INTRODUCTION TO ANALYSIS

CONTEMPORARY UNDERGRADUATE MATHEMATICS SERIES
Robert J. Wisner, Editor

MATHEMATICS FOR THE LIBERAL ARTS STUDENT
Fred Richman, Carol Walker, and Robert J. Wisner
New Mexico State University

MODERN MATHEMATICS: AN ELEMENTARY APPROACH
Ruric E. Wheeler
Samford University

ANALYTIC GEOMETRY
James E. Hall
University of Wisconsin

INTRODUCTORY GEOMETRY: AN INFORMAL APPROACH
James A. Smart
San Jose State College

A PRIMER OF COMPLEX VARIABLES
WITH AN INTRODUCTION TO ADVANCED TECHNIQUES
Hugh J. Hamilton
Pomona College

THEORY AND EXAMPLES OF POINT-SET TOPOLOGY
John Greever
Harvey Mudd College

INTRODUCTION TO ANALYSIS
Edward Gaughan
New Mexico State University

CALCULUS OF SEVERAL VARIABLES
E. K. McLachlan
Oklahoma State University

INTRODUCTION TO ANALYSIS

Edward Gaughan

New Mexico State University, Las Cruces, New Mexico

BROOKS/COLE PUBLISHING COMPANY

Belmont, California
A Division of Wadsworth Publishing Company, Inc.

Brooks/Cole Publishing Company, Belmont, California. A division of Wadsworth Publishing Company, Inc.

L.C. Cat. Card No.: 68-11087
Printed in the United States of America

3 4 5 6 7 8 9 10 – 74 73 72 71

700678

PREFACE

Introduction to Analysis is designed to bridge the gap between the intuitive calculus normally offered at the undergraduate level and the sophisticated analysis courses the student reaches in the senior or first-year-graduate level. Through a rigorous approach to the usual topics handled in one-dimensional calculus—limits, continuity, differentiation, integration, and infinite series—it offers a deeper understanding of the ideas encountered in calculus. Although the text assumes that the reader has completed several semesters of calculus, this assumption is necessary only for some of the motivation (of theorems) and examples.

The book has been written with two important goals in mind for its readers: the development of a rigorous foundation for the basic topics of analysis and the less tangible acquisition of an accurate intuitive feeling for analysis. In the interests of these goals, considerable time is devoted to motivating and developing new concepts. Economy of space is often sacrificed so that ideas can be introduced in a natural fashion.

Very few of the exercises at the end of each chapter are of the computational type. The problems have been chosen with care so that they will not only test the student's understanding of the material covered in the text but also extend his understanding by their thought-provoking nature. The starred exercises of the first three chapters are of particular importance, because they contain facts vital to the development of later sections. The exercises are arranged in such a manner that the reader will gain most from the material in each chapter if he attempts the exercises as he reads along. In particular, some of the starred exercises at the end of a chapter may be needed in the development of that chapter.

Chapter 0 contains introductory material on sets, functions, relations, equivalent sets, and a development of the real numbers via Dedekind cuts. If these concepts are already a part of the reader's experience, he may wish to omit this chapter or skim it quickly.

When time allows, the appendices can be profitably interspersed with the study of the other chapters. The discussion of infinite limits and limits at infinity in Appendix I may be of value to the student after he has completed Chapter 2. However, its fullest benefit will be reaped after completion of Chapters 0 through 6. Appendix II, devoted to convergence and uniform convergence of sequences of functions, may be most profitably read after completing Chapter 6.

In the course of this exposition, a number of famous names are mentioned: Dedekind, Cauchy, Bolzano, Weierstrass, Riemann, Stieltjes, and others. A serious student should complement his mathematical knowledge by seeking to know something about the men who have made important contributions to analysis. He is urged to indulge in a little historical research when encountering the names of these men.

The many students, teachers, and colleagues who contributed to this book by giving me inspiration, encouragement, and many helpful suggestions are too numerous to list. This book is dedicated to them. I am also indebted to James E. Scroggs of the University of Arkansas, H. Elton Lacey of the University of Texas, Gerald S. Silberman of Sacramento State College, Loren N. Argabright of the University of Minnesota, Charles Himmelberg of the University of Kansas, and Robert J. Wisner of New Mexico State University for the contributions made in their reviews of the manuscript. My thanks are also extended to the Brooks/Cole Publishing Company for its patience and help during the publishing of this book.

CONTENTS

INTRODUCTION TO ANALYSIS

CHAPTER 0

PRELIMINARIES

Before attempting to study analysis, one must be able to read and communicate mathematics intelligently. This fact is not unique to analysis but is true in all of mathematics, although there are those who fail to hold this view. To emphasize our point, we suggest you consider the choice between studying the history of the British Empire in medieval English or in modern English.

We shall devote this chapter to some of the basic vocabulary of mathematics; in fact, its contents, with some rearrangements, may appear similar to the beginning chapter of a book at this level in algebra, topology, or other topics in mathematics. This similarity is not accidental. A certain basic vocabulary is common to a good share of mathematics. We have, however, attempted to exclude anything unnecessary for the assimilation of the material to come in this book. Later in this chapter, we shall devote some time to the discussion of the development of the set of real numbers. It will be assumed throughout the book that the reader has reasonable familiarity with the set of rational numbers, the usual arithmetic operations on this set, the ordering on this set, and, of course, the principle of induction. Occasionally, however, some of these facts will be mentioned for the sake of emphasis. The elementary functions will be discussed in some detail in the last chapter, but some of the more familiar properties of these functions will be used throughout the text for illustrative examples. However, none of our proofs will depend on facts we have not already verified.

A few words of both warning and encouragement are in order. First, the reader should realize that he will be given only the fundamentals of his mathematical vocabulary; the proper usage comes only with practice and increasing mathematical maturity. Thus, at the beginning it may seem a bit awkward using these new and unfamiliar ideas in the development of additional concepts. Now the words of encouragement: the initial ideas presented and the theorems proved are quite simple; hence, they will give you many chances to practice your vocabulary in settings where intuition can help to guide your thinking. You are encouraged to play this game quite seriously by giving precise proofs to easy theorems, and, thus, gaining practice in clear and precise mathematical expression—an ability that will be invaluable as the material becomes more difficult in later chapters.

One last bit of admonishment is appropriate. Mathematics, by its very nature, begs to be communicated. It is difficult to imagine a mathematician who, upon discovering a new fact or proof, does not have a burning desire to shout it from the roof tops. In fact, any professional mathematician must be able to communicate with others, be he teacher, researcher, or what have you. Those who say that mathematics is completely incomprehensible have either failed to learn the language of mathematics or have had the misfortune of trying to learn mathematics from someone who cannot or will not use the language properly. Much symbolism is used in mathematics, but each symbol or set of symbols must stand for a word or phrase in the language used, which is English in this case. In particular, the sentences formed with symbols must make sense when translated into words and impart the meaning intended. A good test for your use of symbols is to have someone read your writing with a critical eye, translating it aloud to you. Then you can see if it meets the test for clarity and meaning.

We shall begin with the naive notion of a *set*. A very simple approach will be sufficient for our purposes in this book. We shall think of a set as a collection of objects. Note that the word collection is as undefined in this setting as is the word set. In order to build the intuitive idea of a set, consider the following examples:

(1) The set of all natural numbers.
(2) The set of all the letters of the Greek alphabet.
(3) The set of all rational roots of the equation $x^2 + 1 = 0$.
(4) The set consisting of the rational numbers 1, 2, and 3.
(5) The set of all integers less than 4 and greater than 0.

Note that in examples 1, 2, 3, and 5, the set was described by a rule for determining which objects belong to the set, whereas in example 4, the elements were explicitly named. In particular, observe that those objects which pass the test for membership in the set described in example 5 are precisely the objects listed in 4. It would be quite disconcerting if these two sets were different—that is, if a set were determined by the method used to describe it rather than by the objects belonging to it. That this will not be the case is made clear by the following definition.

DEFINITION   If A and B are sets, then $A = B$ if and only if every object belonging to A also belongs to B and every object belonging to B also belongs to A.

This definition makes it obvious that the sets described in examples 4 and 5 are equal. To show that two sets A and B are not equal, it suffices to find an object that belongs to one set and not to the other.

DEFINITION   If A is a set and x an object which belongs to A, we say "x is an *element* of A" or "x is a *member* of A" and write $x \in A$. If x does not belong to A, we write $x \notin A$.

Let us use this notation to rewrite the definition of equality for sets. If A and B are sets, then $A = B$ if and only if for each object x, $x \in A$ implies $x \in B$, and $x \in B$ implies $x \in A$. Let A_1 be the set in example 1, A_2 the set in example 2, and so on. Now as observed above, $A_4 = A_5$ and $A_1 \neq A_4$, since $13 \in A_1$ and $13 \notin A_4$. Note, however, that each member of A_4 is also a member of A_1. In a sense, A_4 is a part of A_1.

DEFINITION   If A and B are sets such that each member of A is also a member of B, then A is a *subset* of B or A is *contained* in B, written $A \subset B$. If $A \subset B$ and $A \neq B$, then A is a *proper* subset of B.

Consider again these five examples of sets.

Now $A_4 \subset A_1$, since each member of A_4 is also a member of A_1; but note that $A_4 \neq A_1$. The Greek letter α is a member of A_2, which does not belong to any of the other sets; hence, A_2 is not a subset of any of the other sets. If A is not a subset of B, we will sometimes write $A \not\subset B$. In order to show $A \not\subset B$, we must find an object $x \in A$ such that $x \notin B$. For example, consider A_3 and A_2. Since A_3 is described in terms of rational numbers and A_2 in terms of letters of the Greek alphabet, it would seem odd for A_3 to be a subset of A_2. However, to show that $A_3 \not\subset A_2$, we must find an element of A_3 which does not belong to A_2. Upon investigation, it is discovered that there are no rational roots of the equation $x^2 + 1 = 0$, hence that there are no objects which belong to A_3. Since we cannot show $A_3 \not\subset A_2$, then $A_3 \subset A_2$ by default. In fact, if B is any set, $A_3 \subset B$. The set A_3 is special enough to deserve a special name; it is called the *empty set*. Considering again the definition of subset, it is clear that $A \subset A$ for each set A; hence, every set has at least one subset, and if A is not empty, then A has at least two subsets: A and the empty set. Computation of the number of subsets of a set with n elements for n a positive integer is left as an interesting exercise for the reader.

0.1 THEOREM   If A and B are sets, then $A = B$ if and only if $A \subset B$ and $B \subset A$.

Proof: Suppose $A = B$. Then by our remarks preceding this theorem, $A = B \subset B$ and $B = A \subset A$; hence, $A \subset B$ and $B \subset A$.

We have shown that if $A = B$, then $A \subset B$ and $B \subset A$. To complete the proof of the theorem, we must prove that if $A \subset B$ and $B \subset A$, then $A = B$. Now recall the definition of equality for sets. Let $x \in A$. Then since $A \subset B$, we have $x \in B$. If $x \in B$, then since $B \subset A, x \in A$. Thus, the conditions for the equality of A and B are satisfied and the proof is complete.

The usefulness of this theorem will be apparent shortly.

It is convenient to have a variety of ways of describing sets. We have already seen sets defined by a rule for membership and by a list of the members of the set. If $P(x)$ is a statement concerning the object x, then we denote by $\{x : P(x)\}$ the set of all objects x such that $P(x)$ is true. (The kind of statements that are permissible here is a problem beyond the scope of this book. It suffices to declare that the types encountered in this book are permissible.) For example, if A is a set, then $A = \{x : x \in A\}$ where $P(x)$ is the statement "$x \in A$." The set in example 1 may be written as $\{x : x$ is a natural number$\}$, the set in example 5 as $\{x : x$ is an integer and $0 < x < 4\}$.

> DEFINITION   If A and B are sets, the *union* of A and B, written $A \cup B$, is defined to be the set of all objects that belong to either A or B or possibly both. In the notation used previously, $A \cup B = \{x : x \in A \text{ or } x \in B\}$.

> DEFINITION   If A and B are sets, the *intersection* of A and B, written $A \cap B$, is defined to be the set of all objects that belong to both A and B. In other words, $A \cap B = \{x : x \in A \text{ and } x \in B\}$.

To partially digest these new definitions, let us consider a few more examples. Let

$$A = \{\alpha, \beta, \gamma\}, \qquad B = \{1, 2, 4, \alpha, \beta\}, \qquad C = \{1, 2, 3, 4, 5\}.$$

Now $A \cap B = \{\alpha, \beta\}$, $A \cup B = \{1, 2, 4, \alpha, \beta, \gamma\}$ and $A \cap C$ is empty. If two sets A and B have the property that $A \cap B$ is empty, we say that they are *disjoint*.

An appropriate theorem to state at this stage contains some parts that are quite obvious from the definition of union and intersection and some that are not quite so obvious.

> 0.2 THEOREM   Let A, B, and C be sets. Then
> (i) $A \cap B = B \cap A$.
> (ii) $A \cup B = B \cup A$.
> (iii) $(A \cap B) \cap C = A \cap (B \cap C)$.
> (iv) $(A \cup B) \cup C = A \cup (B \cup C)$.
> (v) $A \cap (B \cup C) = (A \cap B) \cup (A \cap C)$.
> (vi) $A \cup (B \cap C) = (A \cup B) \cap (A \cup C)$.

Parts (i) through (iv) have very obvious proofs, which will not be supplied here. The proof of (v) follows, and that for (vi) is left as an exercise for the student.

Proof: In proving (v) we shall use Theorem 0.1 to show that

$$A \cap (B \cup C) \subset (A \cap B) \cup (A \cap C)$$

and

$$(A \cap B) \cup (A \cap C) \subset A \cap (B \cup C),$$

and hence the two sets are equal.

Suppose $x \in A \cap (B \cup C)$. Then $x \in A$ and $x \in B \cup C$. If $x \in B$, then since $x \in A$, $x \in A \cap B$. If $x \notin B$, then since $x \in B \cup C$, $x \in C$ and also $x \in A$; hence $x \in A \cap C$. Thus, in particular, $x \in A \cap B$ or $x \in A \cap C$. In other words,

$$x \in (A \cap B) \cup (A \cap C).$$

We have shown that $A \cap (B \cup C) \subset (A \cap B) \cup (A \cap C)$.
Suppose

$$x \in (A \cap B) \cup (A \cap C).$$

Then $x \in A \cap B$ or $x \in A \cap C$. If $x \in A \cap B$, then $x \in A$ and $x \in B$; hence, $x \in A$ and $x \in B \cup C$ since $B \subset B \cup C$. Thus,

$$x \in A \cap (B \cup C).$$

If $x \notin A \cap B$, then $x \in A \cap C$; hence, $x \in A$ and $x \in C$, but $C \subset B \cup C$, so that $x \in A \cap (B \cup C)$. We have shown

$$(A \cap B) \cup (A \cap C) \subset A \cap (B \cup C),$$

and the proof is complete.

Some of the reasonably easy relations concerning sets given in the exercises will be used later, and the reader is urged to prove them for his own practice—for the simple reason that if one supplies a proof for a theorem, he can usually keep it in mind much more easily.

DEFINITION   Let A and B be sets. Then the *complement* of A *relative* to B, written $B \setminus A$, is defined to be the set of all objects belonging to B but not to A. In other words,

$$B \setminus A = \{x : x \in B \quad \text{and} \quad x \notin A\}.$$

Let $A = \{1, 2, 3, 4, 5, 6\}$ and $B = \{2, 4, 6, 8, 10\}$. Then $B \setminus A = \{8, 10\}$ and $A \setminus B = \{1, 3, 5\}$. The following form of what are called *De Morgan's laws* may look a bit cumbersome because of our decision to speak of the complement of A relative to B rather than the complement of a set relative to some implied universal set. However, this path leaves little room for misunderstanding.

0.3 THEOREM   Let A, B, and C be sets. Then
(i) $A \setminus (B \cap C) = (A \setminus B) \cup (A \setminus C)$,
(ii) $A \setminus (B \cup C) = (A \setminus B) \cap (A \setminus C)$.

Proof: Again, the method of proof will be to use 0.1, showing that the set on the left side of the proposed equality is a subset of the set on the right and vice versa. Although this method of proof will be used quite often in such theorems, it will not always be advertised in the future.
(i)   Let

$$x \in A \setminus (B \cap C).$$

Then $x \in A$ and $x \notin B \cap C$. Since $x \notin B \cap C$, either $x \notin B$ or $x \notin C$. If $x \notin B$, then, since $x \in A$, $x \in A \setminus B$. If $x \notin C$, then since $x \in A$, $x \in A \setminus C$. Hence,

$$x \in (A \setminus B) \cup (A \setminus C).$$

Thus,

$$A \setminus (B \cap C) \subset (A \setminus B) \cup (A \setminus C).$$

Suppose now

$$x \in (A \setminus B) \cup (A \setminus C).$$

Then either $x \in A \setminus B$ or $x \in A \setminus C$. If $x \in A \setminus B$, then $x \in A$ and $x \notin B$, so that $x \notin B \cap C$; thus, $x \in A \setminus (B \cap C)$. If $x \in A \setminus C$, then $x \in A$ and $x \notin C$, so that $x \notin B \cap C$; thus

$$x \in A \setminus (B \cap C).$$

We have already shown that $(A \setminus B) \cup (A \setminus C) \subset A \setminus (B \cap C)$. This result coupled with that of the preceding paragraph completes the proof of (i).

(ii)   Let

$$x \in A \setminus (B \cup C).$$

Then $x \in A$ and $x \notin B \cup C$. If $x \notin B \cup C$, then $x \notin B$ and $x \notin C$. Thus

$$x \in A \setminus B \quad \text{and} \quad x \in A \setminus C;$$

that is, $x \in (A \setminus B) \cap (A \setminus C)$. Therefore,

$$A \setminus (B \cup C) \subset (A \setminus B) \cap (A \setminus C).$$

Let

$$x \in (A \setminus B) \cap (A \setminus C).$$

Then $x \in A \setminus B$ and $x \in A \setminus C$. Since $x \in A \setminus B$, $x \in A$ and $x \notin B$. Likewise, $x \in A$ and $x \notin C$. Thus,

$$x \in A \quad \text{and} \quad x \notin B \cup C;$$

in other words, $x \in A \setminus (B \cup C)$. Thus,

$$(A \setminus B) \cap (A \setminus C) \subset A \setminus (B \cup C).$$

In order to gain a deeper understanding of Theorem 0.3, let us consider a special case and invent some new notation. Suppose B and C are both subsets of A. If S is a subset of A, let S^* denote the complement of S relative to A so that $S^* = A \setminus S$. In this setting, the theorem states that

$$(B \cap C)^* = B^* \cup C^* \quad \text{and} \quad (B \cup C)^* = B^* \cap C^*.$$

In cruder terms, the complement of the intersection is the union of the complements, and the complement of the union is the intersection of the complements.

Given objects x and y, $x \neq y$, it is easy to form the set whose only members are x and y: we can write it either $\{x, y\}$ or $\{y, x\}$, since the method of description doesn't determine the set, but determines just the objects that belong to the set. We are interested in another object one may construct from two objects, namely an *ordered pair*. The distinction we desire here is that each of the objects has a special place—as opposed to the set, in which order is unimportant. This is not an unfamiliar concept, for the notion of an ordered pair of real numbers is encountered in algebra at a tender age—for example as in the case of fractions wherein numerators and denominators are distinguished.

DEFINITION   The *ordered pair* (x, y) is defined to be the set $\{\{x\}, \{x, y\}\}$.

Give this definition a little time to soak in. The ordered pair (x, y) is the set whose members are the set whose only member is x and the set whose members are x and y. This is our first encounter here with a set which has other sets as members. If $x = y$, then $(x, x) = \{\{x\}\}$. Should this definition seem disconcerting, remember that its purpose is to single out one object as the "first coordinate" and another as the "second coordinate." After proving the following theorem, we shall see that the definition serves the desired purpose.

0.4 THEOREM $(x, y) = (u, v)$ if and only if $x = u$ and $y = v$.

Proof: If $x = u$ and $y = v$, then

$$(x, y) = \{\{x\}, \{x, y\}\} = \{\{u\}, \{u, v\}\} = (u, v).$$

Suppose now $(x, y) = (u, v)$. Then $\{\{x\}, \{x, y\}\} = \{\{u\}, \{u, v\}\}$. If $x = y$, then

$$\{\{x\}\} = \{\{u\}, \{u, v\}\}.$$

Since the set on the left has only one member, the same must be true of the set on the right. This can be true only if $\{u\} = \{u, v\}$, which in turn can be true only if $u = v$. Thus, we have

$$\{\{x\}\} = \{\{u\}\},$$

and so $\{x\} = \{u\}$, $x = u$, and, of course, $y = x = u = v$. Now suppose x and y are distinct. Then $\{x\}$ and $\{x, y\}$ are distinct sets and the only members of $\{\{x\}, \{x, y\}\}$. By the assumed equality,

$$\{x\} \in \{\{u\}, \{u, v\}\}.$$

The case $\{x\} = \{u, v\}$ is impossible since u and v must be distinct, and thus $\{u, v\}$ has two elements, whereas $\{x\}$ has only one element. Thus $\{x\} = \{u\}$, so $x = u$. Also

$$\{x, y\} \in \{\{u\}, \{u, v\}\},$$

and the only remaining element that can be equal to $\{x, y\}$ is $\{u, v\}$. But $x = u$, and by the equality $\{x, y\} = \{u, v\}$, we must have $y = v$. This concludes the proof.

The concept of an ordered pair sets the stage for another way of combining two sets to form a new set. In analytic geometry, one considers the set of all ordered pairs of real numbers—a new set constructed from an old one—a generalization of this will be the next definition.

DEFINITION   If A and B are sets, define the *Cartesian product* of A and B, written $A \times B$, to be the set of all ordered pairs (a, b) such that $a \in A$ and $b \in B$. Thus $A \times B = \{(a, b) : a \in A$ and $b \in B\}$.

As an example, let $A = \{1, 2, 3\}$ and $B = \{2, 4, 6\}$. Then

$$A \times B = \{(1, 2), (1, 4), (1, 6), (2, 2), (2, 4), (2, 6), (3, 2), (3, 4), (3, 6)\}.$$

Note that, in general, if A has m elements and B has n elements, then $A \times B$ has mn elements.

Of course, an introduction to analysis must also consider the concept of a function. Intuitively, a function is a gadget which, when fed an object from some set, yields an object, and many functions are familiar from calculus and analytic geometry. Our definition of a function, in the language of sets, fits these preconceived notions about functions.

DEFINITION   A *relation* is a set of ordered pairs. A *function* is a relation F such that if $(x, y) \in F$ and $(x, z) \in F$, then $y = z$.

Note that this condition guarantees that if an object x is the first coordinate of an ordered pair belonging to a function F, then there is precisely one object y such that $(x, y) \in F$. It is customary to call this object $F(x)$. Now observe how the function F works; feed it x and out comes $F(x)$, the second coordinate of the only ordered pair belonging to F with x as first coordinate. Of course, one must be careful what is fed to F: only those objects that are first coordinates of members of F are candidates. If F is a function, we define the *domain* of F to be $\{x : \text{there exists } y \text{ such that } (x, y) \in F\}$, written dom F. If F is a function, we define the *image* (or *range*) of F to be $\{y : \text{there exists } x \text{ such that } (x, y) \in F\}$, written im F.

Consider $\{(x, x^3) : x \text{ is a rational number}\}$. This set of ordered pairs passes the test for being a function, since the second coordinate is completely determined by the first. This, then, is the function defined by the formula $F(x) = x^3$. (Notice that by our definition, a function is the same as what was called the *graph* of a function in analytic geometry.)

Consider now the relation $\{(x^2, x) : x \text{ is a rational number}\}$. In this case, $(9, 3)$ and $(9, -3)$ are members; hence, the condition for being a function is violated and so this relation is not a function. It is for this distinction that we make a choice between the positive and negative square root when we try to define the function $F(x) = \sqrt{x}$. As the reader will recall, the situation becomes even more complicated when inverse trigonometric functions are to be considered. For example, the relation $\{(\sin x, x) : x \text{ a real number}\}$ is not a function, since both $(1, \pi/2)$ and $(1, 5\pi/2)$ belong to it. However, the relation $\{(\sin x, x) : x \text{ a real number}, -\pi/2 \leq x \leq \pi/2\}$ *is* a function.

DEFINITION   Let S be a relation. Then the *converse* of S, written $\hat{S}$, is defined by

$$\hat{S} = \{(x, y) : (y, x) \in S\}.$$

It would be interesting to discover under what conditions the converse of a function is also a function. Suppose F is a function with (x, y) and (x, z) both belonging to $\hat{F}$. In order that $\hat{F}$ be a function, it must be true that $y = z$. Translating back to F, for all (y, x) and (z, x) in F, it must be true that $y = z$; or, in other words, if $F(y) = F(z)$, then $y = z$. This idea is important enough to deserve a special definition.

DEFINITION   A function f is 1–1 (pronounced one-to-one) if and only if for all y, z in the domain of f, $f(y) = f(z)$ implies $y = z$. In essence, this says that a 1–1 function is one that assumes each value in its range exactly once.

Many theorems in mathematics take the following form: Property A is satisfied if and only if Property B is satisfied. It has become accepted practice in mathematics literature to use "iff" as an abbreviation for "if and only if." Thus, the theorem would be written: Property A is satisfied iff Property B is satisfied. We shall now feel free to use this abbreviation, as we do in the theorem that follows.

0.5 THEOREM   Let F be a function. Then $\hat{F}$ is a function iff F is a 1–1 function. If $\hat{F}$ is a function, then $\operatorname{dom}\hat{F} = \operatorname{im}F$ and $\operatorname{im}\hat{F} = \operatorname{dom}F$.

Proof: Assume $\hat{F}$ is a function. Suppose x, y belong to the domain of F with $F(x) = F(y) = z$. Then $(x, z) \in F$ and $(y, z) \in F$ so that $(z, y) \in \hat{F}$ and $(z, x) \in \hat{F}$. Since $\hat{F}$ is a function $y = x$. Thus, if $\hat{F}$ is a function, then F is 1–1.
Now assume F is 1–1. Let $(u, w) \in \hat{F}$ and $(u, v) \in \hat{F}$. To show that $\hat{F}$ is a function, we must show that $w = v$. By the definition of $\hat{F}$, $(w, u) \in F$ and $(v, u) \in F$, making $u = F(w) = F(v)$. By assumption, F is 1–1, hence $w = v$. The facts that $\operatorname{im}F = \operatorname{dom}\hat{F}$ and $\operatorname{dom}F = \operatorname{im}\hat{F}$ are immediate.

In the case that F is a 1–1 function, we shall write F^{-1} in place of $\hat{F}$. Note that $\hat{\hat{F}} = F$ is a function, so if F is a 1–1 function, then by 0.5, $\hat{F}$ is a function and $F = \hat{\hat{F}}$ is a function; hence, by 0.5, $\hat{F} = F^{-1}$ must also be 1–1. If F is a 1–1 function, the function F^{-1} is called the *inverse* of F.

DEFINITION   If f and g are functions and $\operatorname{im} f \subset \operatorname{dom} g$, define the *composition* of g by f, written $g \circ f$, to be the set $\{(x, y) :$ there is $w \in \operatorname{im} f$ such that $(x, w) \in f$ and $(w, y) \in g\}$.

0.6 THEOREM   If f and g are functions and $\operatorname{im} f \subset \operatorname{dom} g$, then $g \circ f$ is a function.

Proof: Let $(x, y) \in g \circ f$ and $(x, z) \in g \circ f$. We must show that $y = z$. By definition, there are $w_1, w_2 \in \operatorname{im} f$ such that $(x, w_1) \in f$, $(w_1, y) \in g$, $(x, w_2) \in f$, and $(w_2, z) \in g$. Since f is a function, $w_1 = w_2$, and since g is a function, $y = z$. Thus $g \circ f$ is a function.

Now if f and g are functions with $\operatorname{im} f \subset \operatorname{dom} g$ and $x \in \operatorname{dom} f$, then $(x, w) \in f$ for some $w \in \operatorname{im} f \subset \operatorname{dom} g$; hence, $(w, y) \in g$ for some $y \in \operatorname{im} g$. This means that $(x, y) \in g \circ f$ and $y = (g \circ f)(x)$, but

$$y = g(w) = g(f(x)).$$

Thus,

$$(g \circ f)(x) = g(f(x)),$$

and we see that the composition of g by f is accomplished by "following" f by g. Also, it is clear that $\operatorname{dom}(g \circ f) = \operatorname{dom} f$. Though we have taken some care to define it, the composition of two functions is not a new idea; for example, the function $h(x) = \sin x^2$ is the composition of the function $g(x) = \sin x$ by $f(x) = x^2$, so that $h = g \circ f$. Note that $f \circ g$ is the function whose value at x is $(\sin x)^2$; hence $f \circ g \neq g \circ f$.

Let f be a function with $\operatorname{dom} f = A$ and $\operatorname{im} f \subset B$. We will find it convenient to denote this in diagram form by "$f : A \rightarrow B$." It will often be useful to express this by writing "f is a function from A into B." If $B = \operatorname{im} f$, then we will write "f is a function from A *onto* B."

If S is a set, denote by 1_S the function from S onto S defined by $1_S(s) = s$ for each $s \in S$. Now if f is a 1–1 function from A onto B, then we have seen that f^{-1} is a 1–1 function from B onto A. Upon examination of the definition of f^{-1}, it becomes clear that $f \circ f^{-1} = 1_B$ and $f^{-1} \circ f = 1_A$.

Suppose $f : A \rightarrow B$ and $T \subset A$. Define

$$f(T) = \{f(t) : t \in T\}.$$

$f(T)$ is called the *image* of T under f. In particular, $f(A) = \operatorname{im} f$. If $C \subset B$, define

$$f^{-1}(C) = \{a \in A : f(a) \in C\}.$$

$f^{-1}(C)$ is called the *inverse image* of C under f. Note that this definition is given without any assumption that f is 1–1, so it is not assumed here that $\hat{f}$ is a function.

Consider now the sets $A = \{1, 2, 3, 4, 5\}$ and $B = \{2, 4, 6, 8, 10\}$. It is clear that $A \neq B$, and in fact $A \not\subset B$ and $B \not\subset A$, so there seems to be no way of comparing the two sets. However, a similarity exists: both sets have exactly five elements, a result we easily obtain by counting the members of each set. If the sets were quite large, counting elements would be a difficult task; in fact, if the sets were infinite, then we would be out of luck. The purpose of the discussion to follow is to consider a way of comparing the size of two sets without the necessity of using the natural numbers as a guide for counting. An obvious way of showing that A and B have the same number of elements is to pair each element of A with an element of B and observe that when this is accomplished, there are no elements of B remaining. The following is one such way of doing this: $(1, 2)$, $(2, 4)$, $(3, 6)$, $(4, 8)$, and $(5, 10)$. The sophisticated reader will recognize that this amounts to defining a 1–1 function from A onto B, in this case the function being easily given by the formula $f(x) = 2x$ for each $x \in A$. There are, of course, many other ways of pairing the elements of A with the elements of B. The reader might be interested in computing how many there are.

> DEFINITION   If A and B are sets, we say that A is *equivalent* to B, written $A \sim B$, iff there is a 1–1 function f from A onto B.

To the reader who has sampled the flavor of modern mathematics, the word *equivalent* carries certain implications. Before considering some examples relating to this definition, let us prove a theorem that justifies the usage.

> 0.7 THEOREM   Let A, B, and C be sets. Then
> (1) $A \sim A$.
> (2)   If $A \sim B$, then $B \sim A$.
> (3)   If $A \sim B$ and $B \sim C$, then $A \sim C$.

Proof: (1)   To show $A \sim A$, we must exhibit a 1–1 function f from A onto A. It seems reasonable to try 1_A. Now if

$$1_A(a_1) = 1_A(a_2),$$

then

$$a_1 = 1_A(a_1) = 1_A(a_2) = a_2 ;$$

hence 1_A is 1–1. It is clear that $\operatorname{im} 1_A = A$ since for any $a \in A$, $1_A(a) = a$. Thus $A \sim A$.

(2)   Suppose $A \sim B$. Then there is a 1–1 function f from A onto B. To show $B \sim A$, one must find a 1–1 function g from B onto A. The discerning reader should now observe that f^{-1} is the logical candidate. It has already been shown that f^{-1} is 1–1, $\operatorname{dom} f^{-1} = \operatorname{im} f = B$, and $\operatorname{im} f^{-1} = \operatorname{dom} f = A$; hence, f^{-1} is onto A. Therefore $B \sim A$.

(3)   Assume $A \sim B$ and $B \sim C$. There are 1–1 functions f from A onto B and g from B onto C. We seek a 1–1 function from A onto C. The only reasonable way to obtain a function from A to C is to consider the composition of g by f, namely $g \circ f$. We know that $\operatorname{dom}(g \circ f) = A$, and it remains to be proved that $(g \circ f)$ is 1–1 and that $\operatorname{im}(g \circ f) = C$. This can be done directly, but it's worthwhile to do it via two lemmas that will be useful.

0.8 LEMMA   Suppose $f : A \to B$ and $g : B \to C$. If f and g are 1–1, then $g \circ f$ is 1–1.

Proof: Suppose f and g are 1–1, $a_1, a_2 \in A$ with $(g \circ f)(a_1) = (g \circ f)(a_2)$. Now

$$g(f(a_1)) = (g \circ f)(a_1) = (g \circ f)(a_2) = g(f(a_2)),$$

and since g is 1–1, $f(a_1) = f(a_2)$. In like fashion, the fact that f is 1–1 guarantees that $a_1 = a_2$. Therefore, $g \circ f$ is 1–1.

0.9 LEMMA   Suppose $f : A \to B$ and $g : B \to C$. If $\operatorname{im} f = B$ and $\operatorname{im} g = C$, then $\operatorname{im}(g \circ f) = C$.

Proof: Suppose $c \in C$. Since $\operatorname{im} g = C$, there is $b \in B$ such that $g(b) = c$, and since $\operatorname{im} f = B$, there is $a \in A$ such that $f(a) = b$. Now

$$(g \circ f)(a) = g(f(a)) = g(b) = c.$$

Thus $C \subset \operatorname{im} (g \circ f)$. Conversely, if $a \in A$, then $f(a) \in B$ and

$$(g \circ f)(a) = g(f(a)) \in \operatorname{im} g = C,$$

so $\operatorname{im} (g \circ f) \subset C$. Thus, $\operatorname{im} (g \circ f) = C$.

With these two lemmas we can now complete the proof of 0.7. Since $f : A \to B$ and $g : B \to C$ are 1–1, then $g \circ f$ is 1–1; and since f is onto B and g is onto C, then $g \circ f$ is onto C. Therefore $A \sim C$.

There is much more to be said concerning the equivalence of two sets. We shall mention only a few instances that are pertinent to what we intend to do later. Let us first consider a few examples.

Let J denote the set of positive integers, and let E denote the set of even positive integers. Define $f : J \to E$ by $f(n) = 2n$ for each $n \in J$. Now if $f(n) = f(m)$, then

$$2n = f(n) = f(m) = 2m,$$

hence $n = m$, so f is 1–1. Since each even positive integer may be written in the form $2n$ where $n \in J$, it is clear that f is 1–1 onto E, hence $J \sim E$. This may seem to be a peculiar state of affairs, the set J being equivalent to one of its proper subsets. However, this is typical of such sets, and in fact one may define an infinite set to be any set which is equivalent to one of its proper subsets.

Let J denote the set of positive integers, and let Z denote the set of all integers. Define $f : J \to Z$ by the following set of rules: if $n \in J$ and n is even,

$$f(n) = \frac{n}{2}$$

and if $n \in J$, n odd,

$$f(n) = (-1)\frac{n - 1}{2}.$$

To show $J \sim Z$, we intend to show that f is a 1–1 function from J onto Z. By construction of f, it is clear that $\operatorname{dom} f = J$ and $\operatorname{im} f \subset Z$. If $m \in Z$ and

m is positive, then $2m \in J$ and $f(2m) = m$. If $m \in Z$ and m is zero or negative, then $1 - 2m \in J$ and

$$f(1 - 2m) = (-1)\frac{(1 - 2m) - 1}{2} = m,$$

since $1 - 2m$ is odd. Thus f is onto Z and it remains to show that f is 1–1. For each $n \in J$ with $n \neq 1$, $f(n) > 0$ if n is even and $f(n) < 0$ if n is odd ($f(1) = 0$). Thus, if $f(s) = f(r) = a$, then s and r must be both 1, both even, or both odd as a is zero, positive, or negative. If s and r are both even, then

$$s = 2\left(\frac{s}{2}\right) = 2f(s) = 2f(r) = 2\left(\frac{r}{2}\right) = r.$$

If s and r are both odd, then

$$s = (-2)\left[-\left(\frac{s-1}{2}\right)\right] + 1 = -2[f(s)] + 1 = -2[f(r)] + 1 = r.$$

Hence f is 1–1.

We have shown that $J \sim E$ and $J \sim Z$, so by use of Theorem 0.7, $Z \sim E$. Sets equivalent to J are of sufficient importance to deserve a special name.

DEFINITION   A set S is *countable* iff S is equivalent to the set J of positive integers. A set S is *finite* iff S is empty or there is $n \in J$ such that S is equivalent to $\{1, 2, 3, \ldots, n\}$. A set S is *at most countable* if it is either finite or countable. A set S is *uncountable* if it is neither finite nor countable.

We shall see examples of uncountable sets later, but let us first consider some more examples of countable sets. Three examples of countable sets have been exhibited, namely E, Z, and, of course, J itself since $J \sim J$. The reader might find it instructive to stop now and discover a few more examples for himself. As a start, try to prove that the set of odd positive integers is countable.

The following theorem shows that in a certain sense, countable sets are the smallest infinite sets.

0.10 THEOREM   Any infinite subset of a countable set is countable.

Proof: Let S be a countable set and T an infinite subset of S. Since S is countable, there is a 1–1 function f from J onto S. Let $M = \{n \in J : f(n) \in T\}$. Since M is a subset of J, it has a least member, n_1. In like fashion, $M \setminus \{n_1\}$ has a least member, n_2. Continuing in this fashion, if $n_1, n_2, \ldots, n_k$ have thus been chosen, $M \setminus \{n_1, n_2, \ldots, n_k\}$ has a least member, n_{k+1}. Note that $M \setminus \{n_1, n_2, \ldots, n_k\}$ is not empty, since otherwise M would be equivalent to $\{1, 2, \ldots, k\}$ and hence finite. Define $g : J \to J$ by $g(r) = n_r$. By the manner of choosing $n_r \in M \setminus \{n_1, \ldots, n_{r-1}\}$, it is clear that g is 1–1 and $f \circ g : J \to S$ is 1–1. The proof will be complete if it can be verified that $\mathrm{im} f \circ g = T$. Let $t \in T$. Then there is $m \in M$ such that $f(m) = t$ and there is an r among $1, 2, \ldots, m$ such that $m = n_r$; so

$$g(r) = n_r = m \quad \text{and} \quad f(g(r)) = t.$$

Thus $T \sim J$; hence T is countable.

0.11 THEOREM   If A and B are countable, then $A \times B$ is countable.

Proof: Suppose A and B are countable. Then there are 1–1 functions f from A onto J and g from B onto J. Define $h : A \times B \to J$ by

$$h(a, b) = 2^{f(a)} \cdot 3^{g(b)}.$$

Since f and g are 1–1, h must be 1–1 by the unique factorization theorem for integers. Now we have shown $A \times B \sim \mathrm{im}\, h$, but since $\mathrm{im}\, h \subset J$, $\mathrm{im}\, h$ must be countable by 0.10, since $A \times B$ is infinite. Hence $A \times B \sim \mathrm{im}\, h$ and $\mathrm{im}\, h \sim J$, so $A \times B \sim J$.

One point in this last proof should be emphasized: namely, that to show a set S is countable, it is sufficient to exhibit a 1–1 function from S onto any countable set, in particular any infinite subset of J.

It is interesting to observe that many ways of combining sets yield countable sets; the preceding theorem gave one way. Before pursuing this matter further, we shall generalize some concepts introduced previously.

DEFINITION   Let Λ be a set, and suppose for each $\lambda \in \Lambda$, a subset A_λ of a given set S is specified. The collection of sets A_λ is called an *indexed family* of subsets of S with Λ as the index set. In more sophisticated terms, an indexed family is a function from the index set to the set of all subsets of S such that the image of λ is the set A_λ. We denote this by $\{A_\lambda\}_{\lambda \in \Lambda}$.

DEFINITION   If $\{A_\lambda\}_{\lambda \in \Lambda}$ is an indexed family of sets, define

$$\bigcup\nolimits_{\lambda \in \Lambda} A_\lambda = \{x : x \in A_\lambda \text{ for some } \lambda \in \Lambda\}$$

and

$$\bigcap\nolimits_{\lambda \in \Lambda} A_\lambda = \{x : x \in A_\lambda \text{ for all } \lambda \in \Lambda\}.$$

The reader is invited to generalize some of the previous theorems in light of these new ideas.

There is one logical difficulty here which needs to be pointed out. If Λ is the empty set, then it is easy to see that $\bigcup_{\lambda \in \Lambda} A_\lambda$ is empty; however, it is not so clear what to expect of $\bigcap_{\lambda \in \Lambda} A_\lambda$. This could be overcome by insisting that all index sets be nonempty, and this shall be done in some cases. In a context where all sets considered are understood to be subsets of a given set S, the common usage is to let

$$S = \bigcap\nolimits_{\lambda \in \Lambda} A_\lambda$$

if Λ is the empty set. The reason for this discussion is to alert the reader to possible problems that might arise from this situation, not to give a solution.

In the event that the index set is the set J of positive integers or a finite subset thereof, some special notation may be adopted. For example, $\bigcup_{n \in J} A_n$ may also be written $\bigcup_{n=1}^{\infty} A_n$, and if $S = \{1, 2, \ldots, k\}$, we may write $\bigcup_{n=1}^{k} A_n$ instead of $\bigcup_{n \in S} A_n$. Of course, similar notation may be used for the intersection of a family of sets.

0.12 THEOREM   If $\{A_\lambda\}_{\lambda \in \Lambda}$ is a family of countable sets with Λ countable, then

$$\bigcup_{\lambda \in \Lambda} A_\lambda$$

is countable.

Proof: Since Λ is countable, there is a 1–1 function f from J onto Λ; hence, for each $\lambda \in \Lambda$, there is a unique $n \in J$ such that $f(n) = \lambda$. In particular, the problem is not changed if we decide to use J as the index set rather than Λ and replace the index λ by the corresponding positive integer n. This will simplify the notation to be used, so we shall now consider the indexed family $\{A_n\}_{n \in J}$. The plan of attack will be the following: Each set A_n is countable, so there is a 1–1 function f_n from J onto A_n. Now if $x \in \bigcup_{n=1}^{\infty} A_n$, then $x \in A_n$ for at least one index n, and thus there is $m \in J$ such that $f_n(m) = x$. We may thereby associate with each $x \in \bigcup_{n=1}^{\infty} A_n$ a pair of positive integers (n, m). Unfortunately, x may belong to several such sets, so the choice of the pair is not completely determined, a situation we shall remedy now. If $x \in \bigcup_{n=1}^{\infty} A_n$, then there is a smallest n such that $x \in A_n$, and then there is $m \in J$ such that $f_n(m) = x$. Now for each $x \in \bigcup_{n=1}^{\infty} A_n$, we have a method of choosing a well-defined pair of positive integers (n, m) as described in the preceding sentence. Define $g : \bigcup_{n=1}^{\infty} A_n \to J \times J$ by $g(x) = (n, m)$ as decided above. The purpose of the discussion above was to show that it is *possible* to define such a function g. Suppose

$$g(x) = g(y) = (n, m).$$

Then $x \in A_n$, and $f_n(m) = x$, and $y \in A_n$ with $f_n(m) = y$; hence $x = y$, and we have shown that g is 1–1. Since $J \times J$ is countable, any infinite subset of $J \times J$ is countable, and $\bigcup_{n=1}^{\infty} A_n$ is equivalent to a countable subset of $J \times J$, namely im g. Thus $\bigcup_{n=1}^{\infty} A_n$ is countable.

We have now come to a point where one must make a big decision. So far, we have operated under the assumption that the reader has a reasonable knowledge of the system of rational numbers. Actually, the only facts used, other than for examples in the theory, concern the set of natural numbers, or—if you prefer—the set of positive integers. The next chapter assumes a good acquaintance with the set of real numbers and the many properties it possesses. There are two extreme strategies that might be used here. One could begin with Peano's postulates and develop completely the set of real numbers, an approach that would require about 100 pages. Or, one could postulate the existence of the real number field and list the desired properties, an approach not really in keeping with the spirit of this book. After many hours of consideration we arrived at what seems to be a reasonable compromise. By this time, the reader should have a reasonable knowledge of rational arithmetic—that is, operations with rational numbers. So we chose to begin at this stage, listing briefly the properties of the set of rational numbers that we need and then outlining a way of developing the set of real numbers via what are called *Dedekind cuts*. Since we shall supply very few proofs, we refer the reader to Landau's *Foundations of Analysis* for a more exhaustive (and exhausting) treatment.[†]

   We begin by considering the set Q of all rational numbers, listing some of the more important properties that we assume to be a part of the reader's store of knowledge. Let Z denote the set of integers. There are functions $+ : Q \times Q \to Q$ and $\cdot : Q \times Q \to Q$ and a relation $<$ on Q such that for all $x, y, z \in Q$, we have

   (1) $(x + y) + z = x + (y + z)$; $(x \cdot y) \cdot z = x \cdot (y \cdot z)$;
   (2) $x + y = y + x$; $x \cdot y = y \cdot x$;
   (3) $x \cdot (y + z) = (x \cdot y) + (x \cdot z)$;
   (4)   there is a unique element $0 \in Q$ such that $0 + x = x$ for all $x \in Q$;
   (5)   for each $x \in Q$, there is a unique $y \in Q$ such that $x + y = 0$, and we write $y = -x$;
   (6)   there is a unique element $1 \in Q$ such that $x \cdot 1 = x$ for all $x \in Q$;
   (7)   for each $x \in Q$ with $x \neq 0$, there is a unique element $y \in Q$ such that $x \cdot y = 1$, and we write $y = x^{-1}$ or $y = 1/x$;
   (8)   for each $r \in Q$ there is $n \in Z$ with $n \neq 0$ such that $nr \in Z$, i.e., $r = mn^{-1}$ for some $m, n \in Z, n \neq 0$;
   (9) $x < y$ implies $x + z < y + z$;
   (10) $x < y$ and $y < z$ implies that $x < z$;
   (11) for x and $y \in Q$, exactly one of the following is true: $x < y, y < x, x = y$;
   (12) $x < y$ and $z > 0$ implies that $xz < yz$.

† Edmund Landau, *Foundations of Analysis* (New York: Chelsea Publishing Co., 1951.)

The moment of truth is now here. In the present setting, any linear equation $ax + b = c$ with $a, b, c \in Q, a \neq 0$, has a solution in Q. However, such a simple equation as $x^2 = 2$ does not have a solution in Q. Since it seems in vogue to prove this and it is so easy to do, let us verify that this is indeed the case.

THEOREM   There is no rational number whose square is 2.

Proof: Suppose there are integers p and q such that $2 = (p/q)^2$ where $p > 0, q > 0$. We may further assume that p and q are relatively prime—that is, their greatest common divisor is 1. Thus we have $2q^2 = p^2$, so p is even (since p odd implies p^2 odd). We may write $p = 2r$ where $r \in Z$. Then $2q^2 = p^2 = 4r^2$, so $q^2 = 2r^2$, and hence q is even. Thus, both p and q are even, contrary to the assumption that p and q are relatively prime.

Now one could attempt to build up our number system by making sure one could solve certain polynomial equations, say for example $x^n = r$ where n is a positive integer and r is a positive rational number. Instead, we seek much bigger and better things.

Let us consider now the set A of all rationals r such that $r \leq 0$ or $r^2 < 2$. Now if $a \in A$ and $b < a$, then either $b \leq 0$, making $b \in A$, or $0 < b < a$, in which case $b^2 < ab < a^2 < 2$, making $b \in A$. Suppose $0 < a$ and $a \in A$. Then $a^2 < 2$. Choose any rational number $\delta > 0$ such that $\delta < 1$ and

$$\delta < \frac{2 - a^2}{(2a + 1)}.$$

(One could choose for example, $\delta = $ smaller of the two numbers $\frac{1}{2}$ and $(2 - a^2)/2(2a + 1)$). Now

$$(a + \delta)^2 = a^2 + 2\delta a + \delta^2 < a^2 + 2\delta a + \delta < a^2 + (2 - a^2) = 2;$$

hence $a + \delta \in A$. The point of this argument is that A contains no largest member although $a \in A$ certainly implies that $a < 2$. If we set

$$B = \{p : p \in Q, p > 0 \quad \text{and} \quad p^2 > 2\},$$

we may also show that B has no smallest member even though every member of B is greater than zero. We see that every rational number lies in either A or B, that $A \cap B$ is empty, that A and B are nonempty, that $a \in A$ and $b \in B$ implies $a < b$, that A does not have a largest member and B does not have a smallest member; therefore, the set Q has a "gap" between A and B. If there were a rational number q such that $q^2 = 2$, then we could write

$$A = \{r : r \in Q, r < q\} \quad \text{and} \quad B = \{r : r \in Q, r > q\};$$

but then $A \cup B \neq Q$ since $q \notin A \cup B$. It is the purpose of the next few paragraphs to fill in these gaps.

A *cut* (Dedekind cut) is a set $A \subset Q$ such that

(a) A is nonempty,

(b) $A \neq Q$,

(c) $a \in A$ and $b < a$ imply that $b \in A$,

(d) A does not contain a largest member.

Let R = set of all cuts. This will be called the set of *real numbers*. If A and B are cuts, define $A < B$ iff $A \subset B$ but $A \neq B$. It is not too difficult to see that the following are true:

(e) for $A, B \in R$, exactly one of the following holds: $A < B$, $A = B$, or $B < A$.

(f) $A < B$ and $B < C$ imply that $A < C$.

We now wish to define addition and multiplication of cuts in such a way that 1–7 and 9–12 of our earlier list are satisfied.

Before going to a formal definition for the arithmetic of cuts, let us survey the situation. As we have seen, $A = \{r : r$ is a rational number, $r < 0$ or $r^2 < 2\}$ is a cut. Also, if r_0 is any rational number whatsoever, the set

$$A_{r_0} = \{r : r \in Q, r < r_0\}$$

is a cut. In the latter case, the cut A_{r_0} is determined by the rational number r_0 in the sense that $r \in A_{r_0}$ iff $r \in Q$ and $r < r_0$, whereas the cut A does not have this property. The purpose of using cuts is to furnish a number system which will remove this defect—that is, fill in the gaps. A cut, then, consists of all rational numbers which sit to the left of a gap or to the left of a fixed rational number. The definitions of addition and multiplication of cuts should then be given such that

$$A_r + A_s = A_{r+s} \quad \text{and} \quad A_r \cdot A_s = A_{r \cdot s}$$

for all rational r and s. If such definitions can be given and phrased only in terms of the elements of the cut, the problem of having to distinguish between the two types of cuts should be partially solved.

It now seems reasonably obvious how to define the sum $A + B$ of two cuts A and B; that is,

$$A + B = \{r + s : r \in A, s \in B\}.$$

We invite the reader to verify that this is indeed a cut and that if p and q are rational numbers, then

$$A_p + A_q = A_{p+q}.$$

It is tempting to try the same trick for multiplication, but note that if A and B are cuts, then $\{r \cdot s : r \in A, s \in B\}$ need not be a cut; in fact, if either A or B contains zero, then

$$\{r \cdot s : r \in A, s \in B\} = Q.$$

This state of affairs forces us to approach the problem with less abandon.
Define

$$\theta = \{r : r < 0\},$$

and if A is any cut, define

$$-A = \{-r : r > u \text{ for some rational } u \notin A\}.$$

Now θ is obviously a cut, and if A is a cut, then $-A$ is also a cut. If $A > \theta$ and $B > \theta$, define

$$A \cdot B = \{r \cdot s : r \geq 0, s \geq 0, r \in A, s \in B\} \cup \theta.$$

Now it's not at all difficult to show that this is a cut and also that if $A < \theta$, then $-A > \theta$. Hence, we complete the definition of multiplication by reducing all cases to the one just given. To sum up,

$$A \cdot B = \{r \cdot s : r \geq 0, s \geq 0, r \in A, s \in B\} \cup \theta \text{ if } A > \theta, B > \theta.$$

$$A \cdot B = -[A \cdot (-B)] \text{ if } A > \theta, B < \theta.$$

$$A \cdot B = -[(-A) \cdot B] \text{ if } A < \theta, B > \theta.$$

$$A \cdot B = [(-A)(-B)] \text{ if } A < \theta, B < \theta.$$

$$A \cdot B = \theta \text{ if either } A = \theta \text{ or } B = \theta.$$

It is a matter of much labor (most of which we choose to omit) to show that the following statements are true in the arithmetic of cuts:

For all $A, B, C \in R$,

(1) $(A + B) + C = A + (B + C)$; $(A \cdot B) \cdot C = A \cdot (B \cdot C)$;
(2) $A + B = B + A$; $A \cdot B = B \cdot A$;
(3) $A \cdot (B + C) = A \cdot B + A \cdot C$;
(4) $\theta + A = A$;
(5) $A + (-A) = \theta$;
(6) $A_1 \cdot A = A, (A_1 = \{r : r \in Q, r < 1\})$;
(7) for each $A \in R$ with $A \neq \theta$, there is a unique element $A^{-1} \in R$ such that $A \cdot A^{-1} = A_1$;
(8) for all rational numbers $r, s, A_r + A_s = A_{r+s}, A_r \cdot A_s = A_{rs}$, and $r < s$ iff $A_r < A_s$;
(9) $A < B$ implies $A + C < B + C$;
(10) $A < B$ and $B < C$ implies $A < C$;
(11) for $A, B \in R$, exactly one of the following is true: $A < B$, $A = B$, or $A > B$;
(12) $A < B$ and $C > \theta$ implies that $AC < BC$.

We shall verify a few of these statements, and we invite the reader to attempt some of those remaining. First, let us verify that $A + B$, $-A$, and $A \cdot B$ are all cuts if A and B are cuts.

Suppose A and B are cuts. Then A and B are nonempty, and so $A + B = \{r + s : r \in A, s \in B\}$ is nonempty. Since A and B are cuts, $A \neq Q$ and $B \neq Q$, so there are rational numbers a and b such that $a \notin A$ and $b \notin B$. If $a' \in A$, then necessarily $a' < a$ since $a \leq a'$ would imply $a \in A$. Similarly, $b' \in B$ implies $b' < b$. Hence for all $a' \in A$ and $b' \in B, a' + b' < a + b$, so $a + b \notin A + B$, which means that $A + B \neq Q$. Suppose

$$s = a + b \in A + B,$$

where $a \in A$ and $b \in B$. If $t < s$ and $t \in Q$, then $t < a + b$, hence $t - a < b$. Since B is a cut, $t - a \in B$, so

$$t = (t - a) + a \in A + B.$$

If we can now prove that $A + B$ does not have a largest member, then we can be sure that $A + B$ is indeed a cut. Choose $a \in A, b \in B$. Since A and B are cuts, there are $a^1 \in A$ and $b^1 \in B$ such that $a < a^1$ and $b < b^1$; hence $a + b < a^1 + b^1$, and indeed $A + B$ has no largest member.

Let A be a cut and define $-A = \{-r : r > u$ for some rational $u \notin A\}$. Since A is a cut, $A \neq Q$, and there must be a rational $u \notin A$. Then, of course, $u + 1 > u$, yielding $-(u+1) \in -A$ and so $-A$ is nonempty. Now since A is nonempty, there is a rational number $s \in A$. We claim $-s \notin -A$. If $-s \in -A$, then there is a rational number u such that $s > u$ and $u \notin A$, contrary to A being a cut. Hence, $-s \notin -A$ and $-A \neq Q$. Let $a \in -A$ and let b be a rational number such that $b < a$. There is a rational number u such that $u \notin A$ and $-a > u$. Thus, $u < -a < -b$, which means $b \in -A$. Supposing that $a \in -A$, we seek $b \in -A$ such that $a < b$. By the definition of $-A$, there is a rational number $u \notin A$ such that $u < -a$. The rational number $-\frac{1}{2}(u - a) = b$ then satisfies $u < -b < -a$, so $b \in -A$ and $a < b$. Thus we have verified that indeed $-A$ is a cut.

In order to verify that $A \cdot B$ is a cut if A and B are cuts, it suffices to prove the statement for $A > 0$ and $B > 0$. Recall in this case that $A \cdot B = \{r \cdot s : r \geq 0, s \geq 0, r \in A, s \in B\} \cup \theta$. Since θ is nonempty, we know that $A \cdot B$ is nonempty. There are rational numbers a and b such that $a \notin A$ and $b \notin B$, and since $0 \in A \cap B$, $a > 0$ and $b > 0$. Now consider $a^1 \in A, b^1 \in B$ where $a^1 \geq 0, b^1 \geq 0$. Since A and B are cuts, $a^1 < a$ and $b^1 < b$; hence $a^1 b^1 < ab$, which implies (since $ab > 0$) that $ab \notin A \cdot B$, and so $A \cdot B \neq Q$. Suppose now that $s \in A \cdot B$ and $t < s$. If $t < 0$, then $t \in \theta \subset A \cdot B$. Suppose $t \geq 0$. Since $0 \leq t < s$, there are $a \in A$ and $b \in B$ such that $a \geq 0$, $b \geq 0$, and $a \cdot b = s$. Now $0 \leq t < s$, and hence $0 \leq t/s < 1$; therefore, $(t/s)a < a$, which means that

$$(t/s)a \in A, \quad \text{and} \quad t = (t/s)(a)(b) \in A \cdot B.$$

It now remains only to show that $A \cdot B$ has no largest member. Since $0 \in A \cdot B$, we need only to show that if $0 < s \in A \cdot B$, then there is $t \in A \cdot B$ such that $s < t$. If $0 < s$ and $s \in A \cdot B$, then there are positive rationals $a \in A$ and $b \in B$ such that $s = a \cdot b$. There is $a^1 \in A$ and $b^1 \in B$ such that $a < a^1$ and $b < b^1$, hence

$$s = a \cdot b < a^1 \cdot b^1 = t \in A \cdot B.$$

We have thus shown that $A \cdot B$ is a cut.

As promised, we shall give a proof of some of the results listed for the arithmetic of cuts. We hope that our proofs of 5, 6, 7, and 8 will be transparent enough to enable the reader to verify the remaining parts without great difficulty. It is highly recommended that the reader attempt at least 3 proofs, one of which should be among 9 to 12.

Proof for 5:   Suppose $a \in A$ and $b \in -A$. Then there is a rational number u such that $u \notin A$ and $u < -b$. Since A is a cut, $a < u$, and $a < -b$.

Thus, $a + b < 0$. Therefore, $A + (-A) \leq \theta$. Now suppose $r < 0$ (that is, $r \in \theta$). Choose $a \in A$. There is $a^1 \notin A$ and of course, $a < a^1$; let $s = a^1 - a$. There is a positive integer n such that $n(-r/2) \geq s$. Consider the points $a, a + (-r/2), a + 2(-r/2), \ldots, a + n(-r/2)$. Again, since A is a cut with $a \in A$ and $a + n(-r/2) \notin A$, there is an integer m satisfying $0 \leq m \leq n - 1$ such that $a + m(-r/2) \in A$ and $a + (m + 1)(-r/2) \notin A$. Thus,

$$a + m\left(\frac{-r}{2}\right) \in A \quad \text{and} \quad -\left(a + (m + 2)\left(\frac{-r}{2}\right)\right) \in -A,$$

hence

$$r = a + m\left(\frac{-r}{2}\right) + \left(-\left(a + (m + 2)\left(\frac{-r}{2}\right)\right)\right) \in A + (-A).$$

Thus, $\theta \leq A + (-A)$, so $\theta = A + (-A)$.

Proof for 6:   Suppose $A > \theta$ and $A_1 = \{t : t \in Q, t < 1\}$. We wish to prove that $A \cdot A_1 = A$. By definition,

$$A \cdot A_1 = \{r \cdot t : r \geq 0, t \geq 0, r \in A, t \in A_1\} \cup \theta.$$

Now if $a \in A$ with $a \geq 0$ and $t \in A_1$, then $a \cdot t \leq a$ since $t < 1$; hence $a \cdot t \in A$. Also, if $b < 0$, then $b \in A$ since $A > \theta$; hence $A \cdot A_1 \leq A$. Now $\theta \subset A$ and $\theta \subset A \cdot A_1, 0 \in A$, and $0 \in A \cdot A_1$. So to complete the proof that $A \cdot A_1 = A$, it is sufficient to show that $a \in A, a > 0$, implies that $a \in A \cdot A_1$. If $a \in A$ with $a > 0$, then there is $b \in A$ such that $a < b$, in which case $0 < a/b < 1$ and $a/b \in A_1$. Thus,

$$a = a/b \cdot b \in A \cdot A_1,$$

and the proof is complete for the case $A > \theta$. If $A = \theta$, then by definition,

$$A \cdot A_1 = \theta \cdot A_1 = \theta = A.$$

If $A < \theta$, then

$$A \cdot A_1 = -[(-A) \cdot A_1] = -[-A] = A.\dagger$$

Thus in each case, $A \cdot A_1 = A$, and 6 is proved.

$\dagger$ It is an elementary fact from modern algebra that in a group, $(a^{-1})^{-1} = a$; in additive notation, $-(-a) = a$. The proof is as follows:
For $a \in A$,

$$-a + (-(-a)) = \theta,$$

hence

$$a = a + \theta = a + (-a) + (-(-a)) = \theta + (-(-a)) = -(-a).$$

Proof for 7:   Let us suppose $A \in R$ and $A > 0$. We must define a cut A^{-1} such that $A \cdot A^{-1} = A_1$. In order to reveal the reasons behind the definition we give for A^{-1}, let us consider the cut that must be used if $A = A_r$, r a positive rational. Then $A_r = \{x : x \text{ is rational and } x < r\}$, so if (7) is to be satisfied, $A^{-1} = A_{1/r} = \{x : x \text{ is rational and } x < 1/r\}$. We seek now a way to describe A^{-1} that will satisfy $A^{-1} = A_{1/r}$ while not appealing to the rational number r. To this end, we define $A^{-1} = \{x : x \in Q, x > 0 \text{ and there is } p \in Q, p \notin A, \text{ such that } p < 1/x\} \cup \theta \cup \{0\}$. We must verify that A^{-1} is a cut and that $A \cdot A^{-1} = A_1$. Clearly A^{-1} is a nonvoid subset of Q. Since $A > \theta$, there is $s > 0$ such that $s \in A$. Then $s < p$ for all $p \notin A$, hence $1/s \notin A^{-1}$. Thus $A^{-1} \neq Q$. Choose $a \in A^{-1}$ and $b \in Q$ such that $b < a$. If $b \leq 0$, then by the definition of $A^{-1}, b \in A^{-1}$. Suppose $b > 0$. Then there is $p \in Q \setminus A$ such that $p < 1/a$, but $0 < b < a$ implies $0 < 1/a < 1/b$; hence $p < 1/b$ and $b \in A^{-1}$. Suppose now that $s \in A^{-1}$ and $s > 0$. (If $s \leq 0$, then there will always be $t \in A^{-1}$ such that $t > s$.) There is $p \in Q \setminus A$ such that $p > 0$ and $p < 1/s$. Let

$$t = \frac{2}{p + \dfrac{1}{s}}$$

then $p < 1/t < 1/s$, hence $t \in A^{-1}$ and $0 < s < t$. Thus, we have established that A^{-1} is a cut. Now we seek to show that $A \cdot A^{-1} = A_1$. We note that

$$0 \in (A \cdot A^{-1}) \cap A_1 \quad \text{and} \quad \theta \subseteq (A \cdot A^{-1}) \cap A_1,$$

so we need only consider positive rational numbers in A_1 and in $A \cdot A^{-1}$. Suppose $a \in A, b \in A^{-1}$ and $a > 0, b > 0$. Then there is $p \in Q \setminus A, p > a$ (since $a \in A, p \notin A$), such that $p < 1/b$. Hence $a \cdot b < a \cdot 1/p < 1$, so $A \cdot A^{-1} \subset A_1$. Now suppose $r \in A_1, r > 0$. We wish to show that $r \in A \cdot A^{-1}$. Since $A > \theta$, there is $a \in A$ such that $a > 0$. By the same argument used in proving that $A + (-A) = 0$, there are $a_1, a_2 \in Q$ such that $a_1 \in A, a_2 \notin A$, and $0 < a_2 - a_1 \leq a(1 - r)$ (consider the numbers $a + n(1 - r)a$ for $n = 0, 1, 2, \ldots$). Thus, in particular, $a < a_2$ since $a \in A$, and so

$$a_2 - a_1 \leq a(1 - r) < a_2(1 - r) = a_2 - ra_2,$$

yielding $a_2 < a_1/r$. Since $a_2 > 0, a_2 \notin A$, and $r/a_1 \in A^{-1}$, we have

$$r = a_1 \cdot r/a_1 \in A \cdot A^{-1}.$$

Thus, $A \cdot A^{-1} = A_1$.

If $A < \theta$, then $-A > \theta$ and $A \cdot (-(-A)^{-1}) = (-A) \cdot (-A)^{-1}$ $= A_1$, so we define $A^{-1} = -[(-A)^{-1}]$. The uniqueness of A^{-1} is left to the reader.

Proof for 8: Suppose now that r and s are rational numbers. Recall again that

$$A_r = \{t : t \in Q, t < r\},$$

$$A_s = \{u : u \in Q, u < s\},$$

$$A_{r+s} = \{w : w \in Q, w < r + s\},$$

and

$$A_{r \cdot s} = \{z : z \in Q, z < r \cdot s\}.$$

Choose $t \in A_r, u \in A_s$. Then $t < r$ and $u < s$, so $t + u < r + s$, which means that $t + u \in A_{r+s}$, or $A_r + A_s \leq A_{r+s}$. Conversely, suppose $w \in A_{r+s}$, so that $w \in Q$ and $w < r + s$. Then $w - r < s$, and hence $w - r < (w - r + s)/2$ $< s$ and $(w - r + s)/2 \in A_s$. Similarly, $w - s < r$, so $(w - s + r)/2 < r$ and $(w - s + r)/2 \in A_r$. Therefore,

$$w = \frac{w - r + s}{2} + \frac{w - s + r}{2} \in A_s + A_r,$$

yielding $A_{s+r} \leq A_s + A_r$. Combining these two relations, we see that

$$A_{s+r} = A_s + A_r.$$

Since $\theta = A_0$, it now follows that $-A_r = A_{-r}$ for each rational r.

If either r or s is zero, then $r \cdot s = 0$ and

$$A_r \cdot A_s = \theta = A_{r \cdot s}.$$

Suppose $r, s > 0$. Then, of course, $r \cdot s > 0$, and hence

$$\theta \cup \{0\} \subset (A_r \cdot A_s) \cap A_{r \cdot s}.$$

So to show that $A_{r \cdot s} = A_r \cdot A_s$, we need only consider the positive rational numbers involved. As in the preceding paragraph, it is easy to see that $A_r \cdot A_s \leq A_{r \cdot s}$. Suppose now that $z \in A_{r \cdot s}$; that is, $z \in Q$ and $z < r \cdot s$. There is a rational number z_1 such that $z < z_1 < r \cdot s$. Thus, we have $z/z_1 < 1$; therefore, $r \cdot z/z_1 < r$, and since $z_1/r < s$,

$$z = (z_1/r)(r \cdot z/z_1) \in A_s \cdot A_r.$$

Thus, $A_{r \cdot s} \leq A_r \cdot A_s$, and $A_{r \cdot s} = A_r \cdot A_s$ for $r, s > 0$.

For the cases $r > 0, s < 0$ and $r < 0, s < 0$, note that

$$A_r \cdot A_s = -(A_r \cdot (-A_s)) = -(A_r \cdot A_{-s}) = -A_{r \cdot (-s)} = A_{rs}$$

and

$$A_r \cdot A_s = (-A_r) \cdot (-A_s) = A_{-r} \cdot A_{-s} = A_{(-r)(-s)} = A_{rs}.$$

The fact that $A_r < A_s$ iff $r < s$ follows immediately from the definition of the ordering for cuts.

In light of (8), we see that there is a 1–1 function $T : Q \to R$ (use $T(r) = A_r$) such that for all $r, s \in Q$,

$$T(r + s) = T(r) + T(s),$$

$$T(r \cdot s) = T(r) \cdot T(s),$$

and

$$r < s \text{ implies } T(r) < T(s).$$

Such a function is called an *order-preserving isomorphism* and tells us that the so-called " rational cuts " behave essentially like the rational numbers. For this reason, we shall now feel free to consider a rational number r as a special type of real number, namely the cut A_r. Those real numbers which are not rational numbers are called *irrational* numbers.

It is important now to consolidate our gains achieved by constructing the set of real numbers. A set $S \subset R$ is said to be *bounded from above* (*below*) if there is a real number M such that for all $x \in S, x \le M$ ($x \ge M$). A set is *bounded* if it is bounded both from above and from below. If $S \subset R$, a real number M is an *upper bound* (*lower bound*) for S if for all $x \in S, x \le M$ ($x \ge M$). If a nonvoid set S is finite, then S is obviously bounded, and in fact, among the members of S there must be a largest, which we denote by *max S*, and a smallest, which we denote by *min S*. For an infinite set S, it is not necessarily true that S has either a largest or a smallest member; in fact, recall that a cut is an infinite set of rational numbers bounded from above but having no largest member. Consider for the moment a rational cut $A_r = \{p : p \in Q, p < r\}$. Now A_r is bounded from above since any real number $a \ge r$ may serve as an upper bound. We wish to point out in this particular case that among all of the upper bounds for A_r, there is a smallest, namely r. It is an important result of our construction that this is *not* really a special case. Let us give the proper definitions and consider the situation in proper detail.

Let S be a set of real numbers bounded from above. A real number a is a *least upper bound* for S if a is an upper bound for S having the property that if b is also an upper bound for S, then $a \leq b$. If S is bounded from below, then a real number a is a *greatest lower bound* for S if a is a lower bound for S having the property that if b is any lower bound for S, then $b \leq a$. It is immediately clear that if S has a least upper bound a, then it is unique, and we write $a = $ l.u.b. S or $a = \sup S$. The abbreviation *sup* is from the word *supremum*, often used as a synonym for least upper bound. Likewise, if S has a greatest lower bound c, then it is unique, and we write $c = $ g.l.b. S or $c = \inf S$. *Inf* comes from *infimum*, a synonym for greatest lower bound.

0.13 THEOREM   Every nonempty set of real numbers bounded from above has a least upper bound. Every nonempty set of real numbers bounded from below has a greatest lower bound. (Notice that this theorem is not true if one deals only with rational numbers.

Proof: Let S be any nonempty set of real numbers, which is bounded from above, say $X \leq M$ for all $X \in S$. Recall now that each real number is a cut and that a cut is a certain kind of set of rational numbers. Let A be the union of all cuts belonging to S. Thus, a rational number r belongs to A iff there is a cut X which belongs to S such that $r \in X$ or, equivalently, iff $A_r < X$. (See Exercise 16.) We shall prove that A is a cut and is in fact the desired least upper bound for S. Since S is nonempty, A is clearly nonempty. The fact that $X \leq M$ for all $X \in S$ implies that $A \subset M$, hence $A \neq Q$ since M is a cut. Now suppose that $a \in A$ and $b \in Q$ with $b < a$. Thus, there is $X \in S$ such that $A_a < X$, so $A_b < A_a < X$ and $b \in A$. Suppose $a \in A$. There is again $X \in S$ such that $a \in X$, and since X is a cut, there is $b \in X$ such that $a < b$. By the definition of $A, b \in A$. Therefore, A is a cut. If $X \in S$, then by the choice of A, $X \subset A$, that is $X \leq A$; hence A is an upper bound for S. If B is also an upper bound for S, then $X \subset B$ for all $X \in S$. But $A = \bigcup_{X \in S} X$, so $A \leq B$. Therefore, A is the desired least upper bound for S.

Suppose now that S is bounded from below. Define $-S = \{-x : x \in S\}$. Now there is a real number a such that

$a \le x$ for all $x \in S$, so $-x \le -a$ for all $x \in S$. Thus, $-S$ is bounded from above, and hence has a least upper bound, which we'll call b. This means that $-x \le b$ for all $x \in S$, so $-b \le x$ for all $x \in S$. The number $-b$ is then a lower bound for S; indeed, it turns out to be the greatest lower bound for S. For if c is also a lower bound for S, then, as before, $-c$ is an upper bound for $-S$; hence $-c \ge b$ since $b = \sup(-S)$. Therefore, $-b \ge c$ as claimed.

This last result is indeed very useful, as we shall soon see. For the present, let us illustrate the usefulness of 0.13 with a theorem of some use later on.

0.14 THEOREM   Let a be a positive real number and n a positive integer. Then there is a unique positive real number x such that $x^n = a$.

Proof: Suppose $x^n - y^n = 0, x, y > 0$. Then

$$x^n - y^n = (x - y)(x^{n-1} + x^{n-2}y + \cdots xy^{n-2} + y^{n-1}) = 0.$$

Since $x, y > 0$, the right hand factor of this product is nonzero, and $x - y = 0$; hence $x = y$. Thus, if there is $x > 0$ such that $x^n = a$, then x is unique.

Suppose $a \ge 1$ and set $S = \{y : y \in R, y \ge 0, y^n \le a\}$. Now $0 \in S$, and for all $y \in S, y \le a$ since $a \ge 1$. Hence, S is a nonempty set of real numbers which is bounded from above. Let $x = \sup S$. It is time to recall the binomial theorem, which states that

$$(x + y)^n = \sum_{k=0}^{n} \binom{n}{k} x^k y^{n-k}$$

where

$$\binom{n}{k} = n!/k!(n - k)!.$$

Suppose that $x^n < a$ and say $a - x^n = \varepsilon > 0$. Let

$$c = \sum_{k=0}^{n-1} \binom{n}{k} x^k.$$

The number c is positive, and so we may choose a positive real number δ such that $\delta < 1$ and $\delta < \varepsilon/c$. Now

$$(x + \delta)^n = x^n + \sum_{k=0}^{n-1}\binom{n}{k}x^k\delta^{n-k} < x^n + \delta c < x^n + \varepsilon = a.$$

Thus, $x + \delta \in S$ with $\delta > 0$, contrary to x being an upper bound for S. Thus, we must have $a \leq x^n$. If we can rule out $a < x^n$, the proof will be complete.

Suppose $a < x^n$, so that $x^n - a = \varepsilon > 0$. Choose $0 < y < x$ such that $x - y < \varepsilon/nx^{n-1}$ (for example, let $y = x - \varepsilon/2nx^{n-1}$). Now

$$x^n - y^n = (x - y)(x^{n-1} + x^{n-2}y + \cdots + xy^{n-2} + y^{n-1})$$

$$< \frac{\varepsilon}{nx^{n-1}}(x^{n-1} + x^{n-2}x + \cdots + xx^{n-2} + x^{n-1})$$

$$= \frac{\varepsilon}{nx^{n-1}}(n)x^{n-1} = \varepsilon.$$

Hence $y^n > a$. We shall show that y is also an upper bound for S. If $z \geq y$, then $z^n \geq y^n > a$; hence $z \notin S$, so for all $z \in S$, $z < y$. We have discovered that if $x = \sup S$, then it is not true that $x^n > a$. Also, we know that it is not true that $x^n < a$, and so the only remaining possibility is the desired one, namely $x^n = a$.

Thus $1 \leq a$ and n a positive integer guarantee the existence of a unique positive real number x such that $x^n = a$. If $0 < a < 1$, then $1/a \geq 1$, and there is x such that $x^n = 1/a$, hence $(x^{-1})^n = a$.

The result of 0.14 guarantees that every positive real number a has a unique positive nth root, denoted by $\sqrt[n]{a}$, for each positive integer n. We shall have recourse to this fact in later chapters.

If x is any real number, define

$$|x| = \begin{cases} x & \text{if } x \geq 0 \\ -x & \text{if } x < 0. \end{cases}$$

We say that $|x|$ is the *absolute value* of x. Note that $|-x| = |x|$ for all real numbers x.

0.15 THEOREM   Let a and b be any real numbers. Then
(1) $|a + b| \leq |a| + |b|$,
(2) $|ab| = |a| \cdot |b|$,
(3) $||a| - |b|| \leq |a - b|$,
(4) if $\varepsilon > 0$, then $|a| < \varepsilon$ iff $-\varepsilon < a < \varepsilon$.

Proof: The proof of 1 and 2 will be left to the reader; it only involves considering the cases in which a and b are both positive, both negative, or have opposite signs.

By 1,

$$|a| = |a - b + b| \leq |a - b| + |b|;$$

hence

$$|a| - |b| \leq |a - b|.$$

In similar fashion, $|b| \leq |a - b| + |a|$; hence $|b| - |a| \leq |a - b|$. Since $||a| - |b||$ is equal to $|b| - |a|$ or $|a| - |b|$, depending on the relative magnitudes of $|a|$ and $|b|$, we have shown that $||a| - |b|| \leq |a - b|$.

Suppose $-\varepsilon < a < \varepsilon$, $\varepsilon > 0$. If $a > 0$, then $|a| = a < \varepsilon$. If $a \leq 0$, then $|a| = -a$ and $-\varepsilon < a$; hence $|a| = -a < \varepsilon$. Thus, $-\varepsilon < a < \varepsilon$, $\varepsilon > 0$, implies that $|a| < \varepsilon$. If $|a| < \varepsilon$ and $a > 0$, then $-\varepsilon < 0 < a = |a| < \varepsilon$. If $a \leq 0$, then $|a| = -a < \varepsilon$, hence $-\varepsilon < a \leq 0 < \varepsilon$. Thus, $|a| < \varepsilon$ implies that $-\varepsilon < a < \varepsilon$.

It is to be noted that (4) implies that the following statements are equivalent:
(i) $|a - b| < \varepsilon$.
(ii) $-\varepsilon < a - b < \varepsilon$.
(iii) $b - \varepsilon < a < b + \varepsilon$.
(iv) $a - \varepsilon < b < a + \varepsilon$.

The reader no doubt uses the set of points on a line as a model for the set of real numbers. In this context, $|a - b|$ represents the distance from a to b, and hence

$$\{b : |a - b| < \varepsilon\} = \{b : a - \varepsilon < b < a + \varepsilon\}$$

is the set of points which are within ε of the point a. Sets of this type play a major role in that which follows.

Suppose a and b are real numbers with $a \leq b$.

Define:

$$[a, b] = \{x : x \text{ is real}, a \leq x \leq b\},$$
$$[a, b) = \{x : x \text{ is real}, a \leq x < b\},$$
$$(a, b] = \{x : x \text{ is real}, a < x \leq b\},$$
$$(a, b) = \{x : x \text{ is real}, a < x < b\}.$$

The set $[a, b]$ is called a *closed interval* and (a, b) is called an *open interval*. In each case, $b - a$ is called the *length* of the interval. Note that if $a = b$, then $[a, b] = \{a\}$ and $[a, b)$, $(a, b]$, and (a, b) are empty. We choose to make the convention now that when using the above notation, we will assume $a < b$ unless otherwise specified.

EXERCISES

1. If A is a set with n elements, determine the numbers of subsets of A. (Hint: the answer is 2^n.)
2. If A, B, and C are sets, prove that $A \cup (B \cap C) = (A \cup B) \cap (A \cup C)$.
3. Prove that for all sets A, B, and C, $A \cap B \subset A \subset A \cup C$.
4. If $A \subset B$, prove that $(C \setminus B) \subset (C \setminus A)$. Is the converse true?
5. Show that $(A \setminus B) \times C = (A \times C) \setminus (B \times C)$.
6. Show that $(A \cup B) \times (C \cup D) = (A \times C) \cup (A \times D) \cup (B \times C) \cup (B \times D)$.
7. Show that $(A \setminus B) \cup (B \setminus A) = (A \cup B) \setminus (A \cap B)$.
*8. If $f: A \to B$ is 1–1 and im $f = B$, prove that $f \circ f^{-1} = 1_B$ and $f^{-1} \circ f = 1_A$.
9. Prove that there is no rational number whose square is 3.
10. Let $A = \{r : r \text{ is rational}, r^2 > 3, \text{ and } r > 0\}$. Prove that A has no smallest member.
11. If A and B are cuts with $A > 0$, prove that $\{r \cdot s : r \in A, s \in B\} = Q$.
*12. If x and y are any real numbers such that $x < y$, prove that there are infinitely many rational numbers r such that $x < r < y$. Prove that there are infinitely many irrational numbers z such that $x < z < y$.
*13. If x and y are real numbers such that $x < y$, prove that $-y < -x$.
*14. If x and y are real numbers such that $x < y$, prove that $x < 1/2 \, (x + y) < y$.
*15. If x and y are real numbers such that $0 < x < y$, prove that $0 < 1/y < 1/x$.
16. Let x be a cut. Prove that a rational number r belongs to x iff $A_r < x$.

CHAPTER 1

SEQUENCES

The aspiring analyst should begin his studies by investigating the folklore of sequences in some detail. A vigorous attempt is made in this chapter to remove the cloud of mystery surrounding the inner workings of sequences. A thorough understanding of sequences is an invaluable aid in the understanding of the rest of this book.

DEFINITION A *sequence* is a function whose domain is the set of positive integers.

If a is a sequence, it is customary to write $a(n) = a_n$ for each positive integer n and write $a = \{a_n\}_{n=1}^{\infty}$. We call a_n the nth term of the sequence. If $m \neq n$, then a_m and a_n are considered to be different terms of the sequence even when $a_n = a_m$. In this fashion, it is sometimes convenient to describe a sequence by giving a formula for the nth term. For example, the sequence whose nth term is $1/n$ may be written $\{1/n\}_{n=1}^{\infty}$; the fifth term of this sequence is $1/5$; the ninth term is $1/9$, etc. If p_n denotes the nth prime, the sequence $\{p_n\}_{n=1}^{\infty}$ is well defined, although it may be rather time-consuming to determine the 97th term. As a matter of policy, we shall try to use notation that conveys the intended meaning most clearly. The sequences mentioned earlier may also be described as follows:

$$\left\{\frac{1}{n}\right\}_{n=1}^{\infty} = \left\{1, \frac{1}{2}, \frac{1}{3}, \frac{1}{4}, \frac{1}{5}, \cdots\right\},$$

$$\{p_n\}_{n=1}^{\infty} = \{2, 3, 5, 7, 11, 13, \ldots\}.$$

This device for describing a sequence seems more useful, for example, in describing the sequence

$$\left\{\frac{1 + (-1)^n}{2}\right\}_{n=1}^{\infty} = \{0, 1, 0, 1, 0, 1, \ldots\}.$$

Care must be exercised that this method be used only when it is clear that misunderstanding will not arise.

Until further notice, all sequences under consideration will be sequences of real numbers. In other words, the range will be a subset of the set of real numbers. This will enable us to dispense with the necessity of referring to such sequences in a special way and still afford us the luxury of using the notion of a sequence in other ways, as is done in Chapter 5. By that time, it will be assumed that the reader has acquired sufficient familiarity with our usage that he will not be offended by this abuse. We beg the indulgence of those purists who view our approach with alarm and claim the immunity supported by our purpose, that of using a language as simple and conventional as possible to convey our ideas in a meaningful fashion.

Before attempting to define the notion of a convergent sequence, let us consider some of the examples we have at hand. Considering the sequence, $\{1/n\}_{n=1}^{\infty}$, we observe that by "going out far enough" in the sequence—that is, choosing n sufficiently large, we find terms that are very close to zero. Likewise, in the sequence $\{0, 1, 0, 1, 0, 1, \ldots\}$, we find terms which are very close to zero, in fact many of which are equal to zero. However, in the latter case we discover that however "far out" in the sequence we look—regardless of how large n is chosen—there are terms farther out in the sequence which are not very close to zero. For example, if we choose $n = 1,000,001$, then $a_{1,000,001} = 0$, but $a_{1,000,002} = 1$, which is not very close to zero. This is a defect not present in the first example. If we decide on a measure of closeness, say within .025 of zero, it is clear that all terms of the sequence $\{1/n\}_{n=1}^{\infty}$ beyond the 40th term satisfy this criterion. We shall use this idea as a skeleton upon which to build our definition of convergence. In language less precise than we require, a sequence should converge to a real number A iff, having settled on how close to A we wish to be, all terms of the sequence from some term on are at least that close to A. Let us now give the formal definition of convergence.

DEFINITION   A sequence $\{a_n\}_{n=1}^{\infty}$ *converges to a real number* A iff for each $\varepsilon > 0$, there is a positive integer N such that for all $n \geq N$ we have $|a_n - A| < \varepsilon$.

It is worthwhile to point out that the choice of N may depend upon the choice of ε. Let us return to the sequence $\{1/n\}_{n=1}^{\infty}$. Intuition leads us to believe that this sequence should converge to zero (we shall prove it a bit later). If this conclusion is correct, then for $\varepsilon > 0$, there is N such that for $n \geq N$, $|a_n - 0| = |1/n - 0| = 1/n < \varepsilon$. For example, if $\varepsilon = .025$, then for $n \geq 41$, $|a_n - 0| = 1/n \leq 1/41 < .025$. Thus for $\varepsilon = .025$, $N = 41$ satisfies the conditions of the definition. For $\varepsilon = .00025$, one may take $N = 4001$. Note that if N is such that for $n \geq N$, $|a_n - A| < \varepsilon$ and $N < M$, then for $n \geq M$, $|a_n - A| < \varepsilon$. Hence if $\{a_n\}_{n=1}^{\infty}$ converges to A, then for each $\varepsilon > 0$, there are many, in fact infinitely many, positive integers N such that for $n \geq N$, $|a_n - A| < \varepsilon$. However to prove that $\{a_n\}_{n=1}^{\infty}$ converges to A, it suffices to show that for each $\varepsilon > 0$, there is at least one number N with the desired property.

In order to completely digest a new idea, we shall look for other ways of expressing the notion. Recall that if a and b are real numbers and $\varepsilon > 0$, then $|a - b| < \varepsilon$ iff $b - \varepsilon < a < b + \varepsilon$. Thus $\{a_n\}_{n=1}^{\infty}$ converges to A iff for each $\varepsilon > 0$ there is a positive integer N such that for $n \geq N$ we have $A - \varepsilon < a_n < A + \varepsilon$. This means that, given $\varepsilon > 0$, $A - \varepsilon < a_n < A + \varepsilon$

is true except for a finite set of subscripts, in the case mentioned above, except for some subscripts from the set $\{1, \ldots, N-1\}$.

To facilitate our study of analysis, we must seek more knowledge of the *topology* of the set of real numbers. Knowledge will come gradually as concepts and facts are introduced and discussed. At this stage it will help to consider the notion of a *neighborhood* of a point.

DEFINITION   A set Q of real numbers is a *neighborhood* of a real number x iff Q contains an interval of positive length centered at x—that is, iff there is $\varepsilon > 0$ such that $(x - \varepsilon, x + \varepsilon) \subseteq Q$.

In particular, for each $\varepsilon > 0$, $(x - \varepsilon, x + \varepsilon)$ is a neighborhood of x. In this setting, a sequence converges to A iff each neighborhood of A contains all but a finite number of terms of the sequence.

It is appropriate to state this as an unnumbered lemma and supply a proof. Although the facts are of an obvious nature, the proof will further an understanding of the definitions of convergence and a neighborhood.

LEMMA   A sequence $\{a_n\}_{n=1}^{\infty}$ converges to A iff each neighborhood of A contains all but a finite number of terms of the sequence.

Proof: Suppose $\{a_n\}_{n=1}^{\infty}$ converges to A and let Q be a neighborhood of A. Then there is $\varepsilon > 0$ such that $(A - \varepsilon, A + \varepsilon) \subset Q$. Since $\{a_n\}_{n=1}^{\infty}$ converges to A and $\varepsilon > 0$, there is a positive integer N such that for $n \geq N$, $|a_n - A| < \varepsilon$. In particular, for $n \geq N$, we have $A - \varepsilon < a_n < A + \varepsilon$; hence $a_n \in (A - \varepsilon, A + \varepsilon) \subset Q$. Thus Q contains all terms of the sequence except possibly some of the terms $a_1, a_2 \ldots$, and a_{N-1}; hence Q contains all but a finite number of terms of the sequence.

Conversely, suppose each neighborhood of A contains all but a finite number of terms of the sequence $\{a_n\}_{n=1}^{\infty}$. Choose $\varepsilon > 0$. Then $Q = (A - \varepsilon, A + \varepsilon)$ is a neighborhood of A and contains all but a finite number of terms of the sequence. This means that there is a finite set $J = \{n_1, n_2, \ldots, n_r\}$ of positive integers such that if $a_n \notin Q$, then $n \in J$. Let $N = (\max J) + 1$. Now if $n \geq N$, then $n \notin J$ and by the definition of J, $a_n \in Q$; that is, $A - \varepsilon < a_n < A + \varepsilon$.

This last statement is equivalent to the statement $|a_n - A| < \varepsilon$. Hence for $n \geq N$, $|a_n - A| < \varepsilon$. We have shown that $\{a_n\}_{n=1}^{\infty}$ converges to A.

We now can answer a question that should be lurking in the back of the reader's mind. Can a sequence $\{a_n\}_{n=1}^{\infty}$ converge to two different real numbers? Let us suppose the answer is yes. Thus, there would be distinct real numbers A and B such that $\{a_n\}_{n=1}^{\infty}$ converges to both A and B. Relying on our mental picture of the real line, we may easily convince ourselves that there are intervals P and Q, each of positive length, centered at A and B respectively, such that $P \cap Q$ is empty. The reader is invited to give a proof of this; see Exercise 1. Now, as we have observed above, P contains all but a finite number of terms of the sequence $\{a_n\}_{n=1}^{\infty}$. Since $\{a_n\}_{n=1}^{\infty}$ also converges to B and since Q is a neighborhood of B, Q contains all but a finite number of terms of the sequence. Recalling that $P \cap Q$ is empty, we see that P must contain infinitely many terms of the sequence and also must contain at most a finite number of terms of the sequence. Thus, the assumption that $\{a_n\}_{n=1}^{\infty}$ converges to both A and B with $A \neq B$ leads to a contradiction. We shall state this as a theorem and give a careful proof. Note that our proof is only a restatement of the preceding argument in precise terms. It is worthwhile to point out at this stage of the game that this is the way a good share of elementary mathematics should be done. Theorems should follow naturally from definitions in an intuitive way; then, of course, adequate proofs should be given. At this level, a difficult theorem might be classified as one that does not seem to have an intuitive proof. Thus, we distinguish between a difficult theorem and a theorem which is difficult to prove although the idea of its proof may be intuitively clear.

1.1 THEOREM   If $\{a_n\}_{n=1}^{\infty}$ converges to A and also to B, then $A = B$.

Proof: Suppose $\{a_n\}_{n=1}^{\infty}$ converges to A and also to B with $A \neq B$, and we may as well suppose $A < B$. Let $\varepsilon = \frac{1}{2}(B - A) > 0$. There is N such that $n \geq N$ implies that

$$A - \varepsilon < a_n < A + \varepsilon = A + \frac{1}{2}(B - A) = \frac{1}{2}(A + B).$$

Observe that $\frac{1}{2}(A + B) = B - \frac{1}{2}(B - A) = B - \varepsilon$. Thus, the statement $B - \varepsilon < a_n < B + \varepsilon$ is false for all $n \geq N$, contrary to $\{a_n\}_{n=1}^{\infty}$ converging to B.

The reader may well be able to supply better proofs for this theorem. In this case we have endeavored to pattern the proof after our initial idea. This is not always the best method of proof and we shall not adhere rigidly to this procedure.

Let us now consider the sequence $\{n\}_{n=1}^{\infty}$, or the sequence whose nth term is the positive integer n. It seems reasonably clear that this sequence cannot converge since the terms get larger and larger without bound. A sequence $\{a_n\}_{n=1}^{\infty}$ is *bounded from above* iff there is a real number M such that $a_n \leq M$ for all n. A sequence $\{a_n\}_{n=1}^{\infty}$ is *bounded from below* iff there is a real number R such that $R \leq a_n$ for all n. A sequence is *bounded* iff it is both bounded from above and bounded from below. Note that a sequence $\{a_n\}_{n=1}^{\infty}$ is bounded iff there are real numbers R and M such that $R \leq a_n \leq M$ for all n or, equivalently, iff there is a real number S such that $|a_n| \leq S$ for all n. Let us now suppose that $\{a_n\}_{n=1}^{\infty}$ converges to A. If we choose a neighborhood of A, there are, at most, a finite number of terms of the sequence outside this neighborhood. In particular, if we consider the neighborhood $(A - 1, A + 1)$, there is a positive integer N such that $A - 1 < a_n < A + 1$ for all $n \geq N$. Now we are assured that all terms of the sequence, except possibly the terms $a_1, a_2, \ldots, a_{N-1}$, are bounded from below by $A - 1$ and from above by $A + 1$. It is now easy to find upper and lower bounds for the possibly wayward terms, $a_1, \ldots, a_{N-1}$, since this is a finite set of real numbers. It should now be clear how upper and lower bounds can be chosen for the sequence $\{a_n\}_{n=1}^{\infty}$.

1.2 THEOREM   If $\{a_n\}_{n=1}^{\infty}$ converges to A, then $\{a_n\}_{n=1}^{\infty}$ is bounded.

Proof: Suppose $\{a_n\}_{n=1}^{\infty}$ converges to A. Choose $\varepsilon = 1$. There is a positive integer N such that if $n \geq N$, then $A - 1 < a_n < A + 1$. Let $R = \min\{a_1, a_2, \ldots, a_{N-1}, A - 1\}$ and let $M = \max\{a_1, a_2, \ldots, a_{N-1}, A + 1\}$. Then for all n, we have $R \leq a_n \leq M$. Thus, $\{a_n\}_{n=1}^{\infty}$ is bounded.

The reader should take note of how easy it is to give a clear, concise, proof for a theorem, such as the preceding one, once the idea of the proof has been laid out. The student of analysis should work to cultivate the skill of formulating proofs so that he can communicate mathematics to fellow mathematicians in a clear, uncluttered style.

Let us now consider again the sequence, $\{0, 1, 0, 1, 0, 1, \ldots\}$. This sequence is certainly bounded, but from our earlier remarks, you may suspect that it does not converge to any real number. It is well to stop and consider this question. Given a sequence $\{a_n\}_{n=1}^{\infty}$ and a real number A, how can one show that the sequence $\{a_n\}_{n=1}^{\infty}$ does not converge to A? According to the definition, there must be an $\varepsilon > 0$ such that infinitely many terms of the sequence lie outside the set $(A - \varepsilon, A + \varepsilon)$, or, equivalently, there must be a neighborhood of A which excludes infinitely many terms of the sequence. However, to show that a sequence does not converge to any real number, we must test all real numbers, a tedious task if not done properly. In due time we shall find more satisfactory tests for convergence. For the moment, let us dispose of the sequence

$$\{0, 1, 0, 1, 0, 1, \ldots\}.$$

Let A be any real number. We now can choose a neighborhood of A which excludes at least one of the two numbers, 0 and 1. (See Exercise 3 at the end of the chapter.) The reader might do well to prove this for his own satisfaction and for the practice in formulating such proofs. Now, since infinitely many terms of the sequence are equal to 0 and infinitely many terms of the sequence are equal to 1, this neighborhood of A must exclude infinitely many terms of the sequence. Thus, the sequence does not converge to A. Since A was an arbitrary real number, we conclude that the sequence does not converge to any real number.

DEFINITION   A sequence $\{a_n\}_{n=1}^{\infty}$ is said to be *convergent* iff there is a real number A such that $\{a_n\}_{n=1}^{\infty}$ converges to A. If $\{a_n\}_{n=1}^{\infty}$ is not convergent, it is said to be *divergent*.

In the light of this definition, let us analyze the facts to this point. If a sequence is convergent, then there is a real number A to which it converges, and, by Theorem 1.1, this number is unique. If a sequence is convergent, the unique number to which it converges is called the *limit* of the sequence. Theorem 1.2 may be restated as follows: Every convergent sequence is bounded. In order to prove that a sequence $\{a_n\}_{n=1}^{\infty}$ is convergent, we must first guess to what real number it converges and then prove this conjecture. In many cases the determination of the supposed limit may be the more difficult task. Once the appropriate choice for the limit is found, the proof of convergence may be very easy.

Consider now the sequences $\{1/n\}_{n=1}^{\infty}$ and $\{1 + 1/n\}_{n=1}^{\infty}$. If our intuition has been properly conditioned, we should recognize that the first sequence should converge to 0 and the second sequence should converge to 1. Let us prove both conjectures. Choose $\varepsilon > 0$. There is a positive integer N such that $N > 1/\varepsilon$ or equivalently $1/N < \varepsilon$. Thus, for $n \geq N$ we have $|1/n - 0| = 1/n \leq 1/N < \varepsilon$ and $|(1 + 1/n) - 1| = 1/n \leq 1/N < \varepsilon$. Note that we were able to use the same N for both sequences. This is not accidental. Observe that the nth term of the second sequence is obtained by adding 1 to the nth term of the first sequence. If one imagines the terms of the two sequences plotted on the real line, the two sequences appear to be in some sense " congruent," each term of the second sequence situated exactly one unit to the right of the corresponding term of the first sequence. It seems reasonable to say that the two sequences behave essentially the same except that they have different limits. We are led to conjecture that convergence is an internal property of a sequence and does not depend on what the limit happens to be. This is the topic we shall pursue next.

Suppose $\{a_n\}_{n=1}^{\infty}$ converges to A. Thus, the terms of the sequence must get close to A; in particular, if a_n and a_m are both close to A, then a_n and a_m must be close to each other. Let us formalize this notion.

DEFINITION   A sequence $\{a_n\}_{n=1}^{\infty}$ is *Cauchy* iff for each $\varepsilon > 0$ there is a positive integer N such that if $m, n \geq N$, then

$$|a_n - a_m| < \varepsilon.$$

Let us reconsider our previous remarks. Suppose $\{a_n\}_{n=1}^{\infty}$ converges to A. Choose $\varepsilon > 0$. There is a positive integer N such that if $n, m \geq N$, then $A - \varepsilon < a_n < A + \varepsilon$ and $A - \varepsilon < a_m < A + \varepsilon$. Thus for all $n, m \geq N$ we find $a_n \in (A - \varepsilon, A + \varepsilon)$ and $a_m \in (A - \varepsilon, A + \varepsilon)$. The set $(A - \varepsilon, A + \varepsilon)$ is an interval of length 2ε; hence, the difference between a_n and a_m is less than 2ε. We will now state a theorem, the proof of which we have just outlined.

1.3 THEOREM   Every convergent sequence is a Cauchy sequence.

Proof: Suppose $\{a_n\}_{n=1}^{\infty}$ converges to A. Choose $\varepsilon > 0$. Then $\varepsilon/2 > 0$. There is a positive integer N such that $n \geq N$ implies $|a_n - A| < \varepsilon/2$. (The choice of $\varepsilon/2$ is not a mere whim. We observed previously that the difference between a_n and a_m was less than twice the original choice of ε.) Now if m, $n \geq N$, then $|a_n - A| < \varepsilon/2$ and $|a_m - A| < \varepsilon/2$; hence,

$$|a_n - a_m| = |a_n - A + A - a_m| \leq |a_n - A| + |A - a_m|$$
$$= |a_n - A| + |a_m - A| < \varepsilon/2 + \varepsilon/2 = \varepsilon.$$

Thus $\{a_n\}_{n=1}^{\infty}$ is Cauchy.

We urge the reader to digest the basic idea rather than memorize the formal details of the proof. The manner of expressing the idea in a clear, precise fashion will come with experience gained by following our good example.

Theorem 1.3 gives a necessary condition for convergence. If a sequence is convergent, it must be Cauchy. Equivalently, if a sequence is not Cauchy, then it is not convergent. Consider the sequences $\{1, 2, 3, \ldots\}$ and $\{1, 0, 1, 0, \ldots\}$. It is clear that neither is Cauchy; hence, according to Theorem 1.3, both fail to converge. As mentioned before, the property of being Cauchy is an internal property of a sequence. One might well suspect that this property is not only necessary but also sufficient for convergence. This is true, but a bit of work to prove. The next task will be to prove this theorem.

Consider a Cauchy sequence $\{a_n\}_{n=1}^{\infty}$. Let $\varepsilon = 1$. There is a positive integer N such that for n, $m \geq N$, $|a_n - a_m| < 1$. In particular $N \geq N$. Hence, for $n \geq N$, $|a_N - a_n| < 1$; that is, $a_N - 1 < a_n < a_N + 1$. If the student will recall the remarks preceding Theorem 1.2, it will be clear to him that every Cauchy sequence is bounded, and he should be able to give a nice proof of this theorem when he arrives at Exercise 4.

1.4 THEOREM   Every Cauchy sequence is bounded.

Proof: Exercise 4.

Consider again a Cauchy sequence $\{a_n\}_{n=1}^{\infty}$. The terms of this sequence all lie in an interval (C, D) since the sequence is bounded;

moreover, the terms of the sequence get closer and closer together as one goes out farther and farther in the sequence. It seems reasonable to suspect that there is a real number A where the terms of the sequence "pile up." We must find this number A and prove that the sequence converges to A. The existence of such a real number will be proven as a corollary to a theorem which we shall have cause to use later. First, the notion of "pile up" must be formulated in precise terminology.

> **DEFINITION**   Let S be a set of real numbers. A real number A is an *accumulation point* of S iff every neighborhood of A contains infinitely many points of S.

A few remarks concerning this definition are in order. First of all, if A is an accumulation point of S, then every neighborhood of A contains at least one point of S which is different from A. (Indeed, A might not belong to S.) On the other hand, if A is not an accumulation point of S, then some neighborhood of A contains only a finite number of members of S. In this case it is possible to find a smaller neighborhood of A which excludes all points of S different from A. Thus, A is an accumulation point of S iff every neighborhood of A contains a member of S which is different from A.

Consider the set $S = \{1/n : n$ is a positive integer$\}$. This set is the range of the sequence $\{1/n\}_{n=1}^{\infty}$. Earlier, we showed that $\{1/n\}_{n=1}^{\infty}$ converges to zero. Thus, every neighborhood of 0 contains infinitely many terms of the sequence; and since all terms of the sequence are distinct (that is, if $m \neq n$, then $a_m \neq a_n$), every neighborhood of 0 contains infinitely many points of the set S. Therefore, 0 is an accumulation point of the set S. Observe that we did not define an accumulation point of a sequence, but rather, an accumulation point of a set. One might be led to conjecture that the limit of a convergent sequence is always an accumulation point of the range of the sequence. To see that this is false, consider the sequence $\{a_n\}_{n=1}^{\infty}$ where $a_n = 1$ for all n. This sequence converges to 1, but its range is finite, and, hence, can have no accumulation points.

The class of finite sets of real numbers is a class of subsets of the real line each of which does not possess accumulation points. A natural question to pursue is the following: Under what conditions can one guarantee that a set will have at least one accumulation point? Of course, such sets must be infinite. Now consider the set S of all positive integers. Given any real number A, it is easy to find a neighborhood of A which will exclude all but a finite number of positive integers (in fact, all if $A \notin S$). Thus, S has no accumulation points. The defect here that allows S to avoid possessing accumulation points is that S has plenty of room to "spread out" its members. Perhaps if S is restricted so that it must be contained in an interval of finite length, this restriction will force the existence of accumulation points. This conjecture is true, as we shall now prove.

1.5 BOLZANO–WEIERSTRASS THEOREM   Every bounded infinite set of real numbers has at least one accumulation point.

We shall preface the proof of this famous theorem with some comments on its meaning. As observed previously, it is impossible for finite sets to have accumulation points; moreover, we have an example— the set of natural numbers—of an infinite set with no accumulation point. Consequently, the boundedness of the set must play some role in forcing the existence of an accumulation point. Note that the theorem does not assert that the accumulation point need belong to the set.

Proof: Let S be a bounded infinite set. Since S is bounded, there are real numbers α and β such that $S \subset [\alpha, \beta]$. If α_1 is the midpoint of this interval, then at least one of the sets $[\alpha, \alpha_1]$ and $[\alpha_1, \beta]$ must contain an infinite set of members of S. Choose one with this property and call it $[a_1, b_1]$. If α_2 is the midpoint of this interval, then at least one of the sets $[a_1, \alpha_2]$ and $[\alpha_2, b_1]$ must contain an infinite set of members of S. Choose one with this property and call it $[a_2, b_2]$. Continuing in this fashion (actually, we are constructing two sequences, $\{a_n\}_{n=1}^{\infty}$ and $\{b_n\}_{n=1}^{\infty}$, by induction) we obtain, for each natural number n, a closed interval $[a_n, b_n]$ with the following properties:

(i) $b_n - a_n = 2^{-n}(\beta - \alpha)$.

(ii) $[a_n, b_n]$ contains infinitely many points of S.

(iii) $[a_n, b_n] \subset [a_{n-1}, b_{n-1}] \subset \cdots \subset [a_1, b_1] \subset [\alpha, \beta]$.

Since $[a_n, b_n] \subset [\alpha, \beta]$ for all n, the set $Q = \{a_n : n = 1, 2, \ldots\}$ is bounded; hence, $t = \sup Q$ exists. This number will turn out to be the desired accumulation point. Recall that to prove this, we need only show that every neighborhood of t contains infinitely many points of S. Let N be any neighborhood of t, then there is $\varepsilon > 0$ such that $(t - \varepsilon, t + \varepsilon) \subset N$. Now $t - \varepsilon$ is not an upper bound for Q, since t is the least upper bound; hence, there is a positive integer n such that $t - \varepsilon < a_n \leq t$. In fact, if $m > n$, then, by the construction above, $t - \varepsilon < a_n \leq a_m \leq t$. Each interval $[a_m, b_m]$ contains infinitely many points of S; hence, the proof would be complete if m could be found such that $t - \varepsilon < a_m < b_m < t + \varepsilon$. As noted above, $t - \varepsilon < a_m \leq t$ for $m \geq n$; hence, it will suffice to choose m large enough so that $m \geq n$ and $2^{-m}(\beta - \alpha) < \varepsilon$. ($2^{-m}(\beta - \alpha)$ is the length of the interval $[a_m, b_m]$.) To summarize, choose $m \geq n$ such that $2^{-m}(\beta - \alpha) < \varepsilon$; then $t - \varepsilon < a_m \leq t \leq b_m = a_m + 2^{-m}(\beta - \alpha) < t + \varepsilon$. Thus N contains $[a_m, b_m]$; hence N contains infinitely many members of S, and t is an accumulation point of S.

Suppose now that $\{a_n\}_{n=1}^{\infty}$ is a Cauchy sequence. If the range is finite, say $\{s_1, \ldots, s_r\}$, and if we choose

$$\varepsilon = \min\{|s_i - s_j| : i \neq j, i, j = 1, \ldots, r\},$$

then there is a positive integer N such that $n, m \geq N$ implies that $|a_n - a_m| < \varepsilon$. Since $a_n = s_j$ and $a_m = s_k$ for some j and k among $\{1, \ldots, r\}$ and ε was chosen to be the least distance between distinct members of the range, we must have $a_n = a_m$ for $m, n \geq N$. Thus, the sequence is constant from some point on and hence converges (see Exercise 6).

If the range of a Cauchy sequence is infinite, then by Theorem 1.4, the range is an infinite bounded set and hence, by the Bolzano–Weierstrass Theorem, has an accumulation point. We have been searching for a point where the sequence "piles up," and this accumulation point should be it.

1.6 THEOREM   Every Cauchy sequence is convergent.

Proof: Let $\{a_n\}_{n=1}^{\infty}$ be a Cauchy sequence. By the remarks above, if the range is finite, the sequence is constant from some point on; hence it converges. Suppose the range is infinite—call it S. By Theorem 1.4, S is bounded; hence, by the Bolzano–Weierstrass

Theorem, S has an accumulation point—call it a. We shall prove that $\{a_n\}_{n=1}^{\infty}$ converges to a. Choose $\varepsilon > 0$. Since the set $(a - \varepsilon/2, a + \varepsilon/2)$ is a neighborhood of a, it contains infinitely many members of the set S. Since $\{a_n\}_{n=1}^{\infty}$ is Cauchy, there is a positive integer N such that $n, m \geq N$ implies $|a_n - a_m| < \varepsilon/2$. Also since $(a - \varepsilon/2, a + \varepsilon/2)$ contains infinitely many points of S, and hence infinitely many terms of the sequence $\{a_n\}_{n=1}^{\infty}$, there is $n_0 \geq N$ such that $a_{n_0} \in (a - \varepsilon/2, a + \varepsilon/2)$. Now if $n \geq n_0$, we have $|a_n - a| < |a_n - a_{n_0}| + |a_{n_0} - a| < \varepsilon/2 + \varepsilon/2 = \varepsilon$.

Thus $\{a_n\}_{n=1}^{\infty}$ converges to a.

By combining Theorems 1.3 and 1.6, we see that a sequence is Cauchy iff it is convergent. It is now possible to recognize a convergent sequence without having any idea what the limit might be. This is not an unpleasant state of affairs, as we shall see later.

We have been sampling the topology of the real line when convenient for our purposes, and our experiences with real numbers have been based mainly on the arithmetic processes—addition, subtraction, multiplication, and division—and the ordering of the real numbers. It is not surprising that these operations and the order relation are "topologically nice." The true meaning of this last sentence will become clearer in following chapters. For the present we shall be content to show the relationship between the arithmetic processes and the ordering on R and the notion of convergence.

Suppose $\{a_n\}_{n=1}^{\infty}$ and $\{b_n\}_{n=1}^{\infty}$ are Cauchy sequences. Considering the sequence $\{a_n + b_n\}_{n=1}^{\infty}$, we observe that the following inequality holds:

$$|(a_n + b_n) - (a_m + b_m)| = |(a_n - a_m) + (b_n - b_m)| \leq |a_n - a_m| + |b_n - b_m|.$$

The reader should now be able to see how to prove that the sequence $\{a_n + b_n\}_{n=1}^{\infty}$ is Cauchy. Thus, if $\{a_n\}_{n=1}^{\infty}$ and $\{b_n\}_{n=1}^{\infty}$ are convergent, so is $\{a_n + b_n\}_{n=1}^{\infty}$. We wish, however, to prove a more informative theorem, which not only states that $\{a_n + b_n\}_{n=1}^{\infty}$ converges, but also asserts what the limit will be.

1.7 THEOREM   If $\{a_n\}_{n=1}^{\infty}$ converges to A and $\{b_n\}_{n=1}^{\infty}$ converges to B, then $\{a_n + b_n\}_{n=1}^{\infty}$ converges to $A + B$.

Proof: Choose $\varepsilon > 0$. There is a positive integer N_1 such that if $n \geq N_1$, then $|a_n - A| < \varepsilon/2$. In like manner, there is a positive integer N_2 such that $n \geq N_2$ implies $|b_n - B| < \varepsilon/2$. Let $N = \max \{N_1, N_2\}$. Then if $n \geq N$, we have $n \geq N_1$, so $|a_n - A| < \varepsilon/2$ and $n \geq N_2$; hence $|b_n - B| < \varepsilon/2$. Thus,

$$|(a_n + b_n) - (A + B)| = |(a_n - A) + (b_n - B)|$$

$$\leq |a_n - A| + |b_n - B| < \frac{\varepsilon}{2} + \frac{\varepsilon}{2} = \varepsilon.$$

Thus $\{a_n + b_n\}_{n=1}^{\infty}$ converges to $A + B$.

Proofs like the preceding do not stem from divine inspiration. One begins with what needs to be shown, namely that $|(a_n + b_n) - (A + B)| < \varepsilon$, and works backward to the appropriate choice of N. Although proofs are not written this way, they are conceived in this manner. Let us follow this process for the product $\{a_n b_n\}_{n=1}^{\infty}$ of two sequences to see how this process works.

Suppose $\{a_n\}_{n=1}^{\infty}$ converges to A and $\{b_n\}_{n=1}^{\infty}$ converges to B. In the light of previous discussion, it seems reasonable to try to prove that $\{a_n b_n\}_{n=1}^{\infty}$ converges to AB. Now for the scratch work:

$$|a_n b_n - AB| = |a_n b_n - a_n B + a_n B - AB| = |a_n(b_n - B) + B(a_n - A)|$$

$$\leq |a_n| \, |b_n - B| + |B| \, |a_n - A|.$$

Since $\{a_n\}_{n=1}^{\infty}$ converges to A and $\{b_n\}_{n=1}^{\infty}$ converges to B, we can make $|a_n - A|$ and $|b_n - B|$ small. The constant $|B|$ poses no problem, but $|a_n|$ depends on the choice of n. Now it is appropriate to recall an earlier theorem, namely that every convergent sequence is bounded. Thus, although $|a_n|$ depends on the choice of n, it can't be very large. Suppose $|a_n| \leq M$ for all n. Then if $\varepsilon > 0$ were chosen, we wish to force the following:

$$|a_n| \, |b_n - B| + |B| \, |a_n - A| \leq M \, |b_n - B| + |B| \, |a_n - A| < \varepsilon.$$

This is satisfied if

$$|b_n - B| < \frac{\varepsilon}{M + |B|} \quad \text{and} \quad |a_n - A| < \frac{\varepsilon}{M + |B|}.$$

It now remains to formulate the proof in an elegant fashion.

1.8. THEOREM   If $\{a_n\}_{n=1}^{\infty}$ converges to A and $\{b_n\}_{n=1}^{\infty}$ converges to B, then $\{a_n b_n\}_{n=1}^{\infty}$ converges to AB.

Proof: Choose $\varepsilon > 0$. Since $\{a_n\}_{n=1}^{\infty}$ is a convergent sequence, it is bounded; hence, there is a positive real number M such that $|a_n| \leq M$ for all n. Now $\varepsilon' = \varepsilon/(|B| + M) > 0$; hence, there is a positive integer N_1 such that $n \geq N_1$ implies $|a_n - A| < \varepsilon'$ and a positive integer N_2 such that $n \geq N_2$ implies $|b_n - B| < \varepsilon'$. Let $N = \max\{N_1, N_2\}$. For $n \geq N$,

$$|a_n b_n - AB| = |(a_n b_n - a_n B) + (a_n B - AB)|$$

$$\leq |a_n||b_n - B| + |B||a_n - A|$$

$$\leq M|b_n - B| + |B||a_n - A| < M\varepsilon' + |B|\varepsilon'$$

$$= \varepsilon.$$

Thus $\{a_n b_n\}_{n=1}^{\infty}$ converges to AB.

Some facts follow immediately from Theorems 1.7 and 1.8. If $\{a_n\}_{n=1}^{\infty}$ converges to A and α is any real number, then the constant sequence $\{\alpha\}_{n=1}^{\infty}$ converges to α; hence, the sequence $\{\alpha a_n\}_{n=1}^{\infty}$ converges to αA. In particular, if $\alpha = -1$, $\{-a_n\}_{n=1}^{\infty}$ converges to $-A$. Combining this observation with Theorem 1.7, we see that if $\{a_n\}_{n=1}^{\infty}$ converges to A and $\{b_n\}_{n=1}^{\infty}$ converges to B, then $\{a_n - b_n\}_{n=1}^{\infty}$ converges to $A - B$. More generally, if α and β are real numbers, then $\{\alpha a_n + \beta b_n\}_{n=1}^{\infty}$ converges to $\alpha A + \beta B$.

The reader is warned not to read any unintended meaning into Theorems 1.7 and 1.8. If $\{a_n\}_{n=1}^{\infty}$ and $\{b_n\}_{n=1}^{\infty}$ are sequences that do not converge, Theorem 1.7 does not assert that $\{a_n + b_n\}_{n=1}^{\infty}$ fails to converge. In like fashion, Theorem 1.8 does not assert that $\{a_n b_n\}_{n=1}^{\infty}$ fails to converge. Exercises 10, 11, and 12 illustrate this point.

The problem with division must be approached with some caution. First of all, consider $\{a_n\}_{n=1}^{\infty}$ converging to A and $\{b_n\}_{n=1}^{\infty}$ converging to B. We wish to consider the sequence $\{a_n/b_n\}_{n=1}^{\infty}$ and might be led to conjecture that this converges to A/B. In order that this even make sense, we must insist that $B \neq 0$ and that $b_n \neq 0$ for all n. Let us proceed with these facts in mind.

$$\left| \frac{a_n}{b_n} - \frac{A}{B} \right| = \left| \frac{a_n B - b_n A}{b_n B} \right| = \left| \frac{a_n B - AB + AB - b_n A}{b_n B} \right|$$

$$\leq \frac{|a_n - A|}{|b_n|} + \frac{|A| \, |B - b_n|}{|b_n| \, |B|}$$

Considering this result in the same fashion as that preceding Theorem 1.8, we see that the quantities $|a_n - A|$ and $|B - b_n|$ can be made small and that the constant $|A|/|B|$ poses no difficulty. However, the factor $1/|b_n|$ must be bounded somehow; indeed, it suffices to keep $|b_n|$ away from zero. However, since $\{b_n\}_{n=1}^{\infty}$ converges to $B \neq 0$, this should not be difficult. Since $B \neq 0$, $\varepsilon = |B|/2 > 0$. The set $(B - \varepsilon/2, B + \varepsilon/2)$ contains all but a finite number of terms of the sequence $\{b_n\}_{n=1}^{\infty}$; hence, the choice of ε makes it clear that all terms in this neighborhood are "bounded away from zero." In other words, there is a positive number M such that $|b_n| \geq M$ for all but a finite number of terms of the sequence. We shall now prove this in a precise and economical fashion.

1.9 LEMMA   If $\{b_n\}_{n=1}^{\infty}$ converges to B and $B \neq 0$, then there is a positive real number M and a positive integer N such that if $n \geq N$, then $|b_n| \geq M$.

Proof: Since $B \neq 0$, $|B|/2 = \varepsilon > 0$. There is N such that if $n \geq N$, then $|b_n - B| < \varepsilon$. Let $M = |B|/2$. Thus for $n \geq N$,

$$|b_n| = |b_n - B + B| \geq |B| - |b_n - B| \geq |B| - \frac{|B|}{2} = \frac{|B|}{2} = M.$$

Note that while the idea of this proof is fairly easy, the inequalities used in the proof are a bit tricky. It is quite tempting to yield to the inclination to give neat, economical proofs like this. In fact, the reader should try his hand at this pleasant pastime as he gains more confidence and experience and begins to be critical of the proofs appearing in this book.

In order to cast aside the veil obscuring the important facts in this proof, we shall give an alternate proof for the case when $B > 0$. The case $B < 0$ may be handled similarly.

Of course, this is more cumbersome than the first proof, but it is much easier to digest. If $B > 0$, then $B/2 > 0$. Now there is a positive integer N such that for $n \geq N$, $B/2 = B - B/2 < b_n < B + B/2$. In the first proof for this lemma, the two cases $B > 0$ and $B < 0$ were handled simultaneously by judicious use of inequalities concerning absolute values. The reader will learn a lot by writing out the proof when $B < 0$ and comparing the two methods of proof.

Equipped with this lemma, we are now ready to state and prove a theorem concerning the quotient of two sequences.

1.10. THEOREM   If $\{a_n\}_{n=1}^{\infty}$ converges to A and $\{b_n\}_{n=1}^{\infty}$ converges to B, with $B \neq 0$ and $b_n \neq 0$ for all n, then $\{a_n/b_n\}_{n=1}^{\infty}$ converges to A/B.

Proof: Choose $\varepsilon > 0$. By Lemma 1.9, there is a positive number M and a positive integer N_1 such that $|b_n| \geq M$ for all $n \geq N_1$. Then

$$\varepsilon' = \frac{M\varepsilon}{1 + \left|\dfrac{A}{B}\right|} > 0.$$

(See the paragraphs preceding Lemma 1.9 to understand the reason for this choice of ε'.) There is a positive integer N_2 such that for $n \geq N_2$, $|a_n - A| < \varepsilon'$, and a positive integer N_3 such that $n \geq N_3$ implies $|b_n - B| < \varepsilon'$. Let $N = \max\{N_1, N_2, N_3\}$. For $n \geq N$, $|b_n - B| < \varepsilon'$, $|a_n - A| < \varepsilon'$, and $|b_n| \geq M$. Thus,

$$\left| \frac{a_n}{b_n} - \frac{A}{B} \right| = \left| \frac{a_n B - b_n A}{b_n B} \right| = \left| \frac{a_n B \quad AB + AB - b_n A}{b_n B} \right|$$

$$\leq \left| \frac{a_n - A}{b_n} \right| + \frac{|A|\,|b_n - B|}{|b_n|\,|B|}$$

$$< \varepsilon'\left(\frac{1}{|b_n|} + \frac{|A|}{|B|\,|b_n|} \right) \leq \varepsilon' \frac{1}{M}\left[1 + \frac{|A|}{|B|} \right] = \varepsilon.$$

The reader has now been initiated into the exclusive club of epsilon-pickers. Since the secrets revealed are representative of the types of epsilon-picking problems to be encountered later in this book, tney should be carefully digested.

As a corollary to Theorem 1.10, observe that if $\{b_n\}_{n=1}^{\infty}$ converges to B with $B \neq 0$ and $b_n \neq 0$ for all n, then $\{1/b_n\}_{n=1}^{\infty}$ converges to $1/B$. (Let $a_n = 1$ for all n and apply Theorem 1.10.)

Let us check our hurried pace for a moment and consider a few applications of the last few theorems. Consider the sequence

$$\left\{\frac{n^3 - 100n^2 + n - 58}{2n^3 + 65n + 69}\right\}_{n=1}^{\infty}.$$

At first glance it would appear that there seems to be little use in trying to apply Theorem 1.10 to this sequence since the sequences

$$\{n^3 - 100n^2 + n - 58\}_{n=1}^{\infty} \quad \text{and} \quad \{2n^3 + 65n + 69\}_{n=1}^{\infty}$$

are both unbounded and, hence, divergent. However, some slight adjustments may improve the situation. Now for each positive integer n,

$$\frac{n^3 - 100n^2 + n - 58}{2n^3 + 65n + 69} = \frac{1 - 100\dfrac{1}{n} + \dfrac{1}{n^2} - 58\dfrac{1}{n^3}}{2 + 65\dfrac{1}{n^2} + 69\dfrac{1}{n^3}}.$$

We have already shown that $\{1/n\}_{n=1}^{\infty}$ converges to 0; hence, by Theorem 1.8, $\{1/n^2\}_{n=1}^{\infty}$ and $\{1/n^3\}_{n=1}^{\infty}$ both converge to 0. If we recall the remarks following 1.8, it is clear that $\{1 - 100(1/n) + 1/n^2 - 58(1/n^3)\}_{n=1}^{\infty}$ converges to

$$1 - (100)(0) + 0 - (58)(0) = 1,$$

and $\{2 + (65)(1/n^2) + 69(1/n^3)\}_{n=1}^{\infty}$ converges to

$$2 + (65)(0) + 69(0) = 2.$$

Now by 1.10,

$$\left\{\frac{n^3 - 100n^2 + n - 58}{2n^3 + 65n + 69}\right\}_{n=1}^{\infty} = \left\{\frac{1 - 100\dfrac{1}{n} + \dfrac{1}{n^2} - 58\dfrac{1}{n^3}}{2 + 65\dfrac{1}{n^2} + 69\dfrac{1}{n^3}}\right\}_{n=1}^{\infty}$$

converges to $\frac{1}{2}$.

In a slightly different vein, consider the sequence

$$\{\sqrt{n+1} - \sqrt{n}\}_{n=1}^{\infty}.$$

As we saw in the example above, the form in which this sequence is given does not lend itself to the use of tools at our disposal, but a familiar algebraic device will remedy this problem. Note that for $n > 0$,

$$\sqrt{n+1} - \sqrt{n} = \frac{n+1-n}{\sqrt{n+1}+\sqrt{n}} = \frac{1}{\sqrt{n+1}+\sqrt{n}}.$$

Now let us appeal to some of the homework exercises rather than attack this problem directly. By Exercise 8, $\{1/\sqrt{n}\}_{n=1}^{\infty}$ converges to 0, since $\{1/n\}_{n=1}^{\infty}$ converges to 0. Thus,

$$0 < \frac{1}{\sqrt{n+1}+\sqrt{n}} \le \frac{1}{2\sqrt{n}},$$

and the sequence $\{1/2\sqrt{n}\}_{n=1}^{\infty}$ converges to 0; hence the sequence

$$\{\sqrt{n+1} - \sqrt{n}\}_{n=1}^{\infty} = \left\{\frac{1}{\sqrt{n+1}+\sqrt{n}}\right\}_{n=1}^{\infty}$$

converges to 0 by Exercise 7.

A relation between order and convergence remains to be shown. We have a specific relation in mind and shall pursue that exclusively. Suppose $\{a_n\}_{n=1}^{\infty}$ and $\{b_n\}_{n=1}^{\infty}$ are sequences converging to A and B, respectively. Suppose further that $a_n \le b_n$ for all n. By this time it should be evident what the conclusion should be—namely, that $A \le B$. However, any attempt to improve this result, by asserting $a_n < b_n$ for all n implies $A < B$, fails. To see this, consider the sequences $\{1/2n^2\}_{n=1}^{\infty}$ and $\{1/n\}_{n=1}^{\infty}$. We have $1/2n^2 < 1/n$ for all n, but both sequences converge to 0. The anticipated theorem will be proved by assuming that $A > B$ and showing that this leads to a contradiction of the hypothesis. If $A > B$, then it is easy to find neighborhoods P and Q of A and B, respectively, that do not overlap and such that if $x \in P$ and $y \in Q$, then $x > y$. All but a finite number of terms of $\{a_n\}_{n=1}^{\infty}$ belong to the set P. The corresponding terms of the sequence $\{b_n\}_{n=1}^{\infty}$ cannot belong to Q, since $a_n \le b_n$ for all n. Thus, there are at most a finite number of terms of the sequence $\{b_n\}_{n=1}^{\infty}$ belonging to the set Q contrary to $\{b_n\}_{n=1}^{\infty}$ converging to B.

1.11 THEOREM   If $\{a_n\}_{n=1}^{\infty}$ converges to A and $\{b_n\}_{n=1}^{\infty}$ converges to B, with $a_n \le b_n$ for all n, then $A \le B$.

Proof: Suppose $B < A$. Then $\varepsilon = (A - B)/2 > 0$. There is a positive integer N_1 such that $n \geq N_1$ imples $A - \varepsilon < a_n < A + \varepsilon$. There is a positive integer N_2 such that $n \geq N_2$ implies $B - \varepsilon < b_n < B + \varepsilon$. Choose $N \geq \max\{N_1, N_2\}$. Then, for $n \geq N$

$$b_n < B + \varepsilon = A - \varepsilon < a_n \leq b_n.$$

This last inequality is clearly impossible.

Note that the contradiction in the proof was not the one mentioned preceding the theorem. But the idea is essentially the same; the choice was motivated by a desire to make the proof simpler to present.

A word of friendly advice to the aspiring student of mathematics is in order here. Contrary to popular belief, mathematics does not consist entirely of formulas and recipes for solving problems. A certain number of them is convenient in mathematics, but unless they are applied with an understanding of the underlying principles and some intuitive feeling for these principles, the rules and formulas have only limited use. The student is encouraged to construct examples other than those given here and to examine them critically. The ideas used in formulating a proof may be very useful in solving a problem in which the theorem may not apply. The next example illustrates this point.

Consider the sequence

$$\left\{ \frac{\sin \dfrac{n\pi}{2}}{n} \right\}_{n=1}^{\infty}.$$

This can be viewed as the product of the two sequences $\{1/n\}_{n=1}^{\infty}$ and $\{\sin(n\pi/2)\}_{n=1}^{\infty}$. Unfortunately, the sequence $\{\sin(n\pi/2)\}_{n=1}^{\infty}$ does not converge since $\sin(n\pi/2) = 0$ if n is divisible by 2, and $\sin(n\pi/2)$ is $+1$ or -1 if n is odd; thus, we cannot apply Theorem 1.8. However, $\{\sin(n\pi/2)\}_{n=1}^{\infty}$ is bounded, and $\{1/n\}_{n=1}^{\infty}$ converges to 0. Referring to the paragraph preceding Theorem 1.8, let $b_n = 1/n$ and $a_n = \sin(n\pi/2)$. Then $B = 0$, and A is unimportant since $|B| |a_n - A| = 0$. Thus, it appears that the sequence converges to 0. Let's check this to make sure. Choose $\varepsilon > 0$. There is a positive integer N such that $1/N < \varepsilon$. Then for $n \geq N$, we have

$$\left| \frac{\sin \dfrac{n\pi}{2}}{n} \right| \leq \frac{1}{n} \leq \frac{1}{N} < \varepsilon.$$

Our conjecture was correct; in fact, we are led to invent a new theorem. Two facts were used in the discussion: namely, $\{1/n\}_{n=1}^{\infty}$ converges to 0, and $\{\sin{(n\pi/2)}\}_{n=1}^{\infty}$ is bounded.

1.12. THEOREM   If $\{a_n\}_{n=1}^{\infty}$ converges to 0 and $\{b_n\}_{n=1}^{\infty}$ is bounded, then $\{a_n b_n\}_{n=1}^{\infty}$ converges to 0.

Proof: Let M be a positive number such that $|b_n| \leq M$ for all n. Choose $\varepsilon > 0$. Then $\varepsilon' = \varepsilon/M > 0$. (This choice of ε' will be apparent shortly, but the reader should have suspected that this would be our choice.) There is a positive integer N such that $n \geq N$ implies $|a_n| = |a_n - 0| < \varepsilon'$. Then

$$|a_n b_n - 0| = |a_n b_n| = |a_n| \, |b_n| \leq |a_n| \, M < \varepsilon' M = \varepsilon.$$

Thus $\{a_n b_n\}_{n=1}^{\infty}$ converges to 0.

Now reconsider one of the equivalent formulations of the idea of convergence: a sequence $\{a_n\}_{n=1}^{\infty}$ converges to A iff each neighborhood of A contains all but a finite number of terms of the sequence. This statement makes it clear that any finite number of terms of a sequence may be changed without affecting either the convergence of the sequence or the limit; in fact, a finite number of terms may be deleted from the sequence and the remaining terms relabeled, retaining the original order, without affecting the convergence or limit. The definition of a subsequence of a sequence will facilitate this discussion.

DEFINITION   Let $\{a_n\}_{n=1}^{\infty}$ be a sequence and $\{n_k\}_{k=1}^{\infty}$ any sequence of positive integers such that $n_1 < n_2 < n_3 \ldots$. The sequence $\{a_{n_k}\}_{k=1}^{\infty}$ is called a *subsequence* of $\{a_n\}_{n=1}^{\infty}$.

In less formal terms, we can say that a subsequence is formed by deleting some (or none, since every sequence is a subsequence of itself) of the terms of the sequence and relabeling the remaining terms while retaining the original order of the terms. Of course, there must be infinitely many terms remaining after the deletion. For example, the sequences

$\{1/k^2\}_{k=1}^{\infty}$, $\{1/2k\}_{k=1}^{\infty}$, and $\{1/2^k\}_{k=1}^{\infty}$ are subsequences of the sequence $\{1/n\}_{n=1}^{\infty}$ formed by setting $n_k = k^2$, $n_k = 2k$, and $n_k = 2^k$, respectively. The sequences $\{1/k^2\}_{k=1}^{\infty}$ and $\{1/2k\}_{k=1}^{\infty}$ converge to 0 according to our previous remarks. The reader is urged to try to prove that $\{1/2^k\}_{k=1}^{\infty}$ also converges to 0, although this fact will be evident from some results that follow.

If $a_n = [1 + (-1)^n]/2$ for each positive integer n and the sequence $\{n_k\}_{k=1}^{\infty}$ is chosen such that $n_k = 2k$ for each positive integer k, then $a_{n_k} = 1$ for each k, and the subsequence thus obtained has all terms equal to 1 and, hence, converges to 1. On the other hand, if n_k is chosen to be $2k - 1$ for each k, then $a_{n_k} = 0$ for all k, and the subsequence thus chosen converges to 0. As noted earlier, every sequence is a subsequence of itself, and this sequence does not converge.

Reflect for a moment on the two examples just given. The first was a convergent sequence, and, of the three subsequences sampled, all converged to the same limit: the limit of the original sequence. While this is not conclusive evidence, it does give some "statistical support" to lead one to conjecture that every subsequence of a convergent sequence must converge and to the same limit. This result should not be surprising in light of the discussion preceding the definition of a subsequence. Proceeding with great confidence in the inherent orderliness of mathematics, we consider the second example given—that of a sequence which does not converge. It has two subsequences with different limits and one subsequence which does not converge at all. By now the reader should have a clear understanding of how the statements of many theorems may be formulated by considering well-chosen examples. In fact, he should associate with each theorem of importance a stock of examples and counterexamples that illustrate both the necessity of the hypotheses and the strength of the conclusions. A theorem used in this fashion becomes a valued aid and tool to be cherished and exploited, rather than a tedious fact to be memorized.

1.13. THEOREM   A sequence converges iff each of its subsequences converges. In fact, if every subsequence converges, then they all converge to the same limit.

Proof: The first half of this theorem is very easy to prove, because every sequence is a subsequence of itself. Indeed, if every subsequence of a sequence converges, then the sequence is convergent, since the sequence is included among the subsequences, all of which were assumed convergent.

Assume now that $\{a_n\}_{n=1}^{\infty}$ is a sequence which converges to A and $\{a_{n_k}\}_{k=1}^{\infty}$ is a subsequence. The proof of the theorem will be complete if it can be shown that $\{a_{n_k}\}_{k=1}^{\infty}$ converges to A. (Before going further, read again the paragraph preceding the definition of a subsequence.) Choose $\varepsilon > 0$. Since $\{a_n\}_{n=1}^{\infty}$ converges to A, there is a positive integer N such that for $n \geq N$, $|a_n - A| < \varepsilon$. Since $\{a_{n_k}\}_{k=1}^{\infty}$ is a subsequence of the given sequence, $n_1 < n_2 < \ldots$; hence, $k \leq n_k$. Thus, for $k \geq N$, $n_k \geq N$, hence $|a_{n_k} - A| < \varepsilon$. Therefore, $\{a_{n_k}\}_{k=1}^{\infty}$ converges to A. Note that if every subsequence of a given sequence converges, then the sequence converges, and, by the argument just given, all subsequences converge to the same limit.

DEFINITION   A sequence $\{a_n\}_{n=1}^{\infty}$ is *increasing* iff $a_n \leq a_{n+1}$ for all positive integers n. A sequence $\{a_n\}_{n=1}^{\infty}$ is *decreasing* iff $a_n \geq a_{n+1}$ for all positive integers n. A sequence is *monotone* iff it is either increasing or decreasing.

1.14. THEOREM   A monotone sequence is convergent iff it is bounded.

Proof: Suppose $\{a_n\}_{n=1}^{\infty}$ is a monotone sequence which is bounded; for definiteness, suppose the sequence is increasing. Since $\{a_n\}_{n=1}^{\infty}$ is bounded, $\sup \{a_n : n = 1, 2, \ldots\}$ exists; call it s. It will be shown that $\{a_n\}_{n=1}^{\infty}$ converges to s. Choose $\varepsilon > 0$. Since s is the least upper bound of $\{a_n : n = 1, 2, \ldots\}$, $s - \varepsilon$ is not an upper bound; hence, there is n_0 such that $s - \varepsilon < a_{n_0}$. Now for $n \geq n_0$,

$$s - \varepsilon < a_{n_0} \leq a_n \leq s < s + \varepsilon;$$

hence $\{a_n\}_{n=1}^{\infty}$ converges to s. For the case in which $\{a_n\}_{n=1}^{\infty}$ is decreasing, let $s = \inf \{a_n : n = 1, \ldots\}$, and the details are quite similar (see Exercise 17).

If the sequence is convergent, then, by Theorem 1.2, it is bounded.

In keeping with our philosophy about examining examples in order to illustrate theorems and show the need for the hypotheses, we shall consider several sequences. First, the sequence $\{n\}_{n=1}^{\infty}$ is indeed monotone, but it does not converge, since it is unbounded. The sequence $\{0, 1, 0, \ldots\}$ is bounded, but the theorem does not apply, because it is not monotone; indeed, it fails to converge.

Consider the sequence $\{s_n\}_{n=1}^{\infty}$ defined as follows:

$$s_1 = \sqrt{2}, s_n = \sqrt{2 + \sqrt{s_{n-1}}} \quad \text{for} \quad n = 2, \ldots.$$

We shall prove that this sequence is increasing and bounded by 2 and, hence, by the preceding theorem, is convergent. Since this sequence is defined inductively, the same device will be used to prove the conjecture stated above. Clearly, $s_1 \le 2$ and

$$s_2 = \sqrt{2 + \sqrt[4]{2}} \ge \sqrt{2} = s_1.$$

We wish to show that $s_n \le 2$ and $s_{n+1} \ge s_n$ for all n; the preceding statement verifies the truth of this for $n = 1$. Assume the condition is satisfied for $n = r$. Then

$$s_{r+1} = \sqrt{2 + \sqrt{s_r}} \le \sqrt{2 + \sqrt{2}} \le \sqrt{2 + 2} = 2$$

and

$$s_{r+2} = \sqrt{2 + \sqrt{s_{r+1}}} \ge \sqrt{2 + \sqrt{s_r}} = s_{r+1};$$

hence, by the principle of induction, the inequalities hold for all n. By use of Theorem 1.14, we are assured that the sequence converges; call the limit L. Now the subsequence $\{s_{n-1}\}_{n=2}^{\infty}$ also converges to L, and since $s_n > 0$ for all n, $\{\sqrt{s_{n-1}}\}_{n=2}^{\infty}$ converges to $\sqrt{L}$. Now observe that since $s_n = \sqrt{2 + \sqrt{s_{n-1}}}$, the sequence

$$\{s_n\}_{n=1}^{\infty} = \{\sqrt{2 + \sqrt{s_{n-1}}}\}_{n=1}^{\infty}$$

converges to $\sqrt{2 + \sqrt{L}}$, and also $\{s_n\}_{n=1}^{\infty}$ converges to L; thus by the uniqueness of the limit of a sequence, $L = \sqrt{2 + \sqrt{L}}$. By eliminating the radicals, we see that L must be a root of the polynomial equation $L^4 - 4L^2 - L + 4 = 0$.

It shall be left as an exercise to the reader to consider the sequence $\{(1 + 1/n)^n\}_{n=1}^{\infty}$. This sequence may be shown to be increasing and bounded, and hence convergent. The limit happens to be e, the base for the natural logarithm, a number which plays a central role in the calculus.

1.15. THEOREM   Let E be a set of real numbers. Then x_0 is an accumulation point of E iff there is a sequence $\{x_n\}_{n=1}^{\infty}$ of members of E, each distinct from x_0, such that $\{x_n\}_{n=1}^{\infty}$ converges to x_0.

Proof: Let x_0 be an accumulation point of E. Then for each positive integer n, there is a point $x_n \in E$ such that $0 < |x_n - x_0| < 1/n$. (The set $(x_0 - 1/n, x_0 + 1/n)$ is a neighborhood of x_0, and so it contains a member of E distinct from x_0.) It now remains to be shown that $\{x_n\}_{n=1}^{\infty}$ converges to x_0. Choose $\varepsilon > 0$. Then there is a positive integer N such that $1/\varepsilon < N$; hence, for $n \geq N, |x_n - x_0| < 1/n \leq 1/N < \varepsilon$. Thus $\{x_n\}_{n=1}^{\infty}$ converges to x_0.

Suppose now that there is a sequence $\{x_n\}_{n=1}^{\infty}$ of members of E, each distinct from x_0, which converges to x_0. Then, since every neighborhood of x_0 contains all but a finite number of terms of the sequence, every neighborhood of x_0 must contain at least one member of E that is distinct from x_0. Hence, x_0 is an accumulation point of E.

We shall close this chapter by examining several examples involving some techniques that are of sufficient interest to be studied with care.

Consider a real number $0 < b < 1$ and form the sequence $\{b^n\}_{n=1}^{\infty}$. Observe that $b^{n-1} - b^n = b^{n-1}(1 - b) > 0$; hence, the sequence is decreasing. In order to show that this sequence converges, it suffices to show that it is bounded from below, an easy task since $b^n > 0$ for all natural numbers n. Although we know now that the sequence converges, we shall seek also to determine its limit. Now $\{b^n\}_{n=1}^{\infty}$ converges; call its limit L. And $\{b^{2n}\}_{n=1}^{\infty}$, being a subsequence of $\{b^n\}_{n=1}^{\infty}$, also converges to L. On the other hand, $\{b^{2n}\}_{n=1}^{\infty}$, which may be considered as the product of the sequence $\{b^n\}_{n=1}^{\infty}$ with itself, converges to L^2. By the uniqueness of the limit, $L^2 = L$, and so $L = 0$ or $L = 1$. Clearly, $L \neq 1$ since the sequence was decreasing and $b < 1$. Hence, $\{b^n\}_{n=1}^{\infty}$ converges to 0. This example is not intended to amaze the reader, but it illustrates a few techniques that are convenient to have at hand.

Consider $0 < c < 1$ and the sequence $\{\sqrt[n]{c}\}_{n=1}^{\infty}$. For all n,

$$\sqrt[n]{c} - {}^{n-1}\!\!\sqrt{c} = \sqrt[n]{c}(1 - {}^{n(n-1)}\!\!\sqrt{c}) > 0,$$

since $c < 1$. Hence the sequence is increasing, and clearly $\sqrt[n]{c} < 1$ for all n. Thus, the sequence converges; call the limit L. By Exercise 8, if $\{x_n\}_{n=1}^{\infty}$ converges to x_0, $x_n \geq 0$ for all n, then $\{\sqrt{x_n}\}_{n=1}^{\infty}$ converges to $\sqrt{x_0}$. Therefore, the sequence $\{\sqrt{\sqrt[n]{c}}\}_{n=1}^{\infty}$ converges to $\sqrt{L}$, but

$$\sqrt{\sqrt[n]{c}} = \sqrt[2n]{c},$$

and $\{\sqrt[2n]{c}\}_{n=1}^{\infty}$ is a subsequence of $\{\sqrt[n]{c}\}_{n=1}^{\infty}$, hence converges to L. By the uniqueness of the limit of a sequence, $\sqrt{L} = L$; hence $L = 0$ or $L = 1$. But $c > 0$ and the sequence is increasing; therefore $L \neq 0$. In conclusion, $\{\sqrt[n]{c}\}_{n=1}^{\infty}$ converges to 1. (See Exercise 18 for the case $c > 1$.)

We shall now consider another sequence which is defined inductively—that is, the first few terms are given, and instructions are given for computing the nth term in terms of some or all of the preceding terms. Let $a_1 = 1$, and for $n \geq 2$, define $a_n = \sqrt{2a_{n-1}}$. We shall also use induction to attack this sequence. First of all, look at a few terms of the sequence,

$$a_1 = 1, \qquad a_2 = \sqrt{2}, \qquad a_3 = \sqrt{2\sqrt{2}},$$

etc. It seems reasonable to expect the sequence to be increasing and, hence, convergent if it is bounded. It may not be clear at first glance what to try for an upper bound; so we shall discover this bound by a very useful device. (Even if you can guess the bound, play the game to see how the device works.) Since the sequence is increasing, if it converges, then the limit will be the least upper bound of the sequence. In an attempt to discover a logical candidate for this limit, let us assume that the sequence converges. Suppose $\{a_n\}_{n=1}^{\infty}$ converges to L; then $\{a_n^2\}_{n=1}^{\infty}$ converges to L^2, but $a_n^2 = 2a_{n-1}$; hence $\{a_n^2\}_{n=1}^{\infty} = \{2a_{n-1}\}_{n=1}^{\infty}$ converges to $2L$. Thus, the only candidates for the limit must be the solutions of the equation $L^2 = 2L$; either $L = 2$ or $L = 0$. It is easy to rule out the possibility $L = 0$, and so $L = 2$ is the obvious choice. Note that it has not been proved that $\{a_n\}_{n=1}^{\infty}$ converges to 2. Our only proof so far is that if the sequence converges, then the limit must be 2. We shall now prove by induction that

$a_n \leq a_{n+1} \leq 2$ for all n and, hence, the sequence is bounded and monotone and, thus, convergent. For $n = 1$, $a_1 = 1 \leq a_2 = \sqrt{2} \leq 2$. Assume the statement is true for $n = r$; in other words, $a_r \leq a_{r+1} \leq 2$. Then

$$a_{r+1} = \sqrt{2a_r} \leq \sqrt{2a_{r+1}} = a_{r+2}$$

and

$$a_{r+2} = \sqrt{2a_{r+1}} < \sqrt{2 \cdot 2} = 2,$$

and the statement holds for $n = r + 1$. By induction, the statement holds for all n, and $\{a_n\}_{n=1}^{\infty}$ converges to 2.

Recall now a word of philosophy mentioned earlier—namely, that determining the limit of a sequence may be half the battle in showing a sequence to be convergent. Consider the sequence $\{\sqrt[n]{n}\}_{n=1}^{\infty}$. Let us try to guess the limit in advance by reasoning similar to that used in the preceding paragraph. Suppose $\{\sqrt[n]{n}\}_{n=1}^{\infty}$ converges; call the limit L. Now consider the subsequence $\{\sqrt[2n]{2n}\}_{n=1}^{\infty}$;

$$\sqrt[2n]{2n} = \sqrt{\sqrt[n]{2} \sqrt[n]{n}},$$

and we know $\{\sqrt[n]{2}\}_{n=1}^{\infty}$ converges to 1 (see Exercise 18). Thus, $\{\sqrt[2n]{2n}\}_{n=1}^{\infty}$ converges to L and also to $\sqrt{L}$; hence, by arguments given before, $L = 1$. We shall try to prove that the sequence converges to 1 or, equivalently, that the sequence $\{\sqrt[n]{n} - 1\}_{n=1}^{\infty}$ converges to 0. Let $x_n = \sqrt[n]{n} - 1$; clearly $x_n \geq 0$ and

$$n = (1 + x_n)^n = 1 + nx_n + \frac{n(n-1)}{2} x_n^{\ 2} + \cdots + x_n^{\ n} \geq \frac{n(n-1)}{2} x_n^{\ 2}.$$

Thus for all n, $0 \leq x_n \leq \sqrt{2/(n-1)}$, for $n \geq 2$. It should be clear now how to complete the proof that $\{x_n\}_{n=1}^{\infty}$ converges to zero.

EXERCISES

1. Let x and y be distinct real numbers. Prove that there is a neighborhood P of x and a neighborhood Q of y such that $P \cap Q$ is empty.

*2. Suppose x is a real number and $\varepsilon > 0$. Prove that $(x - \varepsilon, x + \varepsilon)$ is a neighborhood of each of its members; in other words if $y \in (x - \varepsilon, x + \varepsilon)$ then there is $\delta > 0$ such that $(y - \delta, y + \delta) \subset (x - \varepsilon, x + \varepsilon)$.

3. Let x, y, and z be real numbers with $y \neq z$. Prove that there is a neighborhood of x which excludes either y or z.

4. Prove Theorem 1.4.

* 5. Let S be a nonvoid set of real numbers which is bounded from above (below), and let $x = \sup S (x = \inf S)$. Prove that either $x \in S$ or x is an accumulation point of S.

* 6. Let $\{a_n\}_{n=1}^{\infty}$ be a sequence such that there exist numbers α and N such that for $n \geq N$, $a_n = \alpha$. Prove that $\{a_n\}_{n=1}^{\infty}$ converges to α.

* 7. Suppose $\{a_n\}_{n=1}^{\infty}$, $\{b_n\}_{n=1}^{\infty}$, and $\{c_n\}_{n=1}^{\infty}$ are sequences such that $\{a_n\}_{n=1}^{\infty}$ converges to A, $\{b_n\}_{n=1}^{\infty}$ converges to A, and $a_n \leq c_n \leq b_n$ for all n. Prove that $\{c_n\}_{n=1}^{\infty}$ converges to A.

* 8. If $\{a_n\}_{n=1}^{\infty}$ converges to a with $a_n \geq 0$ for all n, then $\{\sqrt{a_n}\}_{n=1}^{\infty}$ converges to $\sqrt{a}$. (Hint: If $a > 0$, then

$$\sqrt{a_n} - \sqrt{a} = (a_n - a)/(\sqrt{a_n} + \sqrt{a}).)$$

9. Prove that if $\{a_n\}_{n=1}^{\infty}$ and $\{b_n\}_{n=1}^{\infty}$ are Cauchy sequences, then $\{a_n + b_n\}_{n=1}^{\infty}$ is Cauchy, without using Theorem 1.7; and prove that $\{a_n b_n\}_{n=1}^{\infty}$ is Cauchy without using Theorem 1.8.

10. Suppose $\{a_n\}_{n=1}^{\infty}$, $\{b_n\}_{n=1}^{\infty}$ are sequences such that $\{a_n\}_{n=1}^{\infty}$ and $\{a_n + b_n\}_{n=1}^{\infty}$ converge. Prove that $\{b_n\}_{n=1}^{\infty}$ converges.

11. Give an example in which $\{a_n\}_{n=1}^{\infty}$ and $\{b_n\}_{n=1}^{\infty}$ do not converge, but $\{a_n + b_n\}_{n=1}^{\infty}$ converges.

12. Suppose $\{a_n\}_{n=1}^{\infty}$, $\{b_n\}_{n=1}^{\infty}$ are sequences such that $\{a_n\}_{n=1}^{\infty}$ converges to $A \neq 0$, and $\{a_n b_n\}_{n=1}^{\infty}$ converges. Prove that $\{b_n\}_{n=1}^{\infty}$ converges.

13. Prove that

$$\left\{ \frac{\binom{n+k}{k}}{(n+k)^k} \right\}_{n=1}^{\infty}$$

converges to $\dfrac{1}{k!}$.

$$\binom{n+k}{k} = \frac{(n+k)!}{n!\,k!}$$

*14. Prove that if $\{a_n\}_{n=1}^{\infty}$ converges to A, then $\{|a_n|\}_{n=1}^{\infty}$ converges to $|A|$. Is the converse true?

15. Consider a sequence $\{a_n\}_{n=1}^{\infty}$, and for each n, define $\alpha_n = (a_1 + a_2 + \cdots a_n)/n$. Prove that if $\{a_n\}_{n=1}^{\infty}$ converges to A, then $\{\alpha_n\}_{n=1}^{\infty}$ converges to A. Give an example in which $\{\alpha_n\}_{n=1}^{\infty}$ converges but $\{a_n\}_{n=1}^{\infty}$ does not.

16. Prove the following variation on Lemma 1.9: If $\{b_n\}_{n=1}^{\infty}$ converges to $B \neq 0$ and $b_n \neq 0$ for all n, then there is $M > 0$ such that $|b_n| \geq M$ for all n.

*17. Prove that if $\{a_n\}_{n=1}^{\infty}$ is decreasing and bounded, then $\{a_n\}_{n=1}^{\infty}$ converges.

*18. Prove that if $c > 1$, then $\{\sqrt[n]{c}\}_{n=1}^{\infty}$ converges to 1.

*19. Suppose $\{x_n\}_{n=1}^{\infty}$ converges to x_0 and $\{y_n\}_{n=1}^{\infty}$ converges to x_0. Define a sequence $\{z_n\}_{n=1}^{\infty}$ as follows: $z_{2n} = x_n$ and $z_{2n+1} = y_n$. Prove that $\{z_n\}_{n=1}^{\infty}$ converges to x_0.

*20. Let $\{a_n\}_{n=1}^{\infty}$ be a bounded sequence of real numbers. Prove that $\{a_n\}_{n=1}^{\infty}$ has a convergent subsequence. (Hint: You may want to use the Bolzano–Weierstrass Theorem.)

CHAPTER 2

LIMITS OF FUNCTIONS

The notion of the existence of a limit of a function at a point underlies the study of calculus. When students fail to understand this idea, their study of calculus becomes a drudgery of juggling formulas. Before considering continuity, differentiation, and integration, one needs a thorough understanding of limits. The material on sequences presented in Chapter 1 will help in achieving this understanding.

First we shall consider an example commonly found in calculus books. Let

$$f(x) = \frac{x^2 - 1}{x - 1}$$

for $x \neq 1$, and let $f(1) = 6$. We find that $f(x) = x + 1$ for $x \neq 1$ and $f(1) = 6$. To the unsophisticated, it may seem objectionable to define a function this way. Since f behaves so well elsewhere, it seems reasonable to define $f(1) = 1 + 1 = 2$. In this chapter we shall attempt to rearrange any prejudices of the reader concerning the behavior of functions such as this.

First of all, let us examine the intuitive idea of a limit of a function that was presented in elementary calculus. Consider a function $f : D \to R$ where $D \subset R$ and L is a real number.† If $x_0 \in R$, then f has a limit L at x_0 if, as x approaches x_0, $f(x)$ gets close to L. Of course, the values of x to be considered must belong to the domain of the function. The precise formulation of the idea of getting close no longer poses any problem, since this has already been done in Chapter 1 while dealing with convergent sequences. To summarize, in order to formalize the definition of limit of a function, it is necessary to give a precise definition of what is meant by "$f(x)$ gets close to L as x approaches x_0," and to set the stage for this, it is necessary that there be points in D as close to x_0 as one may wish. Finally, the limit should depend only on the behavior of the function near x_0, not on $f(x_0)$; indeed x_0 need not even belong to D.

DEFINITION   Let $f : D \to R$ with x_0 an accumulation point of D. Then f has a limit L at x_0 iff for each $\varepsilon > 0$ there is a $\delta > 0$ such that if $0 < |x - x_0| < \delta$ and $x \in D$, then $|f(x) - L| < \varepsilon$.

Observe that the definition is similar to that concerning a sequence converging to a real number L, in that it does not specify that if L exists, it is unique. However, this is true and the proof is left to the reader (Exercise 1). If f has a limit L at x_0, we write $L = \lim_{x \to x_0} f(x)$.

It is incorrect for a student to think he should memorize all definitions such as the preceding one. That this mistaken impression is widespread among students is evidenced by the fact that many are able to regurgitate the words of the definition, sometimes in the wrong order, without understanding the full meaning. A definition should be carefully examined, dissected, and fully assimilated. The reasons behind it and the full meaning of each part of the statement should be carefully considered.

† Here and throughout the remainder of this book, R will be the set of all real numbers, and the domain of any functions considered will be subsets of R.

The ideas should become not only a part of one's memory, but a part of one's way of thinking, familiar friends and companions along the journey to enjoyment of mathematics.

First of all, the insistence that x_0 be an accumulation point of D, the domain of f, is necessary in order that f be defined at points near x_0. Now, the positive number ε is the desired degree of closeness chosen in advance. To fulfill the definition, one must find $\delta > 0$ (which, of course, will generally depend on ε) such that if $x \in (x_0 - \delta, x_0 + \delta)$, $x \in D$, and $x \neq x_0$ (the behavior of f at x_0 should not affect the limit); then $f(x) \in (L - \varepsilon, L + \varepsilon)$. This last statement is equivalent to insisting that the graph of f for $x \in D \cap (x_0 - \delta, x_0 + \delta)$, $x \neq x_0$, lies in the strip $\{(x, y) : L - \varepsilon < y < L + \varepsilon\}$.

Let us now reconsider the example mentioned at the beginning of the chapter. Let $D = R$, and define $f : D \to R$ by

$$f(x) = \frac{x^2 - 1}{x - 1}$$

for $x \neq 1$ and $f(1) = 6$. For $x \neq 1$, $f(x) = (x^2 - 1)/(x - 1) = x + 1$; hence, f is a linear function, and the graph of f is a line with slope 1, except for $x = 1$. As mentioned above, the number $f(1)$ has nothing to do with the existence of a limit at $x = 1$. Thus, one is led to believe (correctly, by the geometry of the plane) that as x approaches 1, $f(x)$ approaches the value necessary to fill in the gap in the line—namely, $1 + 1 = 2$. Let us prove that f has a limit $L = 2$ at $x = 1$.

Choose $\varepsilon > 0$. Consider the geometric interpretation of the idea of a limit. It is necessary to choose a neighborhood of 1 such that for x in this neighborhood with $x \neq 1$, the corresponding points on the graph of f lie in the strip $\{(x, y) : 2 - \varepsilon < y < 2 + \varepsilon\}$. Now ignoring the point $x = 1$, the graph of f is a straight line of slope 1. Thus, one is tempted to try $\varepsilon = \delta$ to obtain the neighborhood $(1 - \delta, 1 + \delta)$ of $x = 1$. This result could be obtained by direct computation, but it is worthwhile to take this opportunity to emphasize the geometric aspect of the definition. If $0 < |x - 1| < \delta = \varepsilon$, then

$$|f(x) - 2| = \left| \frac{x^2 - 1}{x - 1} - 2 \right| = |(x + 1) - 2| = |x - 1| < \delta = \varepsilon,$$

and the conjecture is shown to be correct.

Define $f: [0, 1] \to R$ by $f(x) = 0$ for x rational and $f(x) = 1$ for x irrational. Every interval in $[0, 1]$ contains both rational and irrational points; hence, in every interval, f assumes the values 0 and 1. Now if f were to have a limit L at some point $x_0 \in [0, 1]$, then all values of f at points near x_0 must lie close to L. Let $\varepsilon = \frac{1}{4}$. Then there must be $\delta > 0$ such that for $0 < |x - x_0| < \delta$ and $x \in [0, 1]$, we have $|f(x) - L| < \frac{1}{4}$. Choose r rational and p irrational such that $0 < |r - x_0| < \delta$, $r \in [0, 1]$ and $0 < |p - x_0| < \delta$, $p \in [0, 1]$. Then

$$1 = |f(p) - f(r)| \leq |f(p) - L + L - f(r)| \leq |f(p) - L| + |L - f(r)|$$

$$< \frac{1}{4} + \frac{1}{4} = \frac{1}{2}.$$

This is obviously false, so f does not have a limit at x_0.

To show that a function f does not have a limit at x_0, it is necessary to show that no real number L has the properties described in the definition, a task which is sometimes difficult in a manner reminiscent of the problems encountered in showing that a sequence did not converge. It will indeed be rewarding if we can simplify this task, as we did for sequences, but let us postpone that for the moment. For the present, we consider a more sophisticated example and attack it only with the tools at hand—namely, the definition and our knowledge of the real line. Define $f: [0, 1] \to R$ by $f(x) = 0$ if x is irrational; and if x is rational, set $f(x) = 1/q$ where $x = p/q$ with p and q non-negative integers that are relatively prime. Thus, we have $f(0) = 1$, $f(\frac{1}{4}) = \frac{1}{4}$, $f(\frac{2}{3}) = \frac{1}{3}$, $f(\sqrt{2}/2) = 0$, $f(6/8) = \frac{1}{4}$, etc. We shall seek to determine those points at which f has a limit and those at which f does not have a limit.

Suppose $x_0 \in [0, 1]$, and let us examine the behavior of f near x_0. Since there are irrational points in every neighborhood of x_0 which are distinct from x_0, it is clear that f takes the value 0 in every neighborhood of x_0 infinitely often. Thus, if there is to be a limit of f at x_0, it is clear that that limit must be zero. It remains to decide if it is reasonable to expect that f has zero as a limit at x_0. For $x \in [0, 1]$, $f(x)$ is small (close to zero), only if x is irrational or if $x = p/q$, p and q relatively prime with q large. However, for a fixed positive integer q, there are but a finite number of points in $[0, 1]$ of the form p/q; in fact, for a fixed positive integer q_0, there are only a finite number of points in $[0, 1]$ of the form p/q, where $q \leq q_0$ with p and q positive integers. Thus, $f(x) \geq 1/q_0$ at only a finite number of points. Now, in view of these observations, the reader should suspect that indeed f has a limit at x and the limit is zero. Let us now give a proof of this fact.

Choose $\varepsilon > 0$. There is a positive integer q_0 such that $1/q_0 < \varepsilon$. There are at most a finite number of rational points in $[0, 1]$ of the form p/q where p and q are positive integers with $q < q_0$, say $r_1, \ldots, r_n$. We may assume that x_0 is deleted from this list if it should happen to be of this form. Now, to guarantee that $f(x)$ is small, it is sufficient to avoid these points. Thus, let

$$\delta = \min \{|x_0 - r_i| : i = 1, \ldots, n\},$$

and observe that $\delta > 0$. Now if $0 < |x - x_0| < \delta$ and $x \in [0, 1]$, then x is either irrational, in which case $f(x) = 0$, or $x = p/q$ where p and q are relatively prime with $q > q_0$, in which case $f(x) = 1/q$. In either case,

$$|f(x) - 0| = |f(x)| \leq \frac{1}{q} < \frac{1}{q_0} < \varepsilon.$$

Thus, f has a limit at each $x \in [0, 1]$ and that limit is zero.

Define $f : (0, 1) \to R$ by $f(x) = \sin 1/x$, and consider the behavior of f at $x = 0$. Although zero is not in the domain of f, it is an accumulation point of the domain of f; hence, it is reasonable to inquire whether or not f has a limit at zero. In this example, it is instructive for the reader to sketch enough of the graph of this function to gain an insight into its behavior as x approaches zero. Since $f(1/n\pi) = 0$ for each positive integer n and $f(2/n\pi)$ is $+1$ or -1 for n an odd positive integer, we see that the function oscillates more and more wildly as x becomes close to zero. Consequently, it is very reasonable to conjecture that f does not have a limit at zero. This will be verified in a fashion similar to that used in showing that the sequence $\{0, 1, 0, 1, 0, \ldots\}$ does not converge. The essence of the idea is to observe that the values of the function cannot all be near some number L when x is near 0, since, in any neighborhood of 0, the function assumes the values 1 and 0.

Let L be any real number and choose $\varepsilon = \frac{1}{3}$. To show that L is not a limit of f at zero, it suffices to show that for any $\delta > 0$, there is $x \in (0, 1)$ such that $0 < |x - 0| < \delta$ and $|f(x) - L| \geq \varepsilon$. By the choice of ε, either $1 \notin (L - \varepsilon, L + \varepsilon)$, or $0 \notin (L - \varepsilon, L + \varepsilon)$. Suppose the latter is the case. Then, given $\delta > 0$, there is a positive integer n such that $1/n\pi < \delta$, and, as observed above, $f(1/n\pi) = 0 \notin (L - \varepsilon, L + \varepsilon)$; hence, $|f(1/n\pi) - L| \geq \varepsilon$.

The case for $1 \notin (L - \varepsilon, L + \varepsilon)$ may be handled similarly. Thus, f does not have a limit at zero.

A word of philosophy seems appropriate at this point. The emphasis on rigor, in both definitions and proofs, is intentional, since this is the only way mathematics can be communicated intelligently. However, one's feelings and intuition about these matters should not be discarded or considered unimportant. On the contrary, intuition is very important and must be cultivated, but it must also be accompanied by the realization that we must provide rigorous proofs for those facts that our intuition tells us are true. Finally, the intuition must constantly be readjusted, because we are occasionally led astray by our feelings. In the preceding example, the oscillatory nature of the function, as evidenced by a sketch of the graph, led our intuition to tell us that the function does not have a limit at zero. The behavior of the function $f(x) = 0$ for x irrational and $f(p/q) = 1/q$ for p and q non-negative integers which are relatively prime, is probably an example that will elude the intuition of the novice. However, the facts are now before us and should be considered as a new experience leading to greater mathematical maturity. The following example should be a familiar friend, and all we shall do is fill in the necessary rigor.

Define $f : (0, 1) \to R$ by $f(x) = 1/x$. Now zero is an accumulation point of $(0, 1)$; hence, we may inquire as to the existence of the limit of f at zero. Again, from a sketch of a part of the graph of this function, it is seen that the function " blows up " at zero. This is not the sort of behavior one expects a function to have if it is to have a limit at zero, so let us prove that f does not have a limit at zero. Let L be any real number, and choose $\varepsilon > 0$ such that $L + \varepsilon > 0$. Now, if $0 < x < 1/(L + \varepsilon)$, then $L + \varepsilon < 1/x = f(x)$; hence, $|f(x) - L| > \varepsilon$. Thus, it is impossible to find a $\delta > 0$ to fulfill the requirements of the definition; that is, L is not a limit of f at zero. Since L is any real number, f does not have a limit at zero.

The four examples thus far considered could be handled more easily with some machinery that can be built up for this purpose. However, the process of considering them directly in terms of the definition should help in the understanding of the concept.

As mentioned in Chapter 1, a very strong relationship exists between limits of sequences and limits of functions. Now is clearly the time to seek out these relationships and exploit them to the fullest. Suppose $f : D \to R$ with x_0 an accumulation point of D, and suppose f has a limit L at x_0. Consider a sequence $\{x_n\}_{n=1}^{\infty}$ converging to x_0 with $x_n \in D$, $x_0 \neq x_n$, for each positive integer n. Since f has a limit L at x_0, as the terms of the sequence get close to x_0, the corresponding values of f must get close to L; in fact, we must have $\{f(x_n)\}_{n=1}^{\infty}$ converging to L. Fortunately, the converse of this theorem is also true. We summarize these results in the following theorem.

2.1 THEOREM   Let $f: D \rightarrow R$ with x_0 an accumulation point of D. Then f has a limit at x_0 iff for each sequence $\{x_n\}_{n=1}^{\infty}$ converging to x_0 with $x_n \in D$ and $x_n \neq x_0$ for all n, the sequence $\{f(x_n)\}_{n=1}^{\infty}$ converges.

Before proving this theorem, let us reflect upon its importance. Consider two sequences $\{x_n\}_{n=1}^{\infty}$ and $\{y_n\}_{n=1}^{\infty}$ such that $x_n, y_n \in D, x_n \neq x_0$, $y_n \neq x_0$ for $n = 1, 2, \ldots$, and such that both $\{x_n\}_{n=1}^{\infty}$ and $\{y_n\}_{n=1}^{\infty}$ converge to x_0. If we assume that the latter condition of the theorem holds, then $\{f(x_n)\}_{n=1}^{\infty}$ and $\{f(y_n)\}_{n=1}^{\infty}$ both converge to, say, L_1 and L_2, respectively. (Note that the condition does not assert that $L_1 = L_2$.) Form a new sequence $\{z_n\}_{n=1}^{\infty}$ where $z_{2n} = x_n$ and $z_{2n-1} = y_n$. This sequence consists of members of D distinct from x_0, and it converges to x_0; hence, $\{f(z_n)\}_{n=1}^{\infty}$ converges. In particular, $\{f(x_n)\}_{n=1}^{\infty}$ and $\{f(y_n)\}_{n=1}^{\infty}$ are subsequences of the convergent sequence $\{f(z_n)\}_{n=1}^{\infty}$, and, hence have the same limit; that is, $L_1 = L_2$. Now, if for every sequence $\{x_n\}_{n=1}^{\infty}$ of members of D distinct from x_0 and converging to x_0, the sequence $\{f(x_n)\}_{n=1}^{\infty}$ converges, then all such sequences have a common limit by use of the above observations. This limit should be the limit of the function, a fact which remains to be seen.

Proof: Suppose f has a limit L at x_0. Let $\{x_n\}_{n=1}^{\infty}$ be a sequence of members of D distinct from x_0 but converging to x_0, and consider the sequence $\{f(x_n)\}_{n=1}^{\infty}$. Choose $\varepsilon > 0$. There is $\delta > 0$ such that if $0 < |x - x_0| < \delta$ with $x \in D$, then $|f(x) - L| < \varepsilon$. Since $\{x_n\}_{n=1}^{\infty}$ converges to x_0, there is N such that for $n \geq N$, $|x_n - x_0| < \delta$. Now for $n \geq N$, $0 < |x_n - x_0| < \delta$ and $x_n \in D$; hence, $|f(x_n) - L| < \varepsilon$. Thus, $\{f(x_n)\}_{n=1}^{\infty}$ converges; indeed, it converges to L.

Suppose now that the latter condition is satisfied; and by the remarks following the theorem, all the sequences $\{f(x_n)\}_{n=1}^{\infty}$ have a common limit, called (with great originality) L. Suppose that L

is not a limit of f at x_0. (We do not assume anything concerning the existence of the limit of f at x_0; we assume only that L is not a limit of f at x_0.) Thus, there is $\varepsilon > 0$ such that for every $\delta > 0$, there is $x \in D$, with $0 < |x - x_0| < \delta$ and such that $|f(x) - L| \geq \varepsilon$. In particular, for each positive integer n, there is $x_n \in D$ with $0 < |x_n - x_0| < 1/n$ such that $|f(x_n) - L| \geq \varepsilon$. The sequence $\{x_n\}_{n=1}^{\infty}$ converges to x_0 and is a sequence of members of D distinct from x_0; hence, $\{f(x_n)\}_{n=1}^{\infty}$ converges to L, contrary to the fact that $|f(x_n) - L| \geq \varepsilon > 0$ for all n. Thus, L must be the limit of f at x_0.

To summarize, f has a limit L at x_0 iff, for each sequence $\{x_n\}_{n=1}^{\infty}$ of members of D distinct from x_0 converging to x_0, the sequence $\{f(x_n)\}_{n=1}^{\infty}$ converges. If the second condition is satisfied, then all the given sequences $\{f(x_n)\}_{n=1}^{\infty}$ have a common limit, which is L, the limit of the function f. An example should serve to reveal the usefulness of this equivalence and the related observation that follows it. Let $f : (0, 1) \rightarrow R$ satisfy the following condition: there is $K > 0$ such that for all $x, y \in (0, 1)$, $|f(x) - f(y)| \leq K |x - y|$. Thus, in particular, whenever $\{x_n\}_{n=1}^{\infty}$ is a Cauchy sequence in $(0, 1)$, then so is $\{f(x_n)\}_{n=1}^{\infty}$; hence, if $\{x_n\}_{n=1}^{\infty}$ is a sequence in $(0, 1)$ converging to 0, the sequence $\{f(x_n)\}_{n=1}^{\infty}$ is convergent. By the theorem, f has a limit at zero; and that may be computed by determining the limit of $\{f(x_n)\}_{n=1}^{\infty}$ for any sequence $\{x_n\}_{n=1}^{\infty}$ in $(0, 1)$ converging to zero. Hopefully, a judicious choice of the sequence $\{x_n\}_{n=1}^{\infty}$ may make the task less tedious.

The urge to reconsider the preceding remarks and to generalize the result is irresistible. Note that the conclusion stems from the fact that $\{x_n\}_{n=1}^{\infty}$ Cauchy implies $\{f(x_n)\}_{n=1}^{\infty}$ Cauchy. The proof of the following theorem is immediate.

2.2 THEOREM Let $f : D \rightarrow R$, and suppose x_0 is an accumulation point of D. If for each sequence $\{x_n\}_{n=1}^{\infty}$ converging to x_0 with $x_n \in D \backslash \{x_0\}$ for each n, the sequence $\{f(x_n)\}_{n=1}^{\infty}$ is Cauchy, then f has a limit at x_0.

Let us now sift through our newly gained knowledge of sequences and hopefully discover theorems concerning limits of functions. Many of these theorems may be proved by exploiting Theorem 2.1, but in some cases we will give a direct proof in order to introduce the reader to the act of finding δ's.

2.3 THEOREM   Let $f : D \to R$, with x_0 an accumulation point of D. If f has a limit at x_0, then there is a neighborhood Q of x_0 and a real number M such that for all $x \in Q \cap D$, $|f(x)| \leq M$.

Proof: Let $\varepsilon = 1$, and let L be the limit of f at x_0. Then there is $\delta > 0$ such that for $0 < |x - x_0| < \delta$ and $x \in D$, we have $|f(x) - L| < \varepsilon = 1$. If $x_0 \in D$, define

$$M = \max \{|L - 1|, |L + 1|, |f(x_0)|\};$$

otherwise, define

$$M = \max \{|L - 1|, |L + 1|\},$$

and let $Q = (x_0 - \delta, x_0 + \delta)$. In either case, if $x \in Q \cap D$, then $|f(x)| \leq M$.

In less formal language, if f has a limit at x_0, then f is bounded near x_0. In particular, this gives another verification that $f(x) = 1/x$ does not have a limit at zero since f is unbounded in every neighborhood of 0.

For each real number x, let $[x]$ denote the largest integer which is less than or equal to x. For example, $[\pi] = 3$, $[3/2] = 1$, and $[2] = 2$. For $n \leq x < n + 1$ with n an integer, $[x] = n$, so the graph of the function looks like a set of stairs with a "jump" of one at each integer. If we have been successful in developing the geometric concept of the limit of a function, it should be apparent that $f(x) = [x]$ has a limit at x_0 iff x_0 is not an integer. Suppose x_0 is not an integer and let $\delta =$ distance from x_0 to the nearest integer. Now $\delta > 0$, and if $0 < |x - x_0| < \delta$, then $[x] = [x_0]$, hence $|f(x) - [x_0]| = 0 < \varepsilon$ for all $\varepsilon > 0$. Thus, f has a limit at x_0 if x_0 is not an integer. If x_0 is an integer, consider the sequence $\{x_0 + (-1)^n 1/n\}_{n=1}^{\infty}$. Now for n odd, $n > 1$, $x_0 + (-1)^n 1/n < x_0$, and thus

$$f\left(x_0 + (-1)^n \frac{1}{n}\right) = x_0 - 1;$$

and for n even, $x_0 + (-1)^n 1/n > x_0$, and thus

$$f\left(x_0 + (-1)^n \frac{1}{n}\right) = x_0.$$

Thus, $\{f(x_0 + (-1)^n 1/n)\}_{n=1}^{\infty}$ does not converge, and so f does not have a limit at x_0 if x_0 is an integer.

Consider the examples $f(x) = [x]$, $g(x) = \sin 1/x$, and $h(x) = 1/x$. Each failed to have a limit at zero for basically different reasons. The function $f(x) = [x]$ "jumped" at zero, taking the value -1 to the left of zero and the value 0 to the right of zero; g oscillated too badly at zero to have a limit there; h was unbounded near zero and so could not have a limit there. In a sense, these three examples describe the sort of behavior one may suspect of a function that does not have a limit at a point. We shall comment more on this at the end of this chapter.

Following the pattern set in Chapter 1, we shall now determine the relationships between limits of functions and the algebraic operations. If $f : D \to R$ and $g : D \to R$, define $f + g : D \to R$ by $(f + g)(x) = f(x) + g(x)$ for all $x \in D$. In a similar fashion, define $fg : D \to R$ by $(fg)(x) = f(x)g(x)$. If $g(x) \neq 0$ for $x \in D$, we may define $f/g : D \to R$ by $(f/g)(x) = f(x)/g(x)$ for all $x \in D$. Now read Theorems 1.7, 1.8, and 1.10, and attempt to formulate corresponding theorems for limits of functions. In each case, the proof can be obtained by use of Theorem 2.1 and the appropriate result from Chapter 1.

2.4 THEOREM Suppose $f, g : D \to R$ with x_0 an accumulation point of D, and further suppose that f and g have limits at x_0. Then,

(1) $f + g$ has a limit at x_0 and

$$\lim_{x \to x_0} (f + g)(x) = \lim_{x \to x_0} f(x) + \lim_{x \to x_0} g(x);$$

(2) fg has a limit at x_0 and

$$\lim_{x \to x_0} (fg)(x) = [\lim_{x \to x_0} f(x)][\lim_{x \to x_0} g(x)];$$

(3) if $g(x) \neq 0$ for all $x \in D$ and $\lim_{x \to x_0} g(x) \neq 0$, then f/g has a limit at x_0 and

$$\lim_{x \to x_0} \left(\frac{f}{g}\right)(x) = \frac{\lim_{x \to x_0} f(x)}{\lim_{x \to x_0} g(x)}.$$

The proofs of (1) and (3) will be accomplished by use of sequences, while the proof of (2) will be direct.

Proof: (1) Let $\{x_n\}_{n=1}^{\infty}$ be any sequence of points in D converging to x_0 with $x_n \neq x_0$ for all n. It suffices to show that $\{(f + g)(x_n)\}_{n=1}^{\infty}$ converges to

$$\lim_{x \to x_0} f(x) + \lim_{x \to x_0} g(x).$$

By assumption, f and g have limits at x_0; hence, $\{f(x_n)\}_{n=1}^{\infty}$ converges to $\lim_{x \to x_0} f(x)$ and $\{g(x_n)\}_{n=1}^{\infty}$ converges to $\lim_{x \to x_0} g(x)$. By Theorem 1.7,

$$\{(f + g)(x_n)\}_{n=1}^{\infty} = \{f(x_n) + g(x_n)\}_{n=1}^{\infty}$$

converges to $\lim_{x \to x_0} f(x) + \lim_{x \to x_0} g(x)$. This concludes the proof of (1).

(2) Given $\varepsilon > 0$, we must find an appropriate $\delta > 0$. The reader is referred to the discussion preceding Theorem 1.8 before beginning the proof. As the plan for finding the δ unfolds, observe the parallel between this search and that for N in Theorem 1.8.

Choose $\varepsilon > 0$. Let

$$A = \lim_{x \to x_0} f(x) \quad \text{and} \quad B = \lim_{x \to x_0} g(x).$$

We wish to find $\delta > 0$ such that if $0 < |x - x_0| < \delta$ and $x \in D$, then $|f(x)g(x) - AB| < \varepsilon$. By Theorem 2.3, there is $\delta_1 > 0$ and a real number $M > 0$ such that for $0 < |x - x_0| < \delta_1$, $x \in D$, we have $|f(x)| \leq M$. Let

$$\varepsilon' = \frac{\varepsilon}{|B| + M} > 0.$$

There is $\delta_2 > 0$ such that if $0 < |x - x_0| < \delta_2$, $x \in D$, then $|f(x) - A| < \varepsilon'$ and $\delta_3 > 0$ such that for $0 < |x - x_0| < \delta_3$, $x \in D$, we have $|g(x) - B| < \varepsilon'$. Let

$$\delta = \min \{\delta_1, \delta_2, \delta_3\}.$$

Now if $0 < |x - x_0| < \delta$, $x \in D$, then,

$$|(fg)(x) - AB| = |f(x)g(x) - AB| \le |f(x)g(x) - f(x)B|$$
$$+ |f(x)B - AB|$$
$$= |f(x)||g(x) - B| + |B||f(x) - A| < M\varepsilon' + |B|\varepsilon'$$
$$= \varepsilon.$$

(3) Suppose $\{x_n\}_{n=1}^{\infty}$ is a sequence of members of D distinct from x_0, converging to x_0. Now $\{f(x_n)\}_{n=1}^{\infty}$ converges to $\lim_{x \to x_0} f(x)$ and $\{g(x_n)\}_{n=1}^{\infty}$ converges to $\lim_{x \to x_0} g(x)$. Since $g(x) \ne 0$ for all $x \in D$, $g(x_n) \ne 0$ for all n. By assumption, $\lim_{x \to x_0} g(x) \ne 0$. Hence

$$\left\{ \left(\frac{f}{g} \right)(x_n) \right\}_{n=1}^{\infty} = \left\{ \frac{f(x_n)}{g(x_n)} \right\}_{n=1}^{\infty}$$

converges to

$$\frac{\lim_{x \to x_0} f(x)}{\lim_{x \to x_0} g(x)}.$$

By Theorem 2.1, f/g has the indicated limit at x_0.

The adventuresome reader may wish to attempt a direct proof of (3). A lemma similar to 1.9 is in order, and then the proof may be patterned after that of Theorem 1.10. Good luck!

2.5 THEOREM   Suppose $f: D \to R$ and $g: D \to R$, x_0 is an accumulation point of D, and f and g have limits at x_0. If $f(x) \le g(x)$ for all $x \in D$, then

$$\lim_{x \to x_0} f(x) \le \lim_{x \to x_0} g(x).$$

Proof: Exercise 7.

Let us now look at an example suggested by the sequence $\{1/n \sin n\pi/4\}_{n=1}^{\infty}$. Consider the function $f: (0, 1) \to R$, defined by $f(x) = x \sin 1/x$. It has been shown that $\sin 1/x$ fails to have a limit at zero;

so, we may not use Theorem 2.4 (2). However, $\sin 1/x$ is bounded above by 1 and below by -1. Now it is clear that

$$|f(x)| = \left| x \sin \frac{1}{x} \right| \leq |x|;$$

hence, f has a limit at zero; in fact, $\lim_{x \to 0} f(x) = 0$. (We merely choose $\delta = \varepsilon$.) Now, a theorem reminiscent of Theorem 1.12 is in order.

2.6 THEOREM   Let $f: D \to R$ and $g: D \to R$, x_0 an accumulation point of D. If f is bounded in a neighborhood of x_0 and g has limit zero at x_0, then fg has a limit at x_0 and $\lim_{x \to x_0} fg(x) = 0$.

Proof: Choose $\varepsilon > 0$. There is a $\delta_1 > 0$ and $M > 0$ such that if $x \in D$, $|x - x_0| < \delta_1$, then $|f(x)| \leq M$. Let $\varepsilon' = \varepsilon/M$. There is $\delta_2 > 0$ such that if $x \in D$ and $0 < |x - x_0| < \delta_2$, then

$$|g(x) - \lim_{x \to x_0} g(x)| = |g(x)| < \varepsilon'.$$

Choose $\delta = \min\{\delta_1, \delta_2\}$. Then if $0 < |x - x_0| < \delta$ with $x \in D$, a computation yields

$$|(fg)(x)| = |f(x)g(x)| = |f(x)||g(x)| \leq M\varepsilon' = \varepsilon.$$

Hence, fg has a limit at x_0, and $\lim_{x \to x_0} (fg)(x) = 0$.

The proper use of the preceding theorems will allow us to handle a rather large class of functions. Suppose $f: R \to R$ is defined by $f(x) = x$ for each $x \in R$. If $x_0 \in R$, then for each sequence $\{x_n\}_{n=1}^{\infty}$ converging to x_0 with $x_n \in R \backslash \{x_0\}$,

$$\{f(x_n)\}_{n=1}^{\infty} = \{x_n\}_{n=1}^{\infty}$$

is convergent to x_0, hence f has a limit at x_0; in particular,

$$\lim_{x \to x_0} f(x) = x_0.$$

Now this is clearly not intended to startle the reader, but we include it for completeness. Choose $k \in R$ and consider the function $g: R \to R$ where

$g(x) = k$ for all $x \in R$. It is clear that g has a limit at x_0 for each $x_0 \in R$ and $\lim_{x \to x_0} g(x) = k$. These last two statements are usually expressed as

$$\lim_{x \to x_0} x = x_0 \quad \text{and} \quad \lim_{x \to x_0} k = k.$$

Now by use of induction and Theorem 2.4 (2), we see that the function $f(x) = x^n$ has a limit at x_0 for each $x_0 \in R$, and $\lim_{x \to x_0} x^n = x_0^n$. By using this result, induction, and parts (1) and (2) of 2.4, we see that for each polynomial

$$p(x) = a_0 + a_1 x + \cdots + a_n x^n,$$

p has a limit at x_0 for each $x_0 \in R$ and $\lim_{x \to x_0} p(x) = p(x_0)$.

If p and q are polynomials and $\{r_1, \ldots, r_n\}$ are the real roots of the equation $q(x) = 0$, then $f: R \backslash \{r_1, \ldots, r_n\} \to R$ defined by

$$f(x) = \frac{p(x)}{q(x)}$$

has a limit at every point x_0 of $R \backslash \{r_1, \ldots, r_n\}$ and

$$\lim_{x \to x_0} f(x) = f(x_0) = \frac{p(x_0)}{q(x_0)}.$$

We are safe in using part (3) of 2.4 in this case since p and q have limits at every point, and $r_1, \ldots, r_n$ are the only points where $\lim_{x \to x_0} q(x) = 0$. The question of the existence of a limit at the points $r_i, i = 1, \ldots, n$, must be handled in a different fashion. We shall postpone the general case until we discuss continuity in Chapter 3.

Recall from an exercise in Chapter 1 that if $\{a_n\}_{n=1}^{\infty}$ is a sequence of non-negative real numbers converging to a, then $\{\sqrt{a_n}\}_{n=1}^{\infty}$ converges to $\sqrt{a}$. Applying this result to this chapter, it becomes clear that if $f: D \to R$ with $f(x) \geq 0$ for all $x \in D$ and if f has a limit at x_0, then the function $g(x) = \sqrt{f(x)}$ has a limit at x_0, and

$$\lim_{x \to x_0} \sqrt{f(x)} = \sqrt{\lim_{x \to x_0} f(x)}.$$

With this in mind, consider the function $h: (0, 1) \to R$ defined by $h(x) = (\sqrt{4 + x} - 2)/x$. The function h is represented as the quotient of two functions, but unfortunately, both have limit 0 at zero, so 2.4 is useless at first glance. Let us attempt to follow a pattern used for sequences by trying to write h in some other form. Now

$$h(x) = \frac{(\sqrt{4+x} - 2)}{x} = \frac{(\sqrt{4+x} - 2)(\sqrt{4+x} + 2)}{x(\sqrt{4+x} + 2)}$$

$$= \frac{4 + x - 4}{x(\sqrt{4+x} + 2)} = \frac{1}{\sqrt{4+x} + 2}.$$

The numerator is the constant function whose value is 1 at each point. By our previous remarks, the denominator is a function which has a limit at zero, namely

$$\lim_{x \to 0} (\sqrt{4+x} + 2) = \sqrt{4} + 2 = 4.$$

Thus, by 2.4, h has a limit at zero and

$$\lim_{x \to 0} h(x) = \lim_{x \to 0} \frac{\sqrt{4+x} - 2}{x} = \frac{1}{4}.$$

Much more about limits will come in later chapters; we end this chapter with a rather interesting theorem.

Previously, we considered three functions that failed to have a limit at a point—one that had a jump, one that is oscillatory, and one that is unbounded. Let us take the first case and seek to determine what behavior can be predicted. Recall that the function $f(x) = 1$ for x irrational and $f(x) = 0$ for x rational had a limit at no point of its domain.

DEFINITION   Let $f : D \to R$. f is said to be *increasing* (*decreasing*) iff for all $x, y \in D$ with $x \le y$,

$$f(x) \le f(y) \quad (f(x) \ge f(y)).$$

If f is either increasing or decreasing, then f is said to be *monotone*.

The function $f(x) = [x]$ was an increasing function, and the only points where f failed to have a limit were the integer points, a countable set. Consider now $f : [\alpha, \beta] \to R$ where f is increasing. Now for all $x \in [\alpha, \beta]$, $f(\alpha) \le f(x) \le f(\beta)$, hence f is bounded; and by the monotonicity, f cannot be oscillatory. Attempt to sketch the graph of some functions increasing on $[0, 1]$ which fail to have a limit at some point. After a few such attempts it should become apparent that the only way for such a function to fail to have a limit at x_0 is to jump at x_0 in a manner similar to the behavior of $f(x) = [x]$ at each integer. Let us get a firmer grip on this idea. For $\alpha < x < \beta$, define $U(x) = \inf \{f(y) : x < y\}$, and for $\alpha < x < \beta$, define $L(x) = \sup \{f(y) : y < x\}$. Since $f(\alpha) \leq f(x) \leq f(\beta)$ for all $x \in [\alpha, \beta]$, $L(x)$ and $U(x)$ exist. Intuitively, $U(x) - L(x)$ measures the jump of f at x; in fact, we shall see later that if $x_0 \in (\alpha, \beta)$, then f has a limit at x_0 iff $U(x_0) - L(x_0) = 0$. Assuming this to be the case, let

$$J_n = \left\{ x \in (\alpha, \beta) : U(x) - L(x) > \frac{1}{n} \right\}.$$

Suppose $\{x_1, \ldots, x_k\} \subset J_n$ with $x_1 < x_2 < \cdots < x_k$. Now if f has a jump greater than $1/n$ at $x_1, \ldots, x_r$, then it seems reasonable to suspect that r can't be too large; in fact r should be less than or equal to $n[f(\beta) - f(\alpha)]$. Thus, J_n should be finite, and the set of points where f fails to have a limit should be $\bigcup_{n=1}^{\infty} J_n$, a countable union of finite sets, hence a set which is at most countable. This is the content of the next theorem; we have outlined the proof in a vague way and must now fill in the details.

2.7 THEOREM   Let $f : [\alpha, \beta] \to R$ be monotone. Then $D = \{x : x \in (\alpha, \beta) \text{ and } f \text{ does not have a limit at } x\}$ is at most countable. If f has a limit at $x_0 \in (\alpha, \beta)$, then $\lim_{x \to x_0} f(x) = f(x_0)$.

As we have seen before, some facts necessary to prove a theorem are of enough importance to warrant presenting them as lemmas before completing the proof of the theorem. The following lemma is such an example.

2.8 LEMMA   Let $f : [\alpha, \beta] \to R$ be increasing. Let

$$U(x) = \inf \{f(y) : x < y\} \quad \text{and} \quad L(x) = \sup \{f(y) : y < x\}$$

for $x \in (\alpha, \beta)$. Then f has a limit at $x_0 \in (\alpha, \beta)$ iff $U(x_0) = L(x_0)$, and in this case

$$\lim_{x \to x_0} f(x) = f(x_0) = U(x_0) = L(x_0).$$

Proof: Suppose f has a limit at $x_0 \in (\alpha, \beta)$, called A. Choose $\varepsilon > 0$. There is $\delta > 0$ such that if $0 < |x - x_0| < \delta$ with $x \in [\alpha, \beta]$, then $|f(x) - A| < \varepsilon$. Since $x_0 \in (\alpha, \beta)$, there are $x, y \in [\alpha, \beta]$ such that $x_0 - \delta < x < x_0 < y < x_0 + \delta$, so by the definition of L and U and the fact that f is increasing,

$$A - \varepsilon < f(x) \le L(x_0) \le f(x_0) \le U(x_0) \le f(y) < A + \varepsilon.$$

Therefore, $U(x_0) - L(x_0) < 2\varepsilon$ for each $\varepsilon > 0$; hence $U(x_0) = L(x_0)$; and since $L(x_0) \le f(x_0) \le U(x_0)$,

$$L(x_0) = f(x_0) = U(x_0).$$

Moreover, $A - \varepsilon < U(x_0) < A + \varepsilon$ for all $\varepsilon > 0$; hence $U(x_0) = A$. Thus

$$\lim_{x \to x_0} f(x) = U(x_0) = L(x_0) = f(x_0).$$

Suppose now that $U(x_0) = L(x_0)$. As observed above, $L(x_0) \le f(x_0) \le U(x_0)$, hence $U(x_0) = f(x_0) = L(x_0)$. It remains to be shown that f has a limit at x_0 and that $\lim_{x \to x_0} f(x) = f(x_0)$. Choose $\varepsilon > 0$. Now $L(x_0) - \varepsilon$ is not an upper bound for $\{f(y) : y < x_0\}$, and $U(x_0) + \varepsilon$ is not a lower bound for $\{f(y) : x_0 < y\}$; hence there are real numbers y_1 and y_2 such that $\alpha \le y_1 < x_0 < y_2 \le \beta$ and such that $L(x_0) - \varepsilon < f(y_1)$ and $f(y_2) < U(x_0) + \varepsilon$. Let $\delta = \min\{x_0 - y_1, y_2 - x_0\}$. Now if $0 < |x - x_0| < \delta$, then $y_1 < x < y_2$, hence

$$f(x_0) - \varepsilon = L(x_0) - \varepsilon < f(y_1) < f(x) < f(y_2) < U(x_0) + \varepsilon$$
$$= f(x_0) + \varepsilon;$$

that is, $|f(x) - f(x_0)| < \varepsilon$. Thus, f has a limit at x_0 and $\lim_{x \to x_0} f(x) = f(x_0)$.

The reader has probably observed that we have neglected considering the behavior at α and β. Of course, we cannot define U at β, since if $\beta < y$, y is not in the domain of f, and similarly we cannot define L at α. We shall leave as an exercise to the reader to prove that f has a limit at α and at β. Equipped with this lemma, we are prepared to prove 2.7.

Proof: Assume f is increasing. Let $D = \{x : x \in (\alpha, \beta)$ and f does not have a limit at $x_0\}$. Now by 2.8, $x \in D$ iff $U(x) - L(x) \neq 0$ and, since f is increasing, iff $U(x) - L(x) > 0$. Let

$$D_n = \{x : U(x) - L(x) > 1/n\}.$$

It is clear that $D = \bigcup_{n=1}^{\infty} D_n$. The proof will be complete if we can show that each D_n is finite. Suppose $\{x_1, \ldots, x_r\} \subset D_n$ with $\alpha < x_1 < x_2 < \cdots < x_r < \beta$. Choose $z_1, \ldots, z_{r+1}$ such that $\alpha < z_1 < x_1, x_i < z_{i+1} < x_{i+1}$ for $i = 1, 2, \ldots, r - 1$ and $x_r < z_{r+1} < \beta$. Now for each $i, f(z_i) \leq L(x_i)$ and $U(x_i) \leq f(z_{i+1})$, hence

$$f(z_{i+1}) - f(z_i) \geq U(x_i) - L(x_i) > 1/n.$$

Now

$$f(\beta) - f(\alpha) = f(\beta) - f(z_{r+1})$$
$$+ \sum_{k=2}^{r+1} [f(z_k) - f(z_{k-1})] + f(z_1) - f(\alpha) \geq r(1/n).$$

Since $f(\beta) - f(\alpha) > 0$ is a fixed real number, it is necessary that $r \leq n(f(\beta) - f(\alpha))$. Therefore, D_n is finite for each n; hence, $D = \bigcup_{n=1}^{\infty} Dn$ is at most countable.

Note that if f is decreasing, then $-f$ is increasing, and f has a limit at x_0 iff $-f$ has a limit at x_0. In particular, a lemma similar to 2.8 may be deduced for decreasing functions.

Reflect a bit on the content of this theorem. With only the assumption that $f : [\alpha, \beta] \to R$ is monotone, it is possible to prove that f has a limit everywhere except at points of an at most countable set and, where the limit exists, $\lim_{x \to x_0} f(x) = f(x_0)$. The full meaning of all this will unfold in later chapters.

EXERCISES

*1. Suppose $f : D \to R$, with x_0 an accumulation point of D. Assume L_1 and L_2 are limits of f at x_0. Prove $L_1 = L_2$. (Use only the definition, as in later theorems, this uniqueness is assumed to have been proved.)

2. Define $f : (0, 1) \to R$ by

$$f(x) = \frac{x^3 + 6x^2 + x}{x^2 - 6x}.$$

Prove that f has a limit at zero and find $\lim_{x \to 0} f(x)$.

3. Define $f : (0, 1) \to R$ by $f(x) = \cos(1/x)$. Does f have a limit at zero? What about $f(x) = x \cos 1/x$.?

4. Consider $f : (0, 1) \to R$ defined by $f(x) = x^x$ (this function will be discussed in detail in Chapter 7). Assume that f has a limit at zero and find that limit. Hint: Choose a sequence $\{x_n\}_{n=1}^{\infty}$ converging to zero such that the limit of the sequence $\{f(x_n)\}_{n=1}^{\infty}$ is easy to determine.

5. Suppose $f : R \to R$ is additive in that for all x, $y \in R$, $f(x + y) = f(x) + f(y)$. Show that f has a limit at each point of R iff there are real numbers a and M such that for all $x \in [-a, a]$, $|f(x)| \leq M$.

* 6. Let $f : D \to R$ with x_0 an accumulation point of D. Prove that f has a limit at x_0 if for each $\varepsilon > 0$, there is a neighborhood Q of x_0 such that for $x, y \, \varepsilon \, Q \cap D$, $x \neq x_0$ and $y \neq x_0$, we have $|f(x) - f(y)| < \varepsilon$.

7. Prove Theorem 2.5.

8. If $f, g, h : D \to R$, where x_0 is an accumulation point of D, $f(x) \leq g(x) \leq h(x)$ for all $x \in D$ and if f and h have limits at x_0 such that $\lim_{x \to x_0} f(x) = \lim_{x \to x_0} h(x)$, prove that g has a limit at x_0 and

$$\lim_{x \to x_0} g(x) = \lim_{x \to x_0} f(x) = \lim_{x \to x_0} h(x).$$

* 9. Suppose $g : D \to R$, with x_0 an accumulation point of D and $g(x) \neq 0$ for all $x \in D$. Further, assume that g has a limit at x_0 and $\lim_{x \to x_0} g(x) \neq 0$. State and prove a theorem similar to 1.9 for such a function.

10. Assume $f : R \to R$ is such that $f(x + y) = f(x)f(y)$ for all $x, y \in R$. If f has a limit at zero, prove that f has a limit at every point and either $\lim_{x \to 0} f(x) = 1$ or $f(x) = 0$ for all $x \in R$.

*11. Show by examples that even though f and g fail to have limits at x_0, it is possible for $f + g$, fg, or f/g to have limits at x_0.

*12. If $f : D \to R$ has a limit at x_0, prove that $|f|$ has a limit at x_0. ($|f|$ is that function defined by $|f|(x) = |f(x)|$.) Is the converse of this statement true?

13. Suppose $f : (a, b) \to R$ and $x \in (a, b)$. Define

$$g(t) = f(x + t) - f(x) \quad \text{and} \quad h(t) = f(x + t) - f(x - t)$$

for all t such that $x + t$ and $x - t$ belong to (a, b). Prove that if g has a limit at zero, then h has a limit at zero and $\lim_{t \to 0} h(t) = 0$. Give an example where h has a limit at zero but g does not.

14. State and prove a lemma similar to 2.8 for decreasing functions.

*15. Let $f : [a, b] \to R$ be monotone. Prove that f has a limit at a and at b.

CHAPTER 3

CONTINUITY

In the discussion of the limit of a function it was emphasized that the value of f at x_0 has no bearing on the question of the existence of the limit of a function f at a point x_0. The concept of continuity of a function at a point brings the value of f at x_0 back into the picture. In very imprecise language, a function f will be continuous at a point x_0 if $f(x)$ lies close to $f(x_0)$ whenever x is sufficiently close to x_0. Let us examine this notion in a very familiar setting. Consider the function $f(x) = \sqrt{x}$ for $x \geq 0$. Since $f(2)$ is an irrational number, it cannot be expressed by any of the conventional means as a decimal. Nevertheless, for purposes of computation, we can attempt to obtain rational numbers fairly close to

$\sqrt{2}$. For example, $(1.4)^2 = 1.96$, $(1.41)^2 = 1.9881$, $(1.414)^2 = 1.999396$, etc. In essence, we are observing that $f(1.96) = 1.4$, $f(1.9881) = 1.41$, and $f(1.999396) = 1.414$, and we assume that 1.414 is close to $\sqrt{2}$ since 1.414 is the value of f at a point close to 2. Thus, the assumption is that $f(x) = \sqrt{x}$ is continuous at 2, a fact to be proved later. As with all new ideas, a precise definition is needed.

> **DEFINITION**   Suppose $E \subset R$ and $f : E \to R$. If $x_0 \in E$, then f is *continuous at* x_0 iff for each $\varepsilon > 0$, there is a $\delta > 0$ such that if
>
> $$|x - x_0| < \delta, \qquad x \in E,$$
>
> then
>
> $$|f(x) - f(x_0)| < \varepsilon.$$
>
> If f is continuous at x for every $x \in E$, then we say f is continuous.

Compare this definition with the definition in the previous chapter concerning the limit of a function at a point x_0. First of all, for continuity at x_0, the number x_0 must belong to E but it need not be an accumulation point of E. Indeed, if $f : E \to R$ with $x_0 \in E$ and x_0 not an accumulation point of E, then there is $\delta > 0$ such that if $|x - x_0| < \delta$ and $x \in E$, then $x = x_0$; hence

$$|f(x) - f(x_0)| = 0 < \varepsilon$$

for every $\varepsilon > 0$. In other words, if x_0 is not an accumulation point of E and $x_0 \in E$, then f is continuous at x_0 by default. Thus, the only interesting case is when x_0 is an accumulation point of E. With this assumption, the following theorem seems the natural conclusion after comparing the two aforementioned definitions and related theorems from Chapter 2.

> **3.1 THEOREM**   Let $f : E \to R$ with $x_0 \in E$ and x_0 an accumulation point of E. Then (i)–(iii) below are equivalent:
> (i) f is continuous at x_0.
> (ii) f has a limit at x_0 and $\lim_{x \to x_0} f(x) = f(x_0)$.
> (iii)   For every sequence $\{x_n\}_{n=1}^{\infty}$ converging to x_0 with $x_n \in E$ for each n, $\{f(x_n)\}_{n=1}^{\infty}$ converges to $f(x_0)$.

Note that if x_0 is not an accumulation point of E with $x_0 \in E$, then (i) is always true, as is (iii). The proof that (iii) holds in this case is left to the reader. In any case, (i) and (iii) are equivalent.

Proof: Assume (iii) holds. In particular, if $\{x_n\}_{n=1}^{\infty}$ converges to x_0 with $x_n \neq x_0$ and $x_n \in E$ for all n, then $\{f(x_n)\}_{n=1}^{\infty}$ converges to $f(x_0)$. Hence, by Theorem 2.1, f has a limit at x_0 and $\lim_{x \to x_0} f(x) = f(x_0)$. Thus, (iii) implies (ii).

Assume (ii) holds and choose $\varepsilon > 0$. Since (ii) holds, there is $\delta > 0$ such that if $0 < |x - x_0| < \delta$ and $x \in E$, then

$$|f(x) - f(x_0)| < \varepsilon.$$

The only fact needed to fulfill the definition of continuity at x_0 is to remove the condition $0 < |x - x_0|$. However, when $|x - x_0| = 0$, then $x = x_0$; hence

$$|f(x) - f(x_0)| = 0 < \varepsilon.$$

Thus, f is continuous at x_0; in other words, (ii) implies (i).

Suppose now that (i) holds and $\{x_n\}_{n=1}^{\infty}$ is a sequence of points in E which converges to x_0. Choose $\varepsilon > 0$. There is $\delta > 0$ such that for $|x - x_0| < \delta$ and $x \in E$, $|f(x) - f(x_0)| < \varepsilon$. Since $\{x_n\}_{n=1}^{\infty}$ converges to x_0, there is N such that for $n \geq N$, $|x_n - x_0| < \delta$. Thus, for $n \geq N$, $|f(x_n) - f(x_0)| < \varepsilon$. This shows that $\{f(x_n)\}_{n=1}^{\infty}$ converges to $f(x_0)$. (Does this paragraph look familiar? It should. Compare it with the proof of 2.1.)

It is worthwhile to reflect on this theorem momentarily and consider some of its less obvious uses. First of all, it may be used to show that a given function f is not continuous at a point x_0 by exhibiting a sequence $\{x_n\}_{n=1}^{\infty}$ converging to x_0 where the sequence $\{f(x_n)\}_{n=1}^{\infty}$ does not converge to $f(x_0)$. From a slightly different point of view, this theorem may be used to show that a certain sequence is convergent. For example, we shall later define the function $f(x) = e^x$ and see that it is continuous on R. Thus, in particular, if the sequence $\{x_n\}_{n=1}^{\infty}$ converges to x_0, then the continuity of $f(x) = e^x$ and Theorem 3.1 guarantees that $\{e^{x_n}\}_{n=1}^{\infty}$ converges to e^{x_0}. We shall call attention to this aspect of Theorem 3.1 later.

We pause momentarily to reconsider some of the results presented in Chapter 2. Recall the function $f: R \to R$ defined by

$$f(x) = \frac{x^2 - 1}{x - 1}$$

for $x \neq 1$ and $f(1) = 6$. It has been shown that f has a limit at 1 and $\lim_{x \to 1} f(x) = 2$. Unfortunately, $\lim_{x \to 1} f(x) = 2 \neq 6 = f(1)$; hence, f is not continuous at 1. In this case, f fails to be continuous at 1 because $f(1)$ does not happen to be the limit of f at 1. Now consider the function $g(x) = \sin(1/x)$ for $0 < x < 1$, and $g(0) = 38$. We have seen that g fails to have a limit at zero, so g is not continuous at zero, regardless of what we try for $g(0)$. The function $h(x) = 1/x$ for $0 < x < 1$ behaves similarly in the sense that h doesn't have a limit at zero, so it is futile to attempt to define $h(0)$ in a way so that h will be continuous at zero.

Recall the function $f: [0, 1] \to R$ defined such that $f(x) = 0$ if x is irrational and $f(p/q) = 1/q$ if p and q are positive integers that are relatively prime. It was shown in Chapter 2 that f has a limit at each point of $[0, 1]$ and that its limit is zero at each point. Thus, f is continuous at $x \in [0, 1]$ iff $f(x) = 0$ (that is, iff x is irrational).

The next theorem is a natural follow-up on Theorem 2.4.

3.2 THEOREM   Suppose $f: D \to R$ and $g: D \to R$ are continuous at $x_0 \in D$. Then

   (1) $f + g$ is continuous at x_0;

   (2) fg is continuous at x_0;

   (3) if $g(x_0) \neq 0$, f/g is continuous at x_0.

(A word of advice is necessary concerning point 3. The function f/g is defined only where $g(x) \neq 0$; hence, when speaking of the function f/g, we assume that the domain consists of those points where $g(x) \neq 0$. Lemma 3.3 will shed some light on this situation.)

Proof: We shall use a different method of proof for each part of this theorem in order to point out the use of facts previously presented on sequences and limits and also to show a direct proof.

Suppose f and g are continuous at $x_0 \in D$. Let $\{x_n\}$ be any sequence of points in D which converges to x_0. Then by 3.1,

$\{f(x_n)\}$ converges to $f(x_0)$ and $\{g(x_n)\}_{n=1}^{\infty}$ converges to $g(x_0)$; hence

$$\{f(x_n) + g(x_n)\}_{n=1}^{\infty}$$

converges to $f(x_0) + g(x_0)$. Thus,

$$\{(f + g)(x_n)\}_{n=1}^{\infty} = \{f(x_n) + g(x_n)\}_{n=1}^{\infty}$$

converges to $f(x_0) + g(x_0) = (f + g)(x_0)$, and hence by 3.1, $f + g$ is continuous at x_0. This concludes the proof of (1).

Suppose f and g are continuous at $x_0 \in D$. If x_0 is not an accumulation point of D, then fg is continuous at x_0 by our observations following the definition of continuity. Suppose now that x_0 is an accumulation point of D. By 3.1, f and g have limits at x_0 and

$$\lim_{x \to x_0} f(x) = f(x_0), \qquad \lim_{x \to x_0} g(x) = g(x_0).$$

By 2.4, fg has a limit at x_0 and

$$\lim_{x \to x_0} (fg)(x) = [\lim_{x \to x_0} f(x)][\lim_{x \to x_0} g(x)] = f(x_0)g(x_0)$$

$$= (fg)(x_0).$$

Thus, by 3.1, fg is continuous at x_0.

We have purposely elected to give a direct proof of (3) because it involves some important facts not yet brought to light. Hopefully, the reader has attempted a direct proof of 2.4 (3) and discovered the need for a lemma similar to the following.

3.3 LEMMA Let $g : D \to R$ be continuous at $x_0 \in D$ with $g(x_0) \neq 0$. Then there is $\delta > 0$ and $\alpha > 0$ such that if $|x - x_0| < \delta$ and $x \in D$, then $|g(x)| \geq \alpha$.

(Note the similarity between this lemma and 1.9, the lemma needed for the theorem concerning the convergence of the quotient of two convergent sequences.)

Proof: Choose

$$\alpha = \frac{|g(x_0)|}{2} > 0.$$

There is $\delta > 0$ such that for $|x - x_0| < \delta, x \in D$, we have

$$|g(x) - g(x_0)| < \alpha.$$

Thus,

$$|g(x)| \geq |g(x_0)| - |g(x) - g(x_0)| > |g(x_0)| - \alpha = \frac{|g(x_0)|}{2} = \alpha.$$

Suppose g is continuous at x_0 and $g(x_0) \neq 0$. By 3.3, there are $\delta > 0$ and $\alpha > 0$ such that for $|x - x_0| < \delta$ and $x \in D$, we have $|g(x)| \geq \alpha$. Choose $\varepsilon > 0$. Let

$$\varepsilon' = \alpha |g(x_0)| \varepsilon > 0.$$

There is $\delta' > 0$ such that for $|x - x_0| < \delta'$ and $x \in D$,

$$|g(x) - g(x_0)| < \varepsilon'.$$

Let

$$\delta'' = \min \{\delta', \delta\}.$$

Now $\delta'' > 0$, and for $|x - x_0| < \delta''$ with $x \in D$, we have

$$\left| \frac{1}{g}(x) - \frac{1}{g}(x_0) \right| = \left| \frac{g(x_0) - g(x)}{g(x)g(x_0)} \right| < \frac{\varepsilon'}{\alpha |g(x_0)|} = \varepsilon.$$

Thus, $1/g$ is continuous at x_0. By part (2) of this theorem, f/g is then continuous at x_0.

From our remarks in Chapter 2 and Theorem 3.1, it is clear that every polynomial is continuous; in fact, if p and q are polynomials, then p/q is continuous at any point x where $q(x) \neq 0$. The case where $q(x) = 0$ is handled in detail in Exercise 5 at the end of this chapter.

The function $f(x) = \sin x$ is undoubtedly familiar to the reader. We observe that for $0 \leq x \leq \pi/2, 0 \leq \sin x \leq x$. From this and the fact that $\sin(-x) = -\sin x$, it is clear that $f(x) = \sin x$ has a limit at zero, namely, $\lim_{x \to 0} \sin x = 0$. From this, we can deduce that the sine function is continuous at every point. Now for all x and y,

$$\sin x - \sin y = 2 \cos \left(\frac{x + y}{2} \right) \sin \left(\frac{x - y}{2} \right).$$

Let x_0 be any real number and $\varepsilon > 0$. Let $\delta = \min \{\varepsilon, \pi/4\}$. Then for $|x_0 - y| < \delta$,

$$|\sin x_0 - \sin y| = \left| 2 \cos \left(\frac{x_0 + y}{2} \right) \sin \left(\frac{x_0 - y}{2} \right) \right| \leq 2 \left| \frac{x_0 - y}{2} \right|$$

$$= |x_0 - y| < \delta \leq \varepsilon.$$

Thus, $\sin x$ is continuous at x_0. For all real x, $\cos x = \sin (\pi/2 - x)$. In order to verify the continuity of $\cos x$ at x_0, let us proceed directly. Choose $\varepsilon > 0$ and let $\delta = \min \{\varepsilon, \pi/4\}$. If $|x - x_0| < \delta$, then

$$\left| \left(\frac{\pi}{2} - x \right) - \left(\frac{\pi}{2} - x_0 \right) \right| = |x_0 - x| < \delta;$$

hence

$$|\cos x - \cos x_0| = \left| \sin \left(\frac{\pi}{2} - x \right) - \sin \left(\frac{\pi}{2} - x_0 \right) \right| < \delta \leq \varepsilon.$$

Thus, $\cos x$ is continuous at x_0. Now it is clear that the functions $\tan x$, $\sec x$, $\csc x$, and $\operatorname{ctn} x$ are continuous where defined, since they may be defined by appropriate products and quotients of the functions $\sin x$ and $\cos x$.

Two points that came to light in this last paragraph deserve some special attention. First of all, a function $f: D \to R$ is continuous at a point $x_0 \in D$ iff for each $\varepsilon > 0$, there is $\delta > 0$ such that for $|x - x_0| < \delta$ and $x \in D$, we have $|f(x) - f(x_0)| < \varepsilon$. Note that the choice of $\delta > 0$ is influenced by two things: the choice of $\varepsilon > 0$ and the point in question, x_0. In the process of investigating the continuity of $f(x) = \sin x$, it was discovered if $\varepsilon > 0$ is given, $\delta > 0$ could be found that would be suitable for any x_0. This is not the usual state of affairs and will be considered in some detail very soon. Secondly, the continuity of the cosine function was deduced from the fact that the sine function was continuous and that $\cos x = \sin (\pi/2 - x)$. If we let $g(x) = \cos x$, $f(x) = \sin x$, and $h(x) = \pi/2 - x$, then this identity may be written $g = f \circ h$. Of course, since h is a polynomial function, it is continuous; indeed, that fact was used to observe that if $|x - x_0| < \delta$, then

$$|h(x) - h(x_0)| = |(\pi/2 - x) - (\pi/2 - x_0)| = |x - x_0| < \delta.$$

We seek now to generalize this idea and shall attempt to prove that the composition of continuous functions is continuous.

3.4 THEOREM   If $f: D \to R$ and $g: D' \to R$ with $\operatorname{im} f \subset D'$, where f is continuous at $x_0 \in D$ and g is continuous at $f(x_0)$, then $g \circ f$ is continuous at x_0.

Proof: Choose $\varepsilon > 0$. There is $\delta_1 > 0$ such that if $|y - f(x_0)| < \delta_1$ and $y \in D'$, then

$$|g(y) - g(f(x_0))| < \varepsilon.$$

There is $\delta_2 > 0$ such that if $|x - x_0| < \delta_2$ and $x \in D$, then

$$|f(x) - f(x_0)| < \delta_1.$$

Now since $\operatorname{im} f \subset D'$, if $|x - x_0| < \delta_2$, and $x \in D$ then $f(x) \in D'$, $f(x_0) \in D'$, and $|f(x) - f(x_0)| < \delta_1$; hence,

$$|(g \circ f)(x) - (g \circ f)(x_0)| = |g(f(x)) - g(f(x_0))| < \varepsilon.$$

Therefore, $g \circ f$ is continuous at x_0.

This theorem, coupled with previous results, allows us to conclude immediately that functions such as $f(x) = \cos x^2$ and $g(x) = \sin(\cos x)$ are continuous at x_0 for all real numbers x_0.

Let us now take up the remaining topic that we want to pursue further. We shall give the appropriate definition and then consider some examples.

DEFINITION   A function $f: D \to R$ is *uniformly continuous on* $E \subset D$ iff for every $\varepsilon > 0$, there is $\delta > 0$ such that if $x, y \in E$ with $|x - y| < \delta$, then $|f(x) - f(y)| < \varepsilon$. In case f is uniformly continuous on D, we say f is uniformly continuous.

As promised, some examples and nonexamples are forthcoming. Now the sine function has been shown to be uniformly continuous on its domain, the set of all real numbers. Therefore, it is an example of a uniformly continuous function. Similarly, the cosine function is uniformly continuous. This is not surprising in light of Exercise 8 of this chapter.

Let us now consider the function $f : (0, \pi/2) \to R$ defined by $f(x) = \tan x$. Elementary identities from trigonometry show that $\tan x = \sin x/\cos x$, for $0 < x < \pi/2$; hence, f is a quotient of uniformly continuous functions. (Since $\sin x$ and $\cos x$ are uniformly continuous on R, then they are certainly uniformly continuous on $(0, \pi/2)$.) Exercises 6 and 7 are designed to show under what conditions the sum, product, or composition of uniformly continuous functions yields a uniformly continuous function. We know by the nature of the tangent function that it is unbounded near $\pi/2$ and so cannot have a limit there. Let us show that this is sufficient to guarantee that $\tan x$ is not uniformly continuous on $(0, \pi/2)$.

3.5 THEOREM   Let $f : D \to R$ be uniformly continuous. Then if x_0 is an accumulation point of D, f has a limit at x_0.

Proof: Let x_0 be an accumulation point of D, and let $\{x_n\}_{n=1}^{\infty}$ be any sequence of members of $D \setminus \{x_0\}$ converging to x_0. Recall that it is sufficient to prove that $\{f(x_n)\}_{n=1}^{\infty}$ is a Cauchy sequence since every Cauchy sequence of real numbers is convergent. Choose $\varepsilon > 0$. Since f is uniformly continuous on D, there is $\delta > 0$ such that for all $x, y \in D$, $|x - y| < \delta$ implies $|f(x) - f(y)| < \varepsilon$. Since $\{x_n\}_{n=1}^{\infty}$ converges to x_0, it is a Cauchy sequence, and there is N such that for $m, n \geq N$, $|x_n - x_m| < \delta$. Now $x_n \in D$ for each n, hence for $m, n \geq N$, $|x_n - x_m| < \delta$, $x_m, x_n \in D$; hence

$$|f(x_n) - f(x_m)| < \varepsilon.$$

Thus, $\{f(x_n)\}_{n=1}^{\infty}$ is Cauchy. By 2.1, f has a limit at x_0.

Observe that this theorem gives a necessary condition for uniform continuity, not one that is sufficient. For example, consider $g : R \to R$ where $g(x) = x^2$ for all real numbers x. Since g is continuous and

$\operatorname{dom} g = R$, the function g has a limit at every accumulation point of R since R contains all its accumulation points. However,

$$|g(x) - g(y)| = |x^2 - y^2| = |x + y||x - y|.$$

Choose $\varepsilon > 0$ and consider any $\delta > 0$. Now choose x and y such that $|x - y| = \delta/2 < \delta$ and $|x + y| = 3\varepsilon/\delta$. Then

$$|g(x) - g(y)| = |x + y||x - y| = \frac{3\varepsilon\,\delta}{\delta}\frac{}{2} = \frac{3}{2}\varepsilon > \varepsilon.$$

In effect, given $\varepsilon > 0$, it is impossible to find $\delta > 0$ such that for $|x - y| < \delta$, we always have $|g(x) - g(y)| < \varepsilon$. Thus, g is not uniformly continuous.

We have seen two examples of continuous functions that were not uniformly continuous; in the first case, the domain was $(0, 1)$, a set with accumulation points which did not belong to the set, and the second function had an unbounded domain. The difficulty in the first example comes about near the accumulation points and perhaps may be overcome by considering functions whose domains contain all their accumulation points. Such sets are of sufficient importance to deserve a name.

DEFINITION   A set $E \subset R$ is *closed* iff every accumulation point of E belongs to E.

As has been observed previously, a finite set has no accumulation points and, by definition, is a closed set. In like fashion, R, the set of all real numbers, is a closed set, since an accumulation point of R is necessarily a real number, hence a member of R. Suppose E is a closed set and $x_0 \in R \setminus E$. Then by the definition of a closed set, x_0 is not an accumulation point of E; hence, there is a neighborhood Q of x_0 which contains no points of E (since $x_0 \notin E$), so $Q \subset R \setminus E$. Thus, if E is closed, there is, for each $x_0 \in R \setminus E$, a neighborhood $Q(x_0)$ of x_0 such that $Q(x_0) \subset R \setminus E$. This is a special type of set which comes about in a natural way by considering the complement of a closed set.

DEFINITION   A set $A \subset R$ is *open* iff for each $x \in A$, there is a neighborhood Q of x such that $Q \subset A$.

The remarks leading up to this definition yield the proof of half of the following theorem:

3.6 THEOREM   A set $E \subset R$ is closed iff $R \setminus E$ is open.

Proof: Suppose E is closed and $x_0 \in R \setminus E$. Then, since E contains all its accumulation points, x_0 is not an accumulation point of E. Hence, there is a neighborhood Q of x_0 which contains no points of E. (Recall $x_0 \notin E$.) But now $Q \subset R \setminus E$, hence (by definition), $R \setminus E$ is open.

Suppose $R \setminus E$ is open. To show E is closed, it suffices to show that if x_0 is an accumulation point of E, then $x_0 \in E$. Let x_0 be an accumulation point of E. Then $x_0 \in E$ or $x_0 \in R \setminus E$. However, $R \setminus E$ is open, so if $x_0 \in R \setminus E$, there is a neighborhood Q of x_0 such that $Q \subset R \setminus E$ or $Q \cap E$ is empty, contrary to x_0 being an accumulation point of E. Thus, $x_0 \in E$ and E is closed.

Now let us return to the problem that precipitated this discussion. Consider $f : E \to R$ with f continuous on E. Choose $\varepsilon > 0$. Now for each $x \in E$ there is $\delta_x > 0$ such that if $y \in E$ and $|x - y| < \delta_x$, then $|f(x) - f(y)| < \varepsilon$. In the search for $\delta > 0$ which will guarantee that $|x - y| < \delta$ and $x, y \in E$ imply that $|f(x) - f(y)| < \varepsilon$, one might try considering

$$\delta = \inf \{\delta_x : x \in E\}.$$

If E is finite, δ is positive; but if E is infinite, δ might be zero, and indeed, if f is not unformly continuous, it will be zero. Consider now the set $(x - \delta_x, x + \delta_x) \cap E$. If

$$y_1, y_2 \in (x - \delta_x, x + \delta_x) \cap E,$$

then $|x - y_1| < \delta_x$ and $|x - y_2| < \delta_x$; hence

$$|f(y_1) - f(y_2)| \leq |f(y_1) - f(x) + f(x) - f(y_2)|$$
$$\leq |f(y_1) - f(x)| + |f(x) - f(y_2)| < \varepsilon + \varepsilon = 2\varepsilon.$$

If one could find $x_1, \ldots, x_n$ such that

$$E \subset \bigcup_{i=1}^{n} (x_i - \delta_{x_i}, x_i + \delta_{x_i}),$$

there might be some hope of showing that f is uniformly continuous. Note that for each x, $(x - \delta_x, x + \delta_x)$ is an open set (see Exercise 10), and $E \subset \bigcup_{x \in E} (x - \delta_x, x + \delta_x)$. Here we have a family of open sets whose union contains E, and we wish to choose a finite subfamily with the same property. A new definition is now in order.

DEFINITION   A set E is *compact* iff for every family $\{G_\alpha\}_{\alpha \in A}$ of open sets such that $E \subset \bigcup_{\alpha \in A} G_\alpha$, there is a finite set $\{\alpha_1, \ldots, \alpha_n\} \subset A$ such that $E \subset \bigcup_{i=1}^n G_{\alpha_i}$.

We shall illustrate this concept by giving some examples of sets which are not compact. Let $E = (0, 1]$, and for each positive integer n, let $G_n = (1/n, 2)$. If $0 < x \le 1$, there is a positive integer n such that $1/n < x$; hence $x \in G_n$, and thus

$$E \subset \bigcup_{n=1}^\infty G_n.$$

If we choose a finite set $n_1, \ldots, n_r$ of positive integers, then

$$\bigcup_{i=1}^r G_{n_i} = G_{n_0}$$

where $n_0 = \max \{n_1, \ldots, n_r\}$ and

$$E \not\subset G_{n_0} = \left(\frac{1}{n_0}, 2\right).$$

Thus, we have a family of open sets $\{G_n\}_{n \in J}$ such that $E \subset \bigcup_{n \in J} G_n$, but no finite subfamily has this property. From the definition, it is clear that E is not compact.

As a second example, consider the set S of all positive integers. For each $n \in S$, define

$$G_n = \left(n - \frac{1}{2}, n + \frac{1}{2}\right).$$

Now $S \subset \bigcup_{n=1}^\infty G_n$, but each G_n contains exactly one member of S, so it is impossible to choose $n_1, \ldots, n_r$ such that $S \subset \bigcup_{i=1}^r G_{n_i}$. Thus, S is not compact.

Let us introduce some new notation to help simplify our language. If E is a set and $\{G_\alpha\}_{\alpha \in A}$ is a collection of sets such that $E \subset \bigcup_{\alpha \in A} G_\alpha$, then the collection $\{G_\alpha\}_{\alpha \in A}$ is called a *cover* of E. If each G_α is an open set, then the collection $\{G_\alpha\}_{\alpha \in A}$ is called an *open cover* of E. If $\{G_\alpha\}_{\alpha \in A}$ is a cover of E and $B \subset A$ such that $E \subset \bigcup_{\alpha \in B} G_\alpha$, then the collection $\{G_\alpha\}_{\alpha \in B}$ is called a *subcover* of E, and if B is finite, then $\{G_\alpha\}_{\alpha \in B}$ is called a *finite subcover* of E. In a sense, we are abusing the language, since every subcover of E is also a cover of E; but in light of the notion of compactness, this is a reasonable abuse. With these additions to our vocabulary, we can restate our definition of compactness: A set E is compact iff every open cover of E has a finite subcover.

The reader should keep the preceding two examples clearly in mind. The first example, $(0, 1]$, is a bounded set that is not closed since 0 is an accumulation point of $(0, 1]$ which does not belong to $(0, 1]$. The second example is a closed set but is unbounded. As the reader might suspect from our choice of examples, the compact sets on the line are precisely those which are both closed and bounded. This is the content of the next theorem.

3.7 THEOREM A set $E \subset R$ is compact iff E is closed and bounded.

Proof: Suppose that E is closed and bounded and that $\{G_\lambda\}_{\lambda \in A}$ is an open cover of E. Since E is bounded, there is a closed interval $[\alpha, \beta]$ such that $E \subset [\alpha, \beta]$. Let us suppose that $\{G_\lambda\}_{\lambda \in A}$ has no finite subcover of E (E is not compact). We shall show that this assumption is self-contradictory. Let γ_0 be the midpoint of $[\alpha, \beta]$. At least one of the two sets $[\alpha, \gamma_0] \cap E$ and $[\gamma_0, \beta] \cap E$ cannot be covered by a finite subfamily of $\{G_\lambda\}_{\lambda \in A}$; choose one and call it $[\alpha_1, \beta_1]$; let γ_1 be the midpoint of $[\alpha_1, \beta_1]$. Then again at least one of the two sets $[\alpha_1, \gamma_1] \cap E$ and $[\gamma_1, \beta_1] \cap E$ cannot be covered by a finite subfamily of $\{G_\lambda\}_{\lambda \in A}$; choose one such and call it $[\alpha_2, \beta_2]$. (Does this game sound familiar? See the proof of the Bolzano–Weierstrass Theorem.) Continuing in this fashion, we obtain a sequence of closed intervals $[\alpha_n, \beta_n]$ with the following properties:

(1) $\beta_n - \alpha_n = 1/2^n (\beta - \alpha)$;

(2) $[\alpha_{n+1}, \beta_{n+1}] \subset [\alpha_n, \beta_n]$ for all n;

(3) for each n, the set $[\alpha_n, \beta_n] \cap E$ cannot be covered by a finite subfamily of $\{G_\lambda\}_{\lambda \in A}$.

By (3), $[\alpha_n, \beta_n] \cap E$ is nonempty for each n; hence, we may choose $x_n \in [\alpha_n, \beta_n] \cap E$ for $n = 1, 2, \ldots$. Consider the set

$$P = \{x_n : n = 1, 2, \ldots\}.$$

If P is finite, then by (2), there is n_0 such that

$$x_{n_0} \in [\alpha_n, \beta_n] \cap E$$

for all n. Since $\{G_\lambda\}_{\lambda \in A}$ is an open cover of E,

$$x_{n_0} \in G_{\lambda_0}$$

for some $\lambda_0 \in A$, and since G_{λ_0} is open, there is $\varepsilon > 0$ such that

$$(x_{n_0} - \varepsilon, x_{n_0} + \varepsilon) \subset G_{\lambda_0}.$$

Choose n such that

$$\beta_n - \alpha_n = \frac{1}{2^n}(\beta - \alpha) < \varepsilon.$$

Then, since $x_{n_0} \in [\alpha_n, \beta_n] \cap E$,

$$x \in [\alpha_n, \beta_n] \cap E$$

implies that $|x - x_{n_0}| \le \beta_n - \alpha_n < \varepsilon$. Hence

$$[\alpha_n, \beta_n] \cap E \subset (x_{n_0} - \varepsilon, x_{n_0} + \varepsilon) \subset G_{\lambda_0}.$$

This means that $[\alpha_n, \beta_n] \cap E$ may be covered by a finite subfamily of $\{G_\lambda\}_{\lambda \in A}$, which is contrary to (3).

Suppose P is infinite. Then P is an infinite bounded set and has an accumulation point x_0; and since $P \subset E$, clearly x_0 is an accumulation point of E and $x_0 \in E$ since E is assumed closed. There is $\lambda_1 \in A$ such that $x_0 \in G_{\lambda_1}$, and, since G_{λ_1} is open, there is $\varepsilon > 0$ such that

$$(x_0 - \varepsilon, x_0 + \varepsilon) \subset G_{\lambda_1}.$$

Choose n such that

$$\beta_n - \alpha_n = \frac{1}{2^n}(\beta - \alpha) < \frac{\varepsilon}{2}.$$

Now x_0 is an accumulation point of P, and $(x_0 - \varepsilon/2, x_0 + \varepsilon/2)$ is a neighborhood of x_0. Hence there are infinitely many numbers of P which belong to $(x_0 - \varepsilon/2, x_0 + \varepsilon/2)$. In particular, there is $m > n$ such that

$$x_m \in \left(x_0 - \frac{\varepsilon}{2}, x_0 + \frac{\varepsilon}{2} \right).$$

Now if $z \in [\alpha_m, \beta_m] \cap E$, then

$$|z - x_0| \le |z - x_m| + |x_m - x_0| < (\beta_m - \alpha_m) + \frac{\varepsilon}{2}$$

$$\le (\beta_n - \alpha_n) + \frac{\varepsilon}{2} < \frac{\varepsilon}{2} + \frac{\varepsilon}{2} = \varepsilon.$$

Thus, $[\alpha_m, \beta_m] \cap E \subset (x_0 - \varepsilon, x_0 + \varepsilon) \subset G_{\lambda_1}$, contrary to (3).

We have now arrived at a contradiction to our original assumption—namely that E was closed and bounded but not compact. Thus, if E is closed and bounded, E is compact.

It now remains to show that every compact set is closed and bounded. We shall accomplish this by showing that if a set is unbounded, it cannot be compact, and if a set is not closed, it cannot be compact.

Assume E is not bounded. For each positive integer n, let $G_n = (-n, n)$. Now G_n is open for each n and $E \subset \bigcup_{n=1}^{\infty} G_n$, so $\{G_n\}_{n=1}^{\infty}$ is an open cover of E. If $n_1, \ldots, n_r$ is any finite set of positive integers, then

$$\bigcup_{i=1}^{r} G_{n_i} = G_{n_0},$$

where $n_0 = \max \{n_1, \ldots, n_r\}$, and since E is unbounded,

$$\{G_{n_i}\}_{i=1,\ldots,r}$$

is not a cover of E. Thus, $\{G_n\}_{n=1}^{\infty}$ is an open cover of E with no finite subcover; hence E is not compact.

Assume E is not closed. Then there is an accumulation point of E (call it x_0) such that $x_0 \notin E$. In much the same way that we did for the set $(0, 1]$, we shall construct an open cover of E with no finite subcover. For each positive integer n, define

$$G_n = R \setminus \left[x_0 - \frac{1}{n}, x_0 + \frac{1}{n} \right].$$

Now $[x_0 - 1/n, x_0 + 1/n]$ is a closed set for each n, hence G_n is open. Observe that $\bigcup_{n=1}^{\infty} G_n = R \setminus \{x_0\}$, so $\{G_n\}_{n=1}^{\infty}$ is an open cover of E. Let $n_1, \ldots, n_r$ be any finite set of positive integers and $n_0 = \max \{n_1, \ldots, n_r\}$. Then

$$\bigcup_{i=1}^{r} G_{n_i} = G_{n_0} = R \setminus \left[x_0 - \frac{1}{n_0}, x_0 + \frac{1}{n_0} \right].$$

In order that $\{G_{n_i}\}_{i=1,\ldots,r}$ be a cover of E, we must have

$$E \subset G_{n_0} = R \setminus \left[x_0 - \frac{1}{n_0}, x_0 + \frac{1}{n_0} \right];$$

hence, $E \cap (x_0 - 1/n_0, x_0 + 1/n_0)$ is empty, contrary to x_0 being an accumulation point of E. Thus, $\{G_n\}_{n=1}^{\infty}$ has no finite subcover and E is not compact.

Having read the proof of this theorem, the student should go back and try to see just what makes it work and where the hypotheses are used. This time, he shouldn't worry about the details, but rather seek out the rough idea of the proof.

In passing, let us point out a few examples of compact sets. Every finite set is compact since it is necessarily closed and bounded. If $a < b$, then the set $[a, b]$ is a closed bounded set and, hence, is compact. It is easy to show that the union of finitely many compact sets is compact, so any set which is the union of a finite number of closed bounded intervals is a compact set.

With this knowledge of the nature of compact sets in mind, we shall exploit this concept with respect to continuity. Our remarks preceding the definition of compactness should make the following theorem no surprise.

3.8 THEOREM   Let $f : D \to R$ be continuous with D compact—that is, closed and bounded. Then f is uniformly continuous.

Proof: Choose $\varepsilon > 0$. Since f is continuous on D, f is continuous at x for each $x \in D$. Thus, for each $x \in D$, there is $\delta_x > 0$ such that if $|x - y| < \delta_x$ and $y \in D$, then $|f(x) - f(y)| < \varepsilon/2$. Consider the family

$$\left\{ \left(x - \frac{\delta_x}{2}, x + \frac{\delta_x}{2} \right) \right\}_{x \in D}.$$

This is an open cover of D and D is compact, so there is a finite subcover of D. In other words, there are $x_1, \ldots, x_n \in D$ such that

$$D \subset \bigcup_{i=1}^{n} \left(x_i - \frac{\delta_{x_i}}{2}, x_i + \frac{\delta_{x_i}}{2} \right).$$

Let

$$\delta = \min \left\{ \frac{\delta_{x_i}}{2} : i = 1, \ldots, n \right\}.$$

Now suppose $x, y \in D$ and $|x - y| < \delta$. There is an integer i among $1, \ldots, n$ such that

$$x \in \left(x_i - \frac{\delta_{x_i}}{2}, x_i + \frac{\delta_{x_i}}{2} \right).$$

Now $|x - y| < \delta \leq \delta_{x_i}/2$, making

$$|y - x_i| \leq |y - x| + |x - x_i| < \frac{\delta_{x_i}}{2} + \frac{\delta_{x_i}}{2} = \delta_{x_i}.$$

Hence,

$$|f(x) - f(y)| \leq |f(x) - f(x_i)| + |f(x_i) - f(y)| < \frac{\varepsilon}{2} + \frac{\varepsilon}{2} = \varepsilon.$$

Therefore, f is uniformly continuous.

In a broad sense, this theorem has a converse. Suppose $f: D \to R$ is uniformly continuous. As has been previously pointed out, f has a limit at each accumulation point of D. As in Exercise 13, let D' be the set of accumulation points of D and $\bar{D} = D \cup D'$. Define $g: \bar{D} \to R$ by $g(x) = f(x)$ for all $x \in D$, and if $x_0 \in \bar{D} \setminus D$, define $g(x_0) = \lim_{x \to x_0} f(x)$. The function $g: \bar{D} \to R$ is called an *extension* of $f: D \to R$ and indeed turns out to be a continuous function. The proof of this will be a challenging exercise for the reader. Thus, if $f : D \to R$ is uniformly continuous with D bounded, then f has a continuous extension $g : \bar{D} \to R$ where $\bar{D}$ is closed and bounded and, hence, compact.

Consider now $f : E \to R$ with E compact. By 3.8, f is uniformly continuous, and since E is compact it is bounded. Hence f is a bounded function, or $f(E)$ is a bounded set (see Exercise 16). If $f(E)$ were also closed, then it would be compact and one would say that the continuous image of a compact set is compact. Let us state this as a theorem and try to prove it.

3.9 THEOREM   Let $f : E \to R$ be continuous with E compact. Then $f(E)$ is compact.

Proof: As pointed out in the preceding paragraph, we need only show that $f(E)$ is closed since we already know $f(E)$ is bounded. Let y_0 be an accumulation point of $f(E)$. Then there is a sequence $\{y_n\}_{n=1}^{\infty}$ of points in $f(E)$ such that $y_n \neq y_0$ for all n and $\{y_n\}_{n=1}^{\infty}$ converges to y_0 (see Theorem 1.15). Since $y_n \in f(E)$ for each n, then there is a sequence $\{x_n\}_{n=1}^{\infty}$ of points in E such that $f(x_n) = y_n$ for each n. There is a subsequence $\{x_{n_k}\}_{k=1}^{\infty}$ which converges to $x_0 \in E$ (see Exercise 17). By Theorem 3.1, the sequence $\{f(x_{n_k})\}_{k=1}^{\infty}$ converges to $f(x_0)$. However,

$$\{f(x_{n_k})\}_{k=1}^{\infty} = \{y_{n_k}\}_{k=1}^{\infty}$$

is a subsequence of $\{y_n\}_{n=1}^{\infty}$ and converges to y_0, so $y_0 = f(x_0) \in E$. Therefore, $f(E)$ is closed.

The following important corollary follows from 3.9.

3.10 COROLLARY   If $f : E \to R$ is continuous with E compact, there are $x_1, x_2 \in E$ such that for all $x \in E$,

$$f(x_1) \leq f(x) \leq f(x_2).$$

Proof: By 3.9, $f(E)$ is a compact set, so by Exercise 11, $\sup f(E)$ and $\inf f(E)$ belong to $f(E)$. Let

$$y_2 = \sup f(E) \quad \text{and} \quad y_1 = \inf f(E).$$

There are $x_1, x_2 \in E$ such that $f(x_1) = y_1$ and $f(x_2) = y_2$. Hence by the choice of y_1 and y_2, for all $x \in E$

$$f(x_1) = y_1 = \inf f(E) \leq f(x) \leq \sup f(E) = y_2 = f(x_2).$$

In essence, this theorem tells us that if $f: E \to R$ is continuous with E compact, then not only is f a bounded function but f actually assumes a maximum and a minimum value on the set E.

Let us explore some examples to illustrate this theorem. Consider $f: (0, 1) \to R$ defined by $f(x) = 1/x$. The function is continuous but not bounded from above. It is bounded from below, but $\inf f((0, 1)) = 1$, and there is no $x \in (0, 1)$ such that $f(x) = 1$.

The function $g: (0, 1) \to R$ defined by $g(x) = x$ is certainly bounded, but $\inf g((0, 1)) = 0$ and $\sup g((0, 1)) = 1$, neither of which is a value of g for the reason that $(0, 1)$ is not compact.

To lay the groundwork for a new theorem worthy of note, suppose $f: E \to R$ is 1-1. Then there is a unique function $f^{-1}: f(E) \to E$ such that $f \circ f^{-1}(x) = x$ for each $x \in f(E)$ and $f^{-1} \circ f(y) = y$ for each $y \in E$. A natural question to raise is the following: if f is continuous, is f^{-1} continuous? The next theorem gives a partial answer.

3.11 THEOREM Suppose $f: E \to R$ is continuous and 1-1 with E compact. Then $f^{-1}: f(E) \to E$ is continuous.

Proof: Let $\{y_n\}_{n=1}^{\infty}$ be any sequence in $f(E)$ converging to y_0. We must show that $\{f^{-1}(y_n)\}_{n=1}^{\infty}$ converges to $f^{-1}(y_0)$. For the sake of notation, let $f^{-1}(y_i) = x_i$ for $i = 0, 1, 2, \ldots$. Then $f(x_i) = y_i$. Let $\{x_{n_k}\}_{k=1}^{\infty}$ be any convergent subsequence of $\{x_n\}_{n=1}^{\infty}$; say it converges to z_0. Then $\{y_{n_k}\}_{n=1}^{\infty}$ converges to $f(z_0)$, by continuity of f, and also to $f(x_0)$ since $\{y_n\}_{n=1}^{\infty}$ converges to $y_0 = f(x_0)$. By hypotheses, f is 1-1; hence $x_0 = z_0$. Thus, $\{x_n\}_{n=1}^{\infty}$ converges to x_0 (see Exercise 18).

To show the necessity of the hypothesis that E be compact, we shall exhibit an example of a function $f: E \to R$ which is 1-1 but such that $f^{-1}: f(E) \to E$ is not continuous. Of course, E must be noncompact. Let

$$E = [0, 1] \cup [2, 3)$$

and define $f(x) = x$ for $0 \leq x \leq 1$ and $f(x) = 4 - x$ for $2 \leq x < 3$. It is left to the reader to satisfy himself that f is indeed 1–1 and continuous. Now $f(E) = [0, 2]$, and for $0 \leq x \leq 1$, $f^{-1}(x) = x$, while for $1 < x \leq 2$, $f^{-1}(x) = 4 - x$. Consider the sequence

$$\left\{1 + \frac{(-1)^n}{n}\right\}_{n=1}^{\infty},$$

which converges to 1. For n odd,

$$f^{-1}\left(1 + \frac{(-1)^n}{n}\right) = 1 + \frac{(-1)^n}{n},$$

and for n even,

$$f^{-1}\left(1 + \frac{(-1)^n}{n}\right) = 4 - \left(1 + \frac{(-1)^n}{n}\right) = 3 - \frac{(-1)^n}{n}.$$

It should be clear then that $\{f^{-1}(1 + (-1)^n/n)\}_{n=1}^{\infty}$ does not converge, and so f^{-1} fails to be continuous at 1.

Consider now a function $f : [-1, 1] \to R$, which is continuous and is such that $f(-1) < 0$ and $f(1) > 0$. An intuitive picture of the geometric nature of the graph of a continuous function leads us to guess that this graph must cross the x-axis somewhere between -1 and $+1$; that is, there is $x \in (-1, 1)$ such that $f(x) = 0$. This indeed turns out to be the case, and in fact it motivates us to state the following theorem.

3.12 THEOREM   (Intermediate-value theorem): Let $f : [a, b] \to R$ be continuous with $f(a) < y < f(b)$ (or $f(b) < y < f(a)$). Then there is $c \in (a, b)$ such that $f(c) = y$.

Proof: Let $A = \{x : x \in [a, b] \text{ and } f(x) \leq y\}$ and $B = \{x : x \in [a, b] \text{ and } f(x) \geq y\}$. Now by hypothesis, $a \in A$ and $b \in B$. Let $c = \sup A$. If $f(c) = y$, we are through. Suppose not. Suppose $f(c) < y$. Let

$$\varepsilon = \frac{1}{2}(y - f(c)) > 0.$$

By the continuity of f, there is $\delta > 0$ such that $|x - c| < \delta$ and $x \in [a, b]$ implies $|f(x) - f(c)| < \varepsilon$; that is,

$$f(x) < f(c) + \varepsilon < y.$$

Now since $f(c) < y$, $c \notin B$; hence $c < b$. Thus, there is $x \in [a, b]$ such that $c < x < c + \delta$; hence $f(x) < y$. This, however, is a contradiction to the choice of $c = \sup A$. Thus, $f(c) = y$.

This theorem is of course the one that is used in attempting to find the zeros of a polynomial. If p is a polynomial with $p(a) < 0$ and $p(b) > 0$, then p has at least one zero between a and b since every polynomial is a continuous function. If p is a polynomial of odd degree, then p will have a change of sign, hence it necessarily has a zero. Let us prove this fact.

3.13 THEOREM   If p is a polynomial of odd degree with real coefficients, then the equation $p(x) = 0$ has at least one real root.

Proof: Assume

$$p(x) = a_0 + a_1 x + \cdots + a_n x^n$$

where n is odd and $a_n \neq 0$. If $a_0 = 0$, then $p(0) = a_0 = 0$ and we are through. Assume now that $a_0 \neq 0$, and let

$$\phi(x) = \frac{a_0}{x^n} + \frac{a_1}{x^{n-1}} + \cdots + a_n$$

for all $x \neq 0$. Choose ε such that $0 < \varepsilon < |a_n|$. For $i = 0, 1, 2, \ldots, n - 1$, there exists $k_i > 1$ such that

$$\frac{|a_i|}{k_i} < \frac{\varepsilon}{n}.$$

Let $K = \max \{k_0, k_1, \ldots, k_{n-1}\}$. Now if $|x| \geq K$, then

$$\left| \frac{a_0}{x^n} + \frac{a_1}{x^{n-1}} + \cdots + \frac{a_{n-1}}{x} \right| \leq \frac{|a_0|}{|x^n|} + \cdots + \frac{|a_{n-1}|}{|x|}$$

$$\leq \frac{|a_0|}{K} + \cdots + \frac{|a_{n-1}|}{K} < \frac{\varepsilon}{n} + \cdots + \frac{\varepsilon}{n} = \varepsilon.$$

Thus, for $|x| \geq K$, $\phi(x)$ has the same sign as a_n. Now $p(x) = \phi(x)x^n$, so if $a_n > 0$ with $x \geq K$, then $p(x) > 0$; and if $x \leq -K$, then

$p(x) < 0$. Similarly, if $a_n < 0$ and $x \geq K$, then $p(x) < 0$, and if $x \leq -K$, then $p(x) > 0$. In any case, we can find points x_1 and x_2 such that $p(x_1) < 0$ and $p(x_2) > 0$; hence, somewhere between x_1 and x_2, p has a zero.

The following theorem is a special case of a much more general theorem.

3.14 THEOREM   Let $f : [0, 1] \to [0, 1]$ be continuous. Then there is $x \in [0, 1]$ such that $f(x) = x$.

Geometrically interpreted, this theorem states that the graph of f crosses the line $y = x$ somewhere in the square

$$\{(x, y) : 0 \leq x \leq 1, 0 \leq y \leq 1\}.$$

Proof: Let $g(x) = f(x) - x$ for $x \in [0, 1]$. Now g is the difference of two continuous functions and, hence, continuous. By hypothesis, $0 \leq f(x) \leq 1$ for all $x \in [0, 1]$; hence

$$g(0) = f(0) - 0 \geq 0 \quad \text{and} \quad g(1) = f(1) - 1 \leq 0,$$

so there is $x_0 \in [0, 1]$ such that $g(x_0) = 0$. This means that $f(x_0) = x_0$.

As a further application, we shall show that the equation $x = \cos x$ has at least one solution in the closed interval $[0, \pi/2]$. Consider the function $f(x) = x - \cos x$ on $[0, \pi/2]$. Clearly, f is continuous, $f(0) = -1$, and $f(\pi/2) = \pi/2$. Therefore, there is $x \in [0, \pi/2]$ such that $f(x) = 0$; in other words, $x = \cos x$.

3.15 THEOREM   Let $f : [a, b] \to R$ be continuous and one-to-one. Then f is monotone.

Proof: Suppose f is 1–1 and not monotone. Then there are x, y, $z \in [a, b]$ such that $x < y < z$, and $f(x) < f(y)$ and $f(y) > f(z)$, or $f(x) > f(y)$ and $f(y) < f(z)$. Let us suppose the latter; in fact, let us suppose $f(x) > f(z) > f(y)$. The other cases may be handled in a similar fashion. By the intermediate-value theorem, there is $w \in (x, y)$ such that $f(w) = f(z)$, contrary to f being 1–1.

Let us now return to a topic considered at the end of Chapter 2. Let $f : [\alpha, \beta] \to R$ be monotone. Then $D = \{x : x \in (\alpha, \beta) \text{ and } f \text{ does not have a limit at } x\}$ is at most countable, and if f has a limit at $x_0 \in (\alpha, \beta)$, then $\lim_{x \to x_0} f(x) = f(x_0)$. The discussion of the behavior of f at α and at β were left to the reader. It is no betrayal of confidence to state now that f has a limit at α and at β and that

$$\lim_{x \to \alpha} f(x) = \inf \{f(x) : \alpha < x \le \beta\}$$

and

$$\lim_{x \to \beta} f(x) = \sup \{f(x) : \alpha \le x < \beta\}$$

if f is increasing. In the case where f is decreasing, both limits still exist, but

$$\lim_{x \to \alpha} f(x) = \sup \{f(x) : \alpha < x \le \beta\}$$

and

$$\lim_{x \to \beta} f(x) = \inf \{f(x) : \alpha \le x < \beta\}.$$

Now it is clear that f is continuous at x for each $x \in (\alpha, \beta) \setminus D$, and possibly at α and β depending on the definition of f at α and β. In particular, the set of points at which f is discontinuous is at most countable.

Perhaps the reader is not too impressed by this last result, since, as far as we know, all infinite sets of real numbers are countable. We now have the machinery at hand to prove that this is indeed *not* the case. The next theorem states that the set $[0, 1]$ is uncountable, and we leave as an exercise to the reader to prove that $R \sim [0, 1]$.

3.16 THEOREM   The set $[0, 1]$ is uncountable.

Proof: Let us assume the theorem is false and $[0, 1]$ is countable. Then there is a 1–1 function $T : J \to [0, 1]$ such that the image of T is $[0,1]$. Now $T(1) \in [0,1]$, and so there is a closed interval $[a_1,b_1] \subset [0,1]$ such that $a_1 < b_1$ and $T(1) \notin [a_1,b_1]$. There is a closed interval $[a_2,b_2] \subset [a_1,b_1]$ such that $a_2 < b_2$ and $T(2) \notin [a_2,b_2]$. Continuing in this fashion, we construct a sequence $\{[a_n,b_n]\}_{n=1}^{\infty}$ of intervals such that for each n,

(1) $[a_n,b_n] \subset [a_{n-1},b_{n-1}] \subset [a_{n-2},b_{n-2}] \subset \cdots \subset [a_1,b_1] \subset [0,1]$;
(2) $T(n) \notin [a_n,b_n]$;
(3) $a_n < b_n$.

Since T maps J onto $[0,1]$ and $T(n) \notin [a_n,b_n]$, the set $\bigcap_{n=1}^{\infty}[a_n,b_n]$ is empty. For each n, define $A_n = R \setminus [a_n,b_n]$. Now

$$\bigcup_{n=1}^{\infty} A_n = \bigcup_{n=1}^{\infty}(R \setminus [a_n,b_n]) = R \setminus (\bigcap_{n=1}^{\infty}[a_n,b_n]) = R,$$

hence $\{A_n\}_{n=1}^{\infty}$ is an open cover of $[0,1]$. By 3.7, $[0,1]$ is compact, so there are integers $n_1, n_2, \ldots, n_r$ such that

$$[0,1] \subset \bigcup_{i=1}^{r} A_{n_i} = A_m,$$

where $m = \max\{n_1, n_2, \ldots, n_r\}$. This means that

$$[0,1] \subseteq A_m = R \setminus [a_m,b_m],$$

contrary to the fact that $[a_m,b_m] \subset [0,1]$.

Thus, the assumption that $[0,1]$ is countable leads us to a contradiction; so the assumption is false. Therefore, the set $[0,1]$ is not a countable set.

One further concept will be useful in Chapter 5. Consider the function $f(x) = [x]$, defined earlier. Now for $0 \le x < 1$, $f(x) = 0$, and for $1 \le x < 2$, $f(x) = 1$. By our previous remarks, f does not have a limit at 1 and so is not continuous at 1. The discontinuity of f is caused by the fact that the behavior of f to the left of 1 is quite different from that to the right of 1. Indeed, if we consider $g : [1,2] \to R$ defined by $g(x) = [x]$, we discover that g is continuous at $x = 1$. With this in mind, we are motivated to offer the following definition.

DEFINITION Suppose $E \subset R$, $f : E \to R$ and $x_0 \in E$. The function f is *right-continuous at* x_0 iff for each $\varepsilon > 0$ there is $\delta > 0$ such that $x_0 \le x < x_0 + \delta$, $x \in E$, implies that $|f(x) - f(x_0)| < \varepsilon$. Similarly, f is *left-continuous at* x_0 iff for each $\varepsilon > 0$, there is $\delta > 0$ such that $x_0 - \delta < x \le x_0$, $x \in E$, implies that $|f(x) - f(x_0)| < \varepsilon$.

In less formal language, f is right-continuous at x_0 iff f is well-behaved when we restrict our attention to points to the right of x_0, and f is left-continuous at x_0 iff f is well-behaved when we restrict our attention to points to the left of x_0. It should be clear to the reader that f is continuous at x_0 iff f is both left- and right-continuous at x_0. We shall now present a theorem, the proof of which is left to the reader.

3.17 THEOREM   Suppose $f: E \to R$ and $x_0 \in E$. Then f is right-continuous at x_0 iff for each sequence $\{x_n\}_{n=1}^{\infty}$ of points of E converging to x_0, with $x_n \in E$ and $x_0 \le x_n$ for all n, it is true that $\{f(x_n)\}_{n=1}^{\infty}$ converges to $f(x_0)$.

The reader is invited to state and prove a similar theorem for left continuity.

EXERCISES

1.   Prove that $f(x) = \sqrt{x}$ is continuous for all $x \ge 0$.
2.   Let $f: R \to R$ have the property that $f(x + y) = f(x) + f(y)$ for all x and y. If f is continuous at zero, prove that f is uniformly continuous and that there is, in fact, $\alpha \in R$ such that $f(x) = \alpha x$ for all x. Prove that f is continuous at zero iff f is bounded on a neighborhood of zero.
3.   Let $f: D \to R$ be continuous at $x_0 \in D$. Prove that there is $M > 0$ and a neighborhood Q of x_0 such that $|f(x)| \le M$ for all $x \in Q \cap D$.
4.   If $f: D \to R$ is continuous at $x_0 \in D$, prove that the function $|f|: D \to R$ such that $|f|(x) = |f(x)|$ is continuous at x_0.
5.   Let p and q be polynomials and x_0 be a zero of q of multiplicity m. Prove that p/q can be assigned a value at x_0 such that the function thus defined will be continuous there iff x_0 is a zero of p of multiplicity greater than or equal to m.
*6. Let $f, g: D \to R$ be uniformly continuous. Prove that $f + g: D \to R$ is uniformly continuous. What can be said about fg?
*7. Let $f: A \to B$ and $g: B \to C$ be uniformly continuous. What can be said about $g \circ f: A \to C$?
8.   A function $f: R \to R$ is periodic iff there is a real number $h \ne 0$ such that $f(x + h) = f(x)$ for all $x \in R$. Prove that if $f: R \to R$ is continuous and periodic, f is uniformly continuous.
*9. Let $E \subset R$. Prove E is closed iff for every x_0 such that there is a sequence $\{x_n\}_{n=1}^{\infty}$ of points of E converging to x_0, it is true that $x_0 \in E$. In other words, E is closed iff it contains all limits of sequences of members of E.

*10. Prove that every set of the form $\{x : a < x < b\}$ is open and every set of the form $\{x : a \leq x \leq b\}$ is closed.

*11. Let E be compact. Prove that sup E and inf E are finite and belong to E.

*12. If $E_1, \ldots, E_n$ are compact, prove that $E = \bigcup_{i=1}^{n} E_i$ is compact.

*13. Let $D \subset R$ and let $D' =$ set of accumulation points of D. Prove that $\overline{D} = D \cup D'$ is the smallest closed set which contains D. ($\overline{D}$ is called the closure of D.)

*14. If $D \subset R$ is bounded, prove that $\overline{D}$ is bounded.

*15. If $D \subset R$, $x \in D$ is said to be an interior point of D iff there is a neighborhood Q of x such that $Q \subset D$. Define $D^\circ =$ set of interior points of D. Prove that D° is the largest open set contained in D.

*16. If $f : D \to R$ is uniformly continuous with D a bounded set, prove that f is bounded.

*17. Let $E \subset R$ be compact and $\{x_n\}_{n=1}^{\infty}$ a sequence of points of E. Prove that there is $x_0 \in E$ and a subsequence $\{x_{n_k}\}_{k=1}^{\infty}$ of $\{x_n\}_{n=1}^{\infty}$ which converges to x_0.

*18. Let $E \subset R$ be compact and $\{x_n\}_{n=1}^{\infty}$ be a sequence of points of E such that every subsequence of $\{x_n\}_{n=1}^{\infty}$ which converges has the same limit—call it x_0. Prove that $\{x_n\}_{n=1}^{\infty}$ converges to x_0. (Hint: If not, there is $\varepsilon > 0$ such that for each k, there is $n_k > k$ such that $|x_{n_k} - x_0| > \varepsilon$. Apply Exercise 17 to $\{x_{n_k}\}_{k=1}^{\infty}$ to get a contradiction.)

*19. Suppose $f : R \to R$ is continuous and let $r_0 \in R$. Prove that $\{x : f(x) \neq r_0\}$ is an open set.

*20. Let $f : [a, b] \to R$ have a limit at each $x \in [a, b]$. Prove that f is bounded.

21. Suppose $f : (a, b) \to R$ is continuous and $f(r) = 0$ for each rational number $r \in (a, b)$. Prove that $f(x) = 0$ for all $x \in (a, b)$.

22. Suppose $f : [a, b] \to R$ and $g : [a, b] \to R$ are both continuous. Let $T = \{x : f(x) = g(x)\}$. Prove that T is closed.

23. Let $f : [a, b] \to R$ be continuous and define

$$g(t) = \sup \{f(x) : a \leq x \leq t\}$$

for $t \in [a, b]$. Prove that g is continuous on $[a, b]$.

24. A real-valued function $f : [a, b] \to R$ is said to be *convex* if

$$f(\lambda x + (1 - \lambda)y) \leq \lambda f(x) + (1 - \lambda)f(y)$$

for $a \leq x \leq b$, $a \leq y \leq b$, and $0 \leq \lambda \leq 1$. Prove that if f is convex on (a, b) then f is continuous on (a, b).

25. Suppose $f : E \to R$ is continuous at x_0 and $x_0 \in F \subset E$. Define $g : F \to R$ by $g(x) = f(x)$ for all $x \in F$. Prove that g is continuous at x_0. Show by example that the continuity of g at x_0 need not imply the continuity of f at x_0.

CHAPTER 4

DIFFERENTIATION

Consider the function $f(x) = x^3$ and choose a fixed point x_0. Choose another point x, and through the points $(x, f(x))$ and $(x_0, f(x_0))$ draw a line $L(x)$. The slope of this line is

$$\frac{f(x) - f(x_0)}{x - x_0},$$

and an easy computation shows us that

$$\frac{f(x) - f(x_0)}{x - x_0} = \left(\frac{1}{x - x_0}\right)[(x - x_0)^3 + 3x_0(x - x_0)^2 + 3x_0^2(x - x_0)]$$

$$= (x - x_0)^2 + 3x_0(x - x_0) + 3x_0^2.$$

Upon careful examination of this expression for the slope of the line $L(x)$, it becomes clear that the slope of $L(x)$ has a limit at x_0 and that limit is $3x_0^2$. If there is a reasonable definition of the slope of a curve at a point, then it should arise from the approach just used.

Suppose now that an object is moving in a rectilinear path with the distance from a fixed point s_0 given at time t by $f(t)$. For fixed choice of t_0 and $t \neq t_0$, the ratio

$$\frac{f(t) - f(t_0)}{t - t_0}$$

gives the average value of the velocity over the time interval $[t, t_0]$ or $[t_0, t]$ as $t < t_0$ or $t > t_0$. Thus, for each $t \neq t_0$, it is possible to compute an average velocity, $A(t)$. If A has a limit at t_0, it seems reasonable to call this limit the *velocity* at t_0.

The two preceding paragraphs are given as a reminder of the many reasons for considering the notion of the derivative of a function at a point. Our approach, though conventional, should extend the reader's knowledge of differentiation and increase his feeling for the subject.

DEFINITION   Let $f: D \to R$ with x_0 an accumulation point of D and $x_0 \in D$. For each $x \in D$ with $x \neq x_0$, define

$$T(x) = \frac{f(x) - f(x_0)}{x - x_0}.$$

The function f is said to be *differentiable at x_0* (or *has a derivative at x_0*) iff T has a limit at x_0, and we write $\lim_{x \to x_0} T(x) = f'(x_0)$. The number $f'(x_0)$ is called the *derivative* of f at x_0. If f is differentiable for each $x \in E \subset D$, we say f is differentiable on E.

First we shall state a basic theorem that gives a condition for differentiability in terms of sequences. Since the definition of differentiability is based on the existence of the limit of a function, this theorem should come as no surprise.

4.1 THEOREM   Suppose $f: D \to R$ and x_0 is an accumulation point of D. Then f is differentiable at x_0 iff for every sequence $\{x_n\}_{n=1}^{\infty}$ of points of $D \setminus \{x_0\}$ converging to x_0, the sequence

$$\left\{ \frac{f(x_n) - f(x_0)}{x_n - x_0} \right\}_{n=1}^{\infty}$$

converges.

No formal proof will be supplied here, since it should be clear from 2.1 that the condition concerning sequences is equivalent to the condition that the function T given in the definition of differentiability have a limit at x_0.

Note also that if f is differentiable at x_0 and $\{x_n\}_{n=1}^{\infty}$ is a sequence of points of $D \setminus \{x_0\}$ converging to x_0, then

$$\left\{ \frac{f(x_n) - f(x_0)}{x_n - x_0} \right\}_{n=1}^{\infty}$$

converges to $f'(x_0)$.

The next few examples will further one's understanding of the definition of differentiation. Consider the function $f(x) = |x|$ for all $x \in R$. Set $x_0 = 0$, and consider the sequence $\{(-1)^n/n\}_{n=1}^{\infty}$; this sequence converges to zero, but zero is not a term of this sequence. For n even,

$$\frac{(-1)^n}{n} = \frac{1}{n} \quad \text{and} \quad \frac{f\left(\frac{1}{n}\right) - f(0)}{\frac{1}{n}} = 1;$$

for n odd,

$$\frac{(-1)^n}{n} = -\frac{1}{n} \quad \text{and} \quad \frac{f\left(\frac{-1}{n}\right) - f(0)}{\frac{-1}{n}} = -1,$$

so the sequence

$$\left\{ \frac{f\left(\frac{(-1)^n}{n}\right) - f(0)}{\frac{(-1)^n}{n}} \right\}_{n=1}^{\infty}$$

does not converge. Thus, by Theorem 4.1, f is not differentiable at zero. If the reader will sketch the graph of $|x|$, he will see why this happens. The graph has a "sharp" corner at zero with the slope suddenly changing from -1 to $+1$ as x increases from negative to positive values, and of course the slope is not defined at zero.

For the moment, assume the usual facts about differentiating the product, sum, and composition of the elementary functions. Define $f(x) = x \sin 1/x$ for $x \neq 0$ and $f(0) = 0$. The fact that f is differentiable at any point other than zero follows from the assumptions made at the beginning of this paragraph. For $x \neq 0$,

$$\frac{f(x) - f(0)}{x - 0} = \sin \frac{1}{x},$$

does not have a limit at zero; hence f is not differentiable at zero, although it is continuous there.

In an attempt to seek a "nicer" function, define $f(x) = x^2 \sin 1/x$ for $x \neq 0$, and $f(0) = 0$. As before, f has a derivative for $x \neq 0$; in fact, $f'(x) = 2x \sin 1/x - \cos 1/x$. Now $f'(x)$ is defined for $x \neq 0$, but it has no limit at zero because of the behavior of $\cos 1/x$ near zero. (See Exercise 2, Chapter 2.) One might suspect that this leads to the fact that f is not differentiable at 0; however, this is false. For $x \neq 0$,

$$\frac{f(x) - f(0)}{x - 0} = x \sin \frac{1}{x},$$

which has a limit at zero, namely $f'(0) = 0$. In this case, we have a function with a derivative at every point, but the derivative is not continuous at one point, and in fact does not have a limit there.

Finally, consider $f(x) = x^3 \sin 1/x$ for $x \neq 0$ and $f(0) = 0$. It will be left to the reader to verify that f is differentiable at every point and that f' is continuous at every point but fails to be differentiable at one point.

Let us now return to the initial definition and seek the facts pertinent to functions differentiable on a set. First of all, consider the difference quotient

$$\frac{f(x) - f(x_0)}{x - x_0} = T(x).$$

For x close to x_0, the denominator is close to zero; hence, in order that T have a limit at x_0, the numerator must be close to zero, otherwise T

would not be bounded near x_0. We are led to predict that if f is differentiable at x_0, then f must be continuous at x_0. The proof may be accomplished by observing that

$$f(x) - f(x_0) = \frac{f(x) - f(x_0)}{x - x_0}(x - x_0)$$

for $x \neq x_0$.

4.2 THEOREM Let $f: D \to R$ be differentiable at x_0. (It is tacitly assumed that $x_0 \in D$ and that x_0 is an accumulation point of D.) Then f is continuous at x_0.

Proof: Let $T: D \setminus \{x_0\} \to R$ be defined by

$$T(x) = \frac{f(x) - f(x_0)}{x - x_0}.$$

T has a limit at x_0 and $\lim_{x \to x_0} T(x) = f'(x_0)$. For $x \neq x_0$,

$$f(x) = \frac{f(x) - f(x_0)}{x - x_0} \cdot (x - x_0) + f(x_0)$$

$$= T(x)(x - x_0) + f(x_0).$$

Now f is a sum of two functions, one of which is constant, the other the product of two functions, each of which has a limit at x_0; so f has a limit at x_0 and

$$\lim_{x \to x_0} f(x) = \lim_{x \to x_0} [T(x)(x - x_0) + f(x_0)]$$

$$= [\lim_{x \to x_0} T(x)][\lim_{x \to x_0} (x - x_0)] + \lim_{x \to x_0} f(x_0)$$

$$= f'(x_0) \cdot 0 + f(x_0) = f(x_0).$$

Thus, f is continuous at x_0.

The next theorem presents the usual facts from calculus about the sum, product, and quotient of differentiable functions.

4.3 THEOREM   Suppose $f, g : D \to R$ are differentiable at x_0.
Then

(a) $f + g$ is differentiable at x_0 and

$$(f + g)'(x_0) = f'(x_0) + g'(x_0);$$

(b) fg is differentiable at x_0 and

$$(fg)'(x_0) = f(x_0)g'(x_0) + f'(x_0)g(x_0);$$

(c) if $g(x_0) \neq 0$, then f/g (the domain is the set of all x such
that $g(x) \neq 0$) is differentiable at x_0 and

$$\left(\frac{f}{g}\right)'(x_0) = \frac{f'(x_0)g(x_0) - g'(x_0)f(x_0)}{[g(x_0)]^2}.$$

Proof: We shall appeal to 4.1 to prove this theorem. Let
$\{x_n\}_{n=1}^{\infty}$ be any sequence of points in $D \setminus \{x_0\}$ converging to x_0.
Since f and g are differentiable at x_0,

$$\left\{\frac{f(x_n) - f(x_0)}{x_n - x_0}\right\}_{n=1}^{\infty}$$

converges to $f'(x_0)$ and

$$\left\{\frac{g(x_n) - g(x_0)}{x_n - x_0}\right\}_{n=1}^{\infty}$$

converges to $g'(x_0)$. Thus,

$$\left\{\frac{(f + g)(x_n) - (f + g)(x_0)}{x_n - x_0}\right\}_{n=1}^{\infty}$$

$$= \left\{\frac{f(x_n) - f(x_0)}{x_n - x_0} + \frac{g(x_n) - g(x_0)}{x_n - x_0}\right\}_{n=1}^{\infty}$$

converges to $f'(x_0) + g'(x_0)$. This means that $f + g$ is differentiable
at x_0 and that

$$(f + g)'(x_0) = f'(x_0) + g'(x_0).$$

By 4.2, f is continuous at x_0, and so $\{f(x_n)\}_{n=1}^{\infty}$ converges to $f(x_0)$.

Thus,

$$\left\{\frac{(fg)(x_n) - (fg)(x_0)}{x_n - x_0}\right\}_{n=1}^{\infty}$$

$$= \left\{\frac{f(x_n)g(x_n) - f(x_n)g(x_0) + f(x_n)g(x_0) - f(x_0)g(x_0)}{x_n - x_0}\right\}_{n=1}^{\infty}$$

$$= \left\{f(x_n)\frac{g(x_n) - g(x_0)}{x_n - x_0} + g(x_0)\frac{f(x_n) - f(x_0)}{x_n - x_0}\right\}_{n=1}^{\infty}$$

converges to $f(x_0)g'(x_0) + g(x_0)f'(x_0)$. Thus, fg is differentiable at x_0 and

$$(fg)'(x_0) = f(x_0)g'(x_0) + g(x_0)f'(x_0).$$

Let $D' = \{x : x \in D \text{ and } g(x) \neq 0\}$. Then D' is the domain of f/g, and x_0 is an accumulation point of D' by the continuity of g at x_0. Let $\{x_n\}_{n=1}^{\infty}$ be any sequence of points of $D' \setminus \{x_0\}$ converging to x_0. Then since g is continuous at x_0 and $g(x_0) \neq 0$, $1/g$ is continuous at x_0; hence, $\{1/g(x_n)\}_{n=1}^{\infty}$ converges to $1/g(x_0)$. Now

$$\left\{\frac{\left(\frac{f}{g}\right)(x_n) - \left(\frac{f}{g}\right)(x_0)}{x_n - x_0}\right\}_{n=1}^{\infty}$$

$$= \left\{\frac{f(x_n)g(x_0) - g(x_n)f(x_0)}{g(x_n)g(x_0)(x_n - x_0)}\right\}_{n=1}^{\infty}$$

$$= \left\{\frac{1}{g(x_n)g(x_0)}\right.$$

$$\times \left.\left[\frac{f(x_n)g(x_0) - f(x_0)g(x_0) + f(x_0)g(x_0) - g(x_n)f(x_0)}{x_n - x_0}\right]\right\}_{n=1}^{\infty}$$

$$= \left\{\frac{1}{g(x_n)g(x_0)}\left[g(x_0)\frac{f(x_n) - f(x_0)}{x_n - x_0} - f(x_0)\frac{g(x_n) - g(x_0)}{x_n - x_0}\right]\right\}_{n=1}^{\infty}$$

converges to

$$\frac{1}{[g(x_0)]^2}[g(x_0)f'(x_0) - f(x_0)g'(x_0)].$$

Thus, f/g is differentiable at x_0 and

$$\left(\frac{f}{g}\right)'(x_0) = \frac{f'(x_0)g(x_0) - f(x_0)g'(x_0)}{[g(x_0)]^2}.$$

Earlier in this chapter we considered $f(x) = \sin 1/x$ for $x \neq 0$. At that time we assumed some facts concerning the differentiation of the sum, product, and composition of differentiable functions. Now we shall justify our assumptions and consider the differentiability of the composition of differentiable functions. The next theorem is often referred to as the chain rule.

4.4 THEOREM   Suppose $f: D \to R$ and $g: D' \to R$ with $f(D) \subset D'$. If f is differentiable at x_0 and g is differentiable at $f(x_0)$, then $g \circ f$ is differentiable at x_0 and

$$(g \circ f)'(x_0) = g'(f(x_0))f'(x_0).$$

(We remind the reader that the hypothesis that f is differentiable at x_0 implies that x_0 is an accumulation point of D, and, similarly, g differentiable at $f(x_0)$ implies $f(x_0)$ is an accumulation point of D'.)

Proof: One might be tempted to prove this theorem by writing

$$\frac{(g \circ f)(x) - (g \circ f)(x_0)}{x - x_0} = \frac{g(f(x)) - g(f(x_0))}{f(x) - f(x_0)} \frac{f(x) - f(x_0)}{x - x_0}$$

and claiming that the right-hand side has $g'(f(x_0))f'(x_0)$ as a limit; hence, $g \circ f$ is differentiable at x_0 as claimed. However, $x \neq x_0$ need not imply that $f(x) \neq f(x_0)$. Hence the denominator may well be zero in the first factor of the right-hand side of the equation. We shall seek to circumvent this trap.

For each $y \in D'$, define

$$h(y) = \frac{g(y) - g(f(x_0))}{y - f(x_0)} - g'(f(x_0))$$

if $y \neq f(x_0)$, and define $h(f(x_0)) = 0$. Since g is differentiable at $f(x_0)$, h has a limit at $f(x_0)$ and

$$\lim_{y \to f(x_0)} h(y) = 0 = h(f(x_0));$$

hence, h is continuous at $f(x_0)$. The differentiability of f at x_0 implies f is continuous at x_0. Since $h \circ f$ is continuous at x_0, it has a limit there, and

$$\phi(x) = \frac{f(x) - f(x_0)}{x - x_0}$$

for $x \neq x_0$ has a limit at x_0; hence, so does

$$[(h \circ f)(x) + g'(f(x_0))]\left[\frac{f(x) - f(x_0)}{x - x_0}\right] = \frac{g(f(x)) - g(f(x_0))}{x - x_0}$$

for $x \neq x_0$. Thus, $g \circ f$ is differentiable at x_0 and

$$(g \circ f)'(x_0) = \lim_{x \to x_0} \frac{g(f(x)) - g(f(x_0))}{x - x_0}$$

$$= \lim_{x \to x_0} [(h \circ f)(x) + g'(f(x_0))] \frac{f(x) - f(x_0)}{x - x_0}$$

$$= g'(f(x_0))f'(x_0).$$

Let us consolidate a few results at this stage of the game. First of all, any constant function is differentiable and has derivative zero everywhere. The function $f(x) = x$ is differentiable everywhere and $f'(x) = 1$ for all x. An easy application of 4.3 shows that every polynomial function is differentiable and every rational function (the quotient of two polynomial functions) is differentiable at each point where the denominator is nonzero. Since it is so easy to do and we already know the answer, let us prove now that if $f(x) = x^n$ for n an integer, then $f'(x) = nx^{n-1}$. (Of course, if $n < 0$, we must assume $x \neq 0$, and if $n = 0$, then $f'(x) = 0$ for all x.)

4.5 THEOREM   If n is an integer and $f(x) = x^n$ for all x, then f is differentiable for all x if $n > 0$ and for all $x \neq 0$ if $n < 0$, and $f'(x) = nx^{n-1}$. If $n = 0$, then $f'(x) = 0$ for all x.

Proof: For $n = 0$, $f(x) = 1$ for all x; hence, f is differentiable for all x and $f'(x) = 0$, and the theorem is true. We shall now prove the theorem by induction for $n > 0$ and appeal to 4.3 to extend to the negative integers. The fact that $f(x) = x^n$ is differentiable for each positive integer n follows from 4.3 by induction, but this is the type of induction proof that should be unnecessary for one who has progressed this far. We shall now proceed to show that $f'(x) = nx^{n-1}$.

For $n = 1$, $f(x) = x$ and $f'(x) = 1 = 1x^0$, so the theorem holds. Suppose the theorem holds for $n = r$; that is, if $f(x) = x^r$, then

$$f'(x) = rx^{r-1}.$$

Consider $g(x) = x^{r+1}$. We may consider this as the product of two functions: $f(x) = x^r$ and $h(x) = x$. By 4.3,

$$g'(x) = f(x)h'(x) + f'(x)h(x) = x^r(1) + (rx^{r-1})x$$
$$= x^r + rx^r = (r+1)x^r.$$

Thus, the theorem holds for $n = r + 1$, and the induction is complete.

It now remains to verify the conclusion for $f(x) = x^n$ for n a negative integer, $x \neq 0$. Now if $n < 0$, then $-n > 0$, and $x^n = 1/x^{-n}$ is differentiable for $x \neq 0$ by our remarks earlier in this proof and 4.3. Moreover, if $f(x) = x^n = 1/x^{-n}$, then

$$f'(x) = \frac{-(-n)x^{-n-1}}{(x^{-n})^2} = nx^{n-1}.$$

This concludes the proof.

The classical maxima and minima problems from the calculus are no doubt familiar to the reader. The fact to be applied here is roughly that the graph of a differentiable function has a horizontal tangent at a maximum or minimum point. This is not quite accurate, but let us define some terms before proceeding further.

DEFINITION   Let $f : D \to R$. A point $x_0 \in D$ is a *relative maximum* (*minimum*) of f iff there is a neighborhood Q of x_0 such that if $x \in Q \cap D$, then

$$f(x) \le f(x_0) \quad (f(x) \ge f(x_0)).$$

Consider a few examples, and reconsider the statement preceding this definition. Perhaps the point is most easily made by looking at the function $f : [0, 1] \to R$ such that $f(x) = x$. Since the domain of f is the interval $[0, 1]$, f has a minimum at 0 and a maximum at 1; indeed, 0 is a relative minimum of f, and 1 is a relative maximum of f. Since $f'(x) = 1$ for all $x \in [0, 1]$, it is clear what is wrong with our statement concerning the existence of a horizontal tangent at a maximum or minimum point. We shall correct this defect in the following theorem.

4.6 THEOREM   Suppose $f : [a, b] \to R$, and suppose f has either a relative maximum or a relative minimum at $x_0 \in (a, b)$. If f is differentiable at x_0, then $f'(x_0) = 0$.

Proof: Assume f has a relative maximum at x_0. Then there is $\delta > 0$ such that if $x_0 - \delta < x < x_0 + \delta$, then $x \in [a, b]$ (since $x_0 \in (a, b)$) and $f(x) \le f(x_0)$. Consider any sequence $\{x_n\}_{n=1}^{\infty}$ converging to x_0 such that $x_0 - \delta < x_n < x_0$. Then, since f is differentiable at x_0,

$$\left\{ \frac{f(x_n) - f(x_0)}{x_n - x_0} \right\}_{n=1}^{\infty}$$

converges to $f'(x_0)$. But

$$\frac{f(x_n) - f(x_0)}{x_n - x_0} \ge 0$$

for each n since $f(x_n) \le f(x_0)$ and $x_n < x_0$, and hence $f'(x_0) \ge 0$. Consider now a sequence $\{y_n\}_{n=1}^{\infty}$ such that $x_0 < y_n < x_0 + \delta$. As before,

$$\left\{ \frac{f(y_n) - f(x_0)}{y_n - x_0} \right\}_{n=1}^{\infty}$$

converges to $f'(x_0)$, but this time

$$\frac{f(y_n) - f(x_0)}{y_n - x_0} \leq 0;$$

hence $f'(x_0) \leq 0$. Therefore, $f'(x_0) = 0$. The case in which f has a relative minimum at x_0 is left to the reader.

The reader should now realize that an important fact in this proof is that we are free to choose points in the domain on either side of x_0 as close as we please. Since both the maximum and the minimum occurred at end points in the preceding example, the theorem did not apply.

The following theorem, known as Rolle's Theorem, is an application of 4.6. We shall postpone a discussion of its geometric interpretation until we have completed the proof.

4.7 ROLLE'S THEOREM   Suppose $f: [a, b] \to R$ is continuous on $[a, b]$ and f is differentiable on (a, b). Then if $f(a) = f(b) = 0$, there is $c \in (a, b)$ such that $f'(c) = 0$.

Proof: If $f(x) = 0$ for all $x \in [a, b]$, then $f'(x) = 0$ for all $x \in [a, b]$, and the theorem is proved.

Suppose $f(x) \neq 0$ for some $x \in [a, b]$. By 3.7, $[a, b]$ is compact since it is closed and bounded; hence, by 3.10, f assumes its maximum and minimum in $[a, b]$, say at x_1 and x_2, respectively. Since f is not identically zero on $[a, b]$ and $f(a) = f(b) = 0$, at least one of x_1 and x_2 must belong to (a, b), say $x_1 \in (a, b)$. Now by 4.6, $f'(x_1) = 0$.

In essence, the theorem states that if the graph of a differentiable function touches the x-axis at a and at b, then somewhere between a and b, there is a horizontal tangent. Draw a few examples to see and appreciate this picture. Now consider some examples of smooth curves where this is not the case. It is clear that the same conclusion cannot be drawn, but the compulsion to generalize cannot be stifled. If f is differentiable on $[a, b]$, then the graph of f is a smooth curve passing through the points $(a, f(a))$

and $(b, f(b))$. Some facts from analytic geometry tell us that it is possible to rotate and translate our set of coordinate axes so that both of these points lie on the x-axis. The geometric interpretation of Rolle's Theorem now leads to the conclusion that there is a point on the curve $(c, f(c))$ where the tangent is parallel to the new x-axis, which contains the line segment joining $(a, f(a))$ and $(b, f(b))$. In terms of the original coordinate system, this geometric condition becomes

$$f'(c) = \frac{f(b) - f(a)}{b - a},$$

since $(f(b) - f(a))/(b - a)$ is the slope of the line segment joining $(a, f(a))$ and $(b, f(b))$. This is the content of the next theorem.

4.8 MEAN-VALUE THEOREM   If $f : [a, b] \to R$ is continuous on $[a, b]$ and differentiable on (a, b), then there is a $c \in (a, b)$ such that

$$f'(c) = \frac{f(b) - f(a)}{b - a}.$$

Proof: To prove this theorem, we shall find a linear function L such that $f - L$ satisfies Rolle's Theorem and apply Rolle's Theorem to obtain the desired result. This corresponds to the change of corrdinate system mentioned preceding this theorem. The function L must be linear and satisfy

$$L(a) = f(a), \qquad L(b) = f(b).$$

This is accomplished by choosing

$$L(x) = \left[\frac{f(b) - f(a)}{b - a} \right] (x - a) + f(a),$$

the equation of the line passing through $(a, f(a))$ and $(b, f(b))$. L is continuous and differentiable everywhere and

$$L'(x) = \frac{f(b) - f(a)}{b - a}.$$

Let $g = f - L$. The function g satisfies the hypotheses of Rolle's Theorem, hence there is $c \in (a, b)$ such that

$$0 = g'(c) = f'(c) - L'(c) = f'(c) - \frac{f(b) - f(a)}{b - a}.$$

Thus

$$f'(c) = \frac{f(b) - f(a)}{b - a}.$$

The mean-value theorem has some very important applications in relating the behavior of f and f'. The next theorem will serve to illustrate this.

4.9 THEOREM Suppose f is continuous on $[a, b]$ and differentiable on (a, b). Under these hypotheses:
   (i)   If $f'(x) \neq 0$ for all $x \in (a, b)$, then f is 1–1.
   (ii) If $f'(x) = 0$ for all $x \in (a, b)$, then f is constant.
   (iii) If $f'(x) > 0$ for all $x \in (a, b)$, then $x < y$ and $x, y \in [a, b]$ imply $f(x) < f(y)$ (that is, f is strictly increasing).
   (iv) If $f'(x) < 0$ for all $x \in (a, b)$, then $x < y$ and $x, y \in [a, b]$ imply $f(x) > f(y)$ (f is strictly decreasing).

Proof: Consider any $x, y \in [a, b]$ with $x < y$. Now f is continuous on $[x, y]$ and differentiable on (x, y); so, by the mean-value theorem, there is $c \in (x, y)$ such that

$$\frac{f(x) - f(y)}{x - y} = f'(c),$$

that is, $f(x) - f(y) = f'(c)(x - y)$. With this fact in mind, we shall proceed.
   (i)   Suppose f is not 1–1. Then there are $x, y \in [a, b]$ with $x < y$ such that $f(x) = f(y)$. Thus, there is $c \in (x, y)$ such that

$$f'(c) = \frac{f(x) - f(y)}{x - y} = 0,$$

contrary to $f'(c) \neq 0$ for all $c \in [a, b]$.

(ii) Suppose f is not constant on $[a,b]$. Then there are x, $y \in [a,b]$, $x < y$, such that $f(x) \neq f(y)$. There is $c \in (a,b)$ such that

$$f'(c) = \frac{f(x) - f(y)}{x - y} \neq 0,$$

contrary to $f'(c) = 0$ for all $c \in [a,b]$.

(iii) Suppose $x < y$ and x, $y \in [a,b]$. There is $c \in (x,y)$ such that

$$\frac{f(x) - f(y)}{x - y} = f'(c) > 0;$$

hence $f(x) < f(y)$.

(iv) Suppose $x < y$, x, $y \in [a,b]$. There is $c \in (x,y)$ such that

$$\frac{f(x) - f(y)}{x - y} = f'(c) < 0;$$

hence $f(x) > f(y)$.

Now that the proof has been presented, it is clear that parts (iii) and (iv) can be changed as follows to give additional information:

(iii') $f'(x) \geq 0$ for all $x \in (a,b)$ implies f is increasing.

(iv') $f'(x) \leq 0$ for all $x \in (a,b)$ implies f is decreasing.

As an obvious corollary to 4.9, we have the following theorem.

4.10 THEOREM Suppose that f and g are continuous on $[a,b]$ and differentiable on (a,b) and that $f'(x) = g'(x)$ for all $x \in (a,b)$. Then there is a real number k such that

$$f(x) = g(x) + k$$

for all $x \in [a,b]$.

Proof: Consider $h(x) = f(x) - g(x)$ for all $x \in [a,b]$. Clearly, h is continuous on $[a,b]$, differentiable on (a,b), and

$$h'(x) = f'(x) - g'(x) = 0$$

for all $x \in (a, b)$. Hence, by 4.9, there is a real number k such that

$$k = h(x) = f(x) - g(x)$$

for all $x \in [a, b]$. Thus, $f(x) = g(x) + k$ for all $x \in [a, b]$.

Consider a function f differentiable on $[a, b]$. If $f'(x) \neq 0$ for all $x \in (a, b)$, then by 4.9, f is 1–1, and by 3.15, f is monotone. If f is increasing, then for all x, $y \in [a, b]$ with $x \neq y$, we have

$$\frac{f(x) - f(y)}{x - y} > 0.$$

Hence $f'(x) \geq 0$ for all $x \in [a, b]$. Similarly, if f is decreasing, $f'(x) \leq 0$ for all $x \in [a, b]$. We have thus proved the following lemma.

LEMMA   If f is differentiable on $[a, b]$ and $f'(x) \neq 0$ for all $x \in (a, b)$, then either $f'(x) \geq 0$ for all $x \in [a, b]$ or $f'(x) \leq 0$ for all $x \in [a, b]$.

Let us consider this result from a slightly different point of view. Suppose f is differentiable on $[a, b]$ and there are x, $y \in [a, b]$ such that $f'(x) > 0$ and $f'(y) < 0$. If we restrict our attention to $[x, y]$ (assuming $x < y$), then by the lemma, there is $c \in (x, y)$ such that $f'(c) = 0$. Thus, we are led to suspect that f' has the intermediate-value property. That this is indeed the case is stated in the following theorem.

4.11 THEOREM   Suppose f is differentiable on $[a, b]$ and λ is a real number such that $f'(a) < \lambda < f'(b)$ or $f'(b) < \lambda < f'(a)$. Then there is $c \in (a, b)$ such that $f'(c) = \lambda$.

Proof: Define

$$g(x) = f(x) - \lambda x$$

for all $x \in [a, b]$. Then g is differentiable on $[a, b]$ and $g'(x) = f'(x) - \lambda$. If $f'(a) < \lambda < f'(b)$, then $g'(a) < 0$ and $g'(b) > 0$; if

$f'(b) < \lambda < f'(a)$, then $g'(a) > 0$ and $g'(b) < 0$. In either case, g' has opposite signs at a and at b. Hence, by the lemma, there is $c \in (a, b)$ such that

$$0 = g'(c) = f'(c) - \lambda,$$

so that $f'(c) = \lambda$.

Suppose $f : [a, b] \rightarrow R$ is such that there is a differentiable function $g : [a, b] \rightarrow R$ such that $g'(x) = f(x)$ for all $x \in [a, b]$. Now f need not be a continuous function, but f must have the intermediate-value property; in other words, if $x, y \in [a, b]$ and $f(x) < \lambda < f(y)$, then there is c between x and y such that $f(c) = \lambda$. This means that a function which is a derivative of some function must be rather special. In particular, $f(x) = [x]$ cannot be the derivative of a function.

The next theorem is a one-dimensional version of the inverse function theorem. In Chapter 3, we observed that if $f : [a, b] \rightarrow R$ is continuous and 1–1, then f^{-1} is also continuous. It is now natural to inquire what can be obtained if it is assumed that f is differentiable. Before proceeding further, let's look at the possibilities. If f is 1–1 and differentiable, and if f^{-1} is differentiable, then by the chain rule,

$$(f^{-1} \circ f)'(x) = (f^{-1})'(f(x))f'(x)$$

but $(f^{-1} \circ f)(x) = x$ for all $x \in [a, b]$; hence

$$1 = (f^{-1} \circ f)'(x) = (f^{-1})'(f(x))f'(x)$$

for all $x \in [a, b]$. This last equation shows that for $x \in [a, b]$,

$$(f^{-1})'(f(x)) = \frac{1}{f'(x)}$$

and, in particular, $f'(x) \neq 0$. These observations give us some insight into what hypotheses are needed and what conclusions might be drawn in the setting mentioned above.

4.12 THEOREM   Suppose $f : [a, b] \rightarrow R$ is continuous and differentiable with $f'(x) \neq 0$ for all $x \in [a, b]$. Then f is 1–1, f^{-1} is continuous and differentiable on $f([a, b])$, and

$$(f^{-1})'(f(x)) = \frac{1}{f'(x)}$$

for all $x \in [a, b]$.

Proof: Since $f'(x) \neq 0$ for all $x \in [a, b]$, then by 4.9, f is 1–1. Let us suppose that $f([a, b]) = [c, d]$. (The fact that f is continuous guarantees that $f([a, b])$ is indeed a closed interval.) We shall now proceed to show that $f^{-1} : [c, d] \to [a, b]$ is differentiable. Choose $y_0 \in [c, d]$ and $\{y_n\}_{n=1}^{\infty}$ any sequence in $[c, d] \setminus \{y_0\}$ converging to y_0. Let

$$x_n = f^{-1}(y_n)$$

for $n = 0, 1, 2, \ldots$. By 3.11, f^{-1} is continuous and $\{x_n\}_{n=1}^{\infty}$ converges to x_0, and, since f^{-1} is 1–1, $x_n \neq x_0$ for $n = 1, 2, \ldots$. By the differentiability of f,

$$\left\{ \frac{f(x_n) - f(x_0)}{x_n - x_0} \right\}_{n=1}^{\infty}$$

converges to $f'(x_0)$. By hypothesis, $f'(x_0) \neq 0$ and

$$\frac{f(x_n) - f(x_0)}{x_n - x_0} \neq 0$$

for $n = 1, 2, \ldots$. Hence

$$\left\{ \frac{f^{-1}(y_n) - f^{-1}(y_0)}{y_n - y_0} \right\}_{n=1}^{\infty} = \left\{ \frac{x_n - x_0}{f(x_n) - f(x_0)} \right\}_{n=1}^{\infty}$$

converges to $1/(f'(x_0))$. Thus, by 4.1, f^{-1} is differentiable and

$$(f^{-1})'(f(x_0)) = \frac{1}{f'(x_0)}.$$

We close this chapter with a few applications of our results. Consider the function $g(x) = x^2$ defined for all real numbers x. Of course, g is differentiable and $g'(x) = 2x$. We shall restrict our attention to the behavior of g on the interval $[8, 10]$. If $x \in [8, 10]$, then $g'(x) = 2x \neq 0$, and, by 4.12, g is 1–1 on $[8, 10]$, g^{-1} is differentiable on $[64, 100]$, and

$(g^{-1})'(g(x)) = 1/(g'(x))$. It is customary to write the inverse of g as $\sqrt{x}$ where, of course, $\sqrt{x}$ denotes the positive square root of x. Now $g([8, 10]) = [64, 100]$, and if $h(x) = \sqrt{x} = g^{-1}(x)$, we have

$$h : [64, 100] \to [8, 10].$$

Also,

$$h'(x) = h'(g(h(x))) = \frac{1}{g'(h(x))} = \frac{1}{2\sqrt{x}}$$

for each $x \in [64, 100]$, by 4.12. Suppose one wants to approximate $\sqrt{80} = h(80)$. Since $h(81) = 9$ is easy to calculate, we shall try to use this result to come close to $\sqrt{80}$. By the mean-value theorem,

$$h(81) - h(80) = h'(x_0)(81 - 80)$$

for some $x_0 \in [80, 81]$. Thus,

$$h(80) = h(81) - h'(x_0) = 9 - \frac{1}{2\sqrt{x_0}}.$$

Although we do not know the exact value of x_0, we do know that $8 < \sqrt{x_0} < 9$. We may conclude that

$$9 - \frac{1}{18} < \sqrt{80} < 9 - \frac{1}{16}.$$

Suppose $g : [0, 1] \to [0, 1]$ is continuous. By 3.14, there is $x_0 \in [0, 1]$ such that $g(x_0) = x_0$; such a point is called a *fixed point* of g. Define $g_1(x) = g(x)$, and for each $n \geq 1$, define $g_{n+1}(x) = g(g_n(x))$. The function g_n is called the nth *iterate* of g. A fixed point x_0 of g is said to be *attractive* iff there is $\varepsilon > 0$ such that $x \in [0, 1]$ and $|x - x_0| < \varepsilon$ imply that $\{g_n(x)\}_{n=1}^{\infty}$ converges to x_0. Suppose now that g is differentiable at x_0, x_0 is a fixed point of g, and $|g'(x_0)| < 1$. We shall prove that x_0 is an attractive fixed point. Since $|g'(x_0)| < 1$, there are real numbers α and ε such that $\varepsilon > 0$ and if $0 < |x - x_0| < \varepsilon$, $x \in [0, 1]$, then

$$\left| \frac{g(x) - g(x_0)}{x - x_0} \right| < \alpha < 1.$$

Choose $x \in [0, 1]$ such that $0 < |x - x_0| < \varepsilon$. If $g_n(x) = x_0$ for some n, then for $m \geq n$, $g_m(x) = x_0$ and $\{g_m(x)\}_{m=1}^{\infty}$ converges to x_0. Suppose now that $g_n(x) \neq x_0$ for all n. Recall that x_0 is a fixed point of g, so that

$$g(x_0) = x_0 = g_1(x_0).$$

Now since $0 < |x - x_0| < \varepsilon$,

$$\left| \frac{g_1(x) - g_1(x_0)}{x - x_0} \right| = \left| \frac{g(x) - g(x_0)}{x - x_0} \right| < \alpha < 1;$$

hence $|g(x) - x_0| < \alpha |x - x_0| < \varepsilon$. We shall use induction to show that

$$|g_n(x) - x_0| < \alpha^n |x - x_0|,$$

and, since $0 \le \alpha < 1$, $\{\alpha^n\}_{n=1}^{\infty}$ converges to zero; hence, $\{g_n(x)\}_{n=1}^{\infty}$ converges to x_0. We have already verified the result for $n = 1$. Suppose now that $|g_n(x) - x_0| < \alpha^n |x - x_0|$. Since $\alpha < 1$ and $|x - x_0| < \varepsilon$, then $|g_n(x) - x_0| < \varepsilon$, and

$$\left| \frac{g_{n+1}(x) - x_0}{g_n(x) - x_0} \right| = \left| \frac{g(g_n(x)) - g(g_n(x_0))}{g_n(x) - g_n(x_0)} \right| < \alpha.$$

Therefore, $|g_{n+1}(x) - x_0| < \alpha |g_n(x) - x_0| < \alpha^{n+1} |x - x_0|$, and the induction is complete.

EXERCISES

1. Consider the function $f : R \to R$ where $f(x) = x^3 \sin 1/x$ for $x \ne 0$, $f(0) = 0$. Prove that f is differentiable everywhere and compute f'. Where is f' continuous? Where is it differentiable?

2. Suppose $f : (a, b) \to R$ is differentiable at $x \in (a, b)$. Prove that

$$\lim_{h \to 0} \frac{f(x + h) - f(x - h)}{2h}$$

exists and equals $f'(x)$. Give an example of a function where this limit exists but the function is not differentiable.

3. Search the literature for an example of a continuous function that is nowhere differentiable.

4. Use the definition to determine $f'(x)$ for $x > 0$ when $f(x) = \sqrt{x}$.

5. Suppose $f : (a, b) \to R$ is differentiable and $|f'(x)| \le M$ for all $x \in (a, b)$. Prove that f is uniformly continuous on (a, b). Give an example of a function $f : (0, 1) \to R$ which is differentiable and uniformly continuous on $(0, 1)$ but such that f' is unbounded.

6. A function $f : (a, b) \to R$ satisfies a Lipschitz condition at $x \in (a, b)$ iff there is $M > 0$ and $\varepsilon > 0$ such that $|x - y| < \varepsilon$, $y \in (a, b)$ imply that $|f(x) - f(y)| \le M |x - y|$. Give an example of a function that fails to satisfy a Lipschitz condition at a point of continuity. If f is differentiable at x, prove that f satisfies a Lipschitz condition at x.

7. Suppose f is differentiable on (a, b), except possibly at $x_0 \in (a, b)$, and continuous on $[a, b]$; assume $\lim_{x \to x_0} f'(x)$ exists. Prove that f is differentiable at x_0 and f' is continuous at x_0.

8. A function $f : (a, b) \to R$ is said to be uniformly differentiable iff f is differentiable on (a, b) and for each $\varepsilon > 0$, there is $\delta > 0$ such that $0 < |x - y| < \delta, x, y \in (a, b)$ imply that

$$\left| \frac{f(x) - f(y)}{x - y} - f'(x) \right| < \varepsilon.$$

Prove that if f is uniformly differentiable on (a, b), then f' is continuous on (a, b).

9. Generalized mean-value theorem: Suppose g, $f : [a, b] \to R$ are continuous on $[a, b]$ and differentiable on (a, b). Prove that there is $c \in (a, b)$ such that

$$f'(c)(g(b) - g(a)) = g'(c)(f(b) - f(a)).$$

10. Prove the following version of L'Hospital's rule: Let f and g be differentiable on (a, b). Assume that $x_0 \in (a, b)$ and $f(x_0) = g(x_0) = 0$ but that $g'(x) \neq 0$ for all $x \in (a, b)$. Prove that $\lim_{x \to x_0} f(x)/g(x)$ exists and equals $f'(x_0)/g'(x_0)$.

11. Define $f(x) = x + 2x^2 \sin 1/x$ for $x \neq 0$ and $f(0) = 0$. Prove that f is differentiable everywhere. Show that there exists a number a such that $f'(a) > 0$ but there does not exist a neighborhood of a in which f is increasing.

12. Use the mean-value theorem to prove that $\sqrt{1 + h} < 1 + \frac{1}{2}h$ for $h > 0$.

13. Suppose $f : [a, b] \to [c, d]$ and $g : [c, d] \to R$ are differentiable on $[a, b]$ and $[c, d]$, respectively. Suppose

$$f' : [a, b] \to R \quad \text{and} \quad g' : [c, d] \to R$$

are also differentiable on $[a, b]$ and $[c, d]$, respectively. Show that $(g \circ f)' : [a, b] \to R$ is differentiable, and compute its derivative.

14. Suppose $f : (a, b) \to R$ is differentiable at $x_0 \in (a, b)$ with $\{\alpha_n\}_{n=1}^{\infty}$ and $\{\beta_n\}_{n=1}^{\infty}$ two sequences in $(a, b) \setminus \{x_0\}$ converging to x_0 such that the sequence

$$\left\{ \frac{\beta_n - x_0}{\beta_n - \alpha_n} \right\}_{n=1}^{\infty}$$

is bounded. Prove that

$$\left\{ \frac{f(\beta_n) - f(\alpha_n)}{\beta_n - \alpha_n} \right\}_{n=1}^{\infty}$$

converges to $f'(x_0)$.

CHAPTER 5

THE RIEMANN–STIELTJES INTEGRAL

Our first concept in this chapter is one the reader should have some familiarity with—that of the Riemann integral. Beginning with an intuitive idea of the area under a curve, we shall progress to a deeper understanding of this concept. By considering a very special case at the outset, we can see what is reasonable to try for a definition.

Suppose $f : [a, b] \to R$ is bounded and $f(x) \geq 0$ for all $x \in [a, b]$. For the purpose of visualizing the notion of area under the curve, it is worthwhile to assume for the moment that f is continuous. We want to determine some reasonable manner of assigning an area to the portion of the plane bounded by the lines $x = a$, $x = b$, $y = 0$ and the graph of f. The approach will be to attempt to approximate the area by use of rectangles, whose areas are easy to compute, and then to use some type of limit process to arrive at our result. Because of the possible pathological nature of f (if we don't assume continuity), it is reasonable to expect some difficulty with this limit idea.

Choose points $x_0, x_1, x_2, \ldots, x_n$ such that $a = x_0 < x_1 < \cdots$ $< x_n = b$. For each i among $1, \ldots, n$, erect a rectangle R_i with the interval $[x_{i-1}, x_i]$ as base and with altitude such that the portion of the graph of f for $x \in [x_{i-1}, x_i]$ lies in this rectangle. This is possible since f is bounded; in fact, we may choose the altitude of R_i to be

$$M_i = \sup \{f(x) : x \in [x_{i-1}, x_i]\}.$$

The area in question lies in the union of the rectangles $R_1, \ldots, R_n$, and these rectangles are nonoverlapping; hence, the area should be less than or equal to the sum of these areas—that is, less than or equal to

$$\sum_{i=1}^{n} M_i(x_i - x_{i-1}).$$

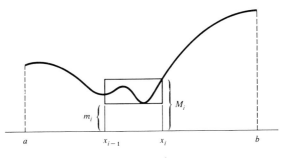

FIGURE 1

For the more conservative reader, possibly one should try underestimating the area. This time, for each i, erect a rectangle S_i with base $[x_{i-1}, x_i]$ and with altitude such that the rectangle S_i lies entirely inside the region in question. Here we shall choose the altitude of S_i to be

$$m_i = \inf \{f(x) : x \in [x_{i-1}, x_i]\}.$$

The rectangles $S_1, \ldots, S_n$ are nonoverlapping, and all lie inside the portion of the plane bounded by the lines $x = a$, $x = b$, $y = 0$ and the graph of f, hence the sum of their areas,

$$\sum_{i=1}^{n} m_i(x_i - x_{i-1}),$$

must be less than or equal to the sought-after area.

Let us temporarily refer to $\sum_{i=1}^{n} M_i(x_i - x_{i-1})$ as an *upper sum* for f and to $\sum_{i=1}^{n} m_i(x_i - x_{i-1})$ as a *lower sum* for f. The upper sum clearly overestimates the area, and the lower sum underestimates it. Observe that as one chooses more points in the interval, the upper sum decreases and the lower sum increases; hence they should "converge" to the "area" to be found. The words in quotation marks are used only because these notions have not been formalized in this setting. Let us now formulate a policy concerning the limiting process to which we have made vague reference above. Roughly, we will insist that the upper and lower sums get closer and closer together as we choose more points in $[a, b]$. The discussion just presented is intended to prepare the reader for the precise formulation that is necessary to give the full meaning of the Riemann integral.

Consider $a < b$. A *partition* P of $[a, b]$ is any finite set $\{x_0, x_1, \ldots, x_n\}$ such that $a = x_0 < x_1 < \cdots < x_n = b$. If P and Q are partitions of $[a, b]$ with $P \subset Q$, then Q is said to be a *refinement* of P.

Suppose that $f : [a, b] \rightarrow R$ is a bounded function and

$$P = \{x_0, x_1, \ldots, x_n\}$$

is a partition of $[a, b]$. For each i among $1, \ldots, n$, define

$$M_i(f) = \sup \{f(x) : x \in [x_{i-1}, x_i]\}$$

and

$$m_i(f) = \inf \{f(x) : x \in [x_{i-1}, x_i]\}.$$

Define

$$U(P, f) = \sum_{i=1}^{n} M_i(f)(x_i - x_{i-1})$$

and

$$L(P, f) = \sum_{i=1}^{n} m_i(f)(x_i - x_{i-1}).$$

We shall call $U(P, f)$ an *upper sum* of f and $L(P, f)$ a *lower sum* of f. Now f is assumed bounded on $[a, b]$, so there is a real number M such that $-M \leq f(x) \leq M$ for all $x \in [a, b]$. Thus, in particular, for any partition P of $[a, b]$, $U(P, f) \geq -M(b - a)$ and $L(P, f) \leq M(b - a)$. Let

$$\overline{\int_a^b} f\, dx = \inf \{U(P, f) : P \text{ a partition of } [a, b]\}$$

and

$$\overline{\int_a^b} f\,dx = \sup\{L(P,f) : P \text{ a partition of } [a,b]\};$$

in light of the previous sentence, $\overline{\int_a^b} f\,dx$ and $\underline{\int_a^b} f\,dx$ exist and are referred to as the upper and lower integrals of f, respectively. We say that f is *Riemann-integrable* on $[a,b]$ if and only if

$$\overline{\int_a^b} f\,dx = \underline{\int_a^b} f\,dx, \quad \text{and} \quad \overline{\int_a^b} f\,dx = \underline{\int_a^b} f\,dx = \int_a^b f\,dx$$

is called the *Riemann integral* of f on $[a,b]$. It will be convenient to write $f \in R(x)$ on $[a,b]$ when f is Riemann-integrable on $[a,b]$. The reader is probably accustomed to writing $\int_a^b f(x)\,dx$ in place of our notation $\int_a^b f\,dx$, and we shall use that notation when convenient. We shall also omit the reference to Riemann from time to time and speak of f being *integrable* on $[a,b]$ and refer to $\int_a^b f\,dx$ as the *integral* of f.

A more general definition of an integral has already been introduced to the student in the discussion of integration by parts and in certain applications of integration in calculus. Since many of the proofs and theorems remain much the same for the more general case, we have chosen to discuss the Riemann–Stieltjes integral in this chapter with appropriate special cases which are applicable only to the Riemann integral.

Let $f : [a,b] \to R$ be bounded and $\alpha : [a,b] \to R$ be an increasing function. For each partition $P = \{x_0, x_1, \ldots, x_n\}$, define

$$U(P,f,\alpha) = \sum_{i=1}^n M_i(f)(\alpha(x) - \alpha(x_{i-1}))$$

$$L(P,f,\alpha) = \sum_{i=1}^n m_i(f)(\alpha(x_i) - \alpha(x_{i-1}))$$

and set $\overline{\int_a^b} f\,d\alpha = \inf\{U(P,f,\alpha) : P \text{ is a partition of } [a,b]\}$, $\underline{\int_a^b} f\,d\alpha = \sup\{L(P,f,\alpha): P \text{ is a partition of } [a,b]\}$. Since f is bounded and α is increasing, if $m \le f(x) \le M$ for all $x \in [a,b]$, then

$$m(\alpha(b) - \alpha(a)) \le \underline{\int_a^b} f\,d\alpha \quad \text{and} \quad \overline{\int_a^b} f\,d\alpha \le M(\alpha(b) - \alpha(a)).$$

If $\underline{\int_a^b} f\,d\alpha = \overline{\int_a^b} f\,d\alpha$, we denote their common value by $\int_a^b f\,d\alpha$ or by $\int_a^b f(x)\,d\alpha(x)$ and we say that f is *Riemann-integrable with respect to α on*

$[a, b]$ and write $f \in R(\alpha)$ on $[a, b]$. The number $\int_a^b f \, d\alpha$ is called the *Riemann–Stieltjes integral of f with respect to α over the interval* $[a, b]$. Note that if $\alpha(x) = x$ for all $x \in [a, b]$, then the Riemann–Stieltjes integral with respect to α reduces to the Riemann integral, so the Riemann integral will be included as a special case in what is to follow.

Perhaps a word of motivation is in order here. Suppose we wish to define the mass-moment of a rod of length k with respect to one end of the rod. Suppose further that a coordinate system is chosen in such a way that the end in question is at 0, the other end is at k, and a function α is given such that for $0 \le x \le k$, $\alpha(0) = 0$ and $\alpha(x) = $ mass of that section of the rod from 0 to x. If we choose a partition $P = \{x_0, x_1, \ldots, x_n\}$ of the interval $[0, k]$, then $\alpha(x_i) - \alpha(x_{i-1})$ is the mass of that section of the rod extending from x_{i-1} to x_i. The number we seek and wish to define to be the mass moment should be less than

$$\sum_{i=1}^n x_i(\alpha(x_i) - \alpha(x_{i-1}))$$

and greater than

$$\sum_{i=1}^n x_{i-1}(\alpha(x_i) - \alpha(x_{i-1})).$$

Observe that these two numbers are $U(P, f, \alpha)$ and $L(P, f, \alpha)$ respectively, for the function $f(x) = x$ on $[0, k]$. It now seems reasonable to define the mass moment to be $\int_0^k x \, d\alpha(x)$, and in fact, we shall prove soon that the function $f(x) = x$ is integrable with respect to α on $[a, b]$ for any increasing α on any $[a, b]$.

The first theorem to be presented will be an aid in understanding this approach to integration.

5.1 THEOREM   Let $f : [a, b] \to R$ be bounded and $\alpha : [a, b] \to R$ increasing. Then if P and Q are any partitions of $[a, b]$, we have
  (1) if $P \subseteq Q$, then $L(P, f, \alpha) \le L(Q, f, \alpha)$ and
       $U(Q, f, \alpha) \le U(P, f, \alpha)$,
  (2) $L(P, f, \alpha) \le U(Q, f, \alpha)$,
  (3) $\underline{\int_a^b} f \, d\alpha \le \overline{\int_a^b} f \, d\alpha$.

Proof: (1)   Let $P = \{x_0, x_1, \ldots, x_n\}$, and suppose we add one point z to this partition, $x_{j-1} < z < x_j$, call the new partition P'.

Let

$$M_i(f) = \sup \{f(x) : x \in [x_{i-1}, x_i]\},$$

$$m_i(f) = \inf \{f(x) : x \in [x_{i-1}, x_i]\},$$

$$r_1 = \sup \{f(x) : x \in [x_{j-1}, z]\},$$

$$r_2 = \sup \{f(x) : x \in [z, x_j]\},$$

$$s_1 = \inf \{f(x) : x \in [x_{j-1}, z]\},$$

$$s_2 = \inf \{f(x) : x \in [z, x_j]\}.$$

Now $M_j(f) \geq \max \{r_1, r_2\}$ and $m_j(f) \leq \min \{s_1, s_2\}$. Then

$$
\begin{aligned}
L(P, f, \alpha) &= \sum_{i=1}^{n} m_i(f)(\alpha(x_i) - \alpha(x_{i-1})) \\
&= \sum_{i=1}^{j-1} m_i(f)(\alpha(x_i) - \alpha(x_{i-1})) + m_j(f)(\alpha(x_j) - \alpha(x_{j-1})) \\
&\quad + \sum_{i=j+1}^{n} m_i(f)(\alpha(x_i) - \alpha(x_{i-1})) \\
&\leq \sum_{i=1}^{j-1} m_i(f)(\alpha(x_i) - \alpha(x_{i-1})) + s_1(\alpha(z) - \alpha(x_{j-1})) \\
&\quad + s_2(\alpha(x_j) - \alpha(z)) \\
&\quad + \sum_{i=j+1}^{n} m_i(f)(\alpha(x_i) - \alpha(x_{i-1})) \\
&= L(P', f, \alpha)
\end{aligned}
$$

and

$$
\begin{aligned}
U(P, f, \alpha) &= \sum_{i=1}^{j-1} M_i(f)(\alpha(x_i) - \alpha(x_{i-1})) \\
&\quad + M_j(f)(\alpha(x_j) - \alpha(x_{j-1})) \\
&\quad + \sum_{i=j+1}^{n} M_i(f)(\alpha(x_i) - \alpha(x_{i-1})) \\
&\geq \sum_{i=1}^{j-1} M_i(f)(\alpha(x_i) - \alpha(x_{i-1})) + r_1(\alpha(z) - \alpha(x_{j-1})) \\
&\quad + r_2(\alpha(x_j) - \alpha(z)) \\
&\quad + \sum_{i=j+1}^{n} M_i(f)(\alpha(x_i) - \alpha(x_{i-1})) \\
&= U(P', f, \alpha).
\end{aligned}
$$

If Q contains k points not in P, repeat this argument k times to obtain $L(P, f, \alpha) \leq L(Q, f, \alpha)$ and $U(P, f, \alpha) \geq U(Q, f, \alpha)$.

(2)   Note first of all that for any partition P of $[a, b]$, $m_i(f)$ $\leq M_i(f)$; hence $L(P, f) \leq U(P, f)$. Now if P and Q are partitions of $[a, b]$, then $P \cup Q$ is also a partition of $[a, b]$ which is a refinement of both P and Q. Then by (1), we have

$$L(P, f, \alpha) \leq L(P \cup Q, f, \alpha) \leq U(P \cup Q, f, \alpha) \leq U(Q, f, \alpha).$$

(3)   By (2), $L(P, f, \alpha) \leq U(Q, f, \alpha)$ for all partitions P and Q of $[a, b]$; hence for each partition P of $[a, b]$, $L(P, f, \alpha)$ is a lower bound for $\{U(Q, f, \alpha) : Q$ is a partition of $[a, b]\}$. Thus, $L(P, f, \alpha)$ $\leq \overline{\int_a^b} f \, d\alpha$ for all partitions P; hence $\overline{\int_a^b} f \, d\alpha = \sup\{L(P, f, \alpha) : P$ a partition of $[a, b]\} \leq \overline{\int_a^b} f \, d\alpha$.

Consider what is implied by the statement "f is Riemann-integrable with respect to α on $[a, b]$." First of all, f must be a bounded real-valued function defined on $[a, b]$. Secondly,

$$\underline{\int_a^b} f \, d\alpha = \overline{\int_a^b} f \, d\alpha.$$

Since $\underline{\int_a^b} f \, d\alpha$ is the supremum of all the lower sums, there must be lower sums very close to $\underline{\int_a^b} f \, d\alpha$. Likewise, since $\overline{\int_a^b} f \, d\alpha$ is the infimum of all the upper sums, there must be upper sums very close to $\overline{\int_a^b} f \, d\alpha$. The integrability of f with respect to α implies that

$$\overline{\int_a^b} f \, d\alpha = \underline{\int_a^b} f \, d\alpha;$$

hence there must be upper and lower sums close to each other. It is not at all surprising that the converse is also true. Of course, we are referring to a theorem to be stated in more precise terms than those given in this paragraph.

5.2 THEOREM   Let $f : [a, b] \to R$ be bounded and $\alpha : [a, b] \to R$ be increasing. Then $f \in R(\alpha)$ on $[a, b]$ iff for each $\varepsilon > 0$, there is a partition P such that

$$U(P, f, \alpha) - L(P, f, \alpha) \leq \varepsilon.$$

Proof: Suppose $f \in R(\alpha)$ on $[a, b]$. Then

$$\overline{\int_a^b} f \, d\alpha = \underline{\int_a^b} f \, d\alpha = \int_a^b f \, d\alpha.$$

Choose $\varepsilon > 0$. Now $\underline{\int_a^b} f \, d\alpha = \sup \{L(P, f, \alpha) : P$ a partition of $[a, b]\}$, hence $\int_a^b f \, d\alpha - \varepsilon/2$ is not an upper bound for the set of all lower sums, so there is a partition P_1 such that

$$\int_a^b f \, d\alpha - \varepsilon/2 < L(P_1, f, \alpha).$$

Similarly, $\overline{\int_a^b} f \, d\alpha = \inf \{U(P, f, \alpha) : P$ is a partition of $[a, b]\}$, hence $\int_a^b f \, d\alpha + \varepsilon/2$ is not a lower bound for the set of all upper sums; thus, there is a partition P_2 such that

$$U(P_2, f, \alpha) < \int_a^b f \, d\alpha + \varepsilon/2.$$

Let $P = P_1 \cup P_2$. Then

$$\int_a^b f \, d\alpha - \varepsilon/2 < L(P_1, f, \alpha) \le L(P, f, \alpha) \le U(P, f, \alpha)$$

$$\le U(P_2, f, \alpha) < \int_a^b f \, d\alpha + \varepsilon/2.$$

Thus, $U(P, f, \alpha) - L(P, f, \alpha) \le \varepsilon$.

Suppose $f : [a, b] \to R$ is bounded and such that for each $\varepsilon > 0$, there is a partition P such that

$$U(P, f, \alpha) - L(P, f, \alpha) \le \varepsilon.$$

We need to show that

$$\overline{\int_a^b} f \, d\alpha = \underline{\int_a^b} f \, d\alpha.$$

By 5.1, $\overline{\int_a^b} f \, d\alpha - \underline{\int_a^b} f \, d\alpha \ge 0$. We shall show that for each $\varepsilon > 0$,

$$0 \le \overline{\int_a^b} f \, d\alpha - \underline{\int_a^b} f \, d\alpha < \varepsilon,$$

hence

$$\overline{\int_a^b} f \, d\alpha = \underline{\int_a^b} f \, d\alpha.$$

Choose $\varepsilon > 0$. There is a partition P such that

$$U(P,f,\alpha) - L(P,f,\alpha) \le \varepsilon/2.$$

Thus, we have

$$L(P,f,\alpha) \le \underline{\int_a^b} f \, d\alpha \le \overline{\int_a^b} f \, d\alpha \le U(P,f,\alpha) \le L(P,f,\alpha) + \varepsilon/2.$$

Therefore, $0 \le \overline{\int_a^b} f \, d\alpha - \underline{\int_a^b} f \, d\alpha \le \varepsilon$, hence

$$\overline{\int_a^b} f \, d\alpha = \underline{\int_a^b} f \, d\alpha$$

and $f \in R(\alpha)$ on $[a,b]$.

Consider the geometric interpretation of $U(P,f) - L(P,f)$ for the case where $f(x) \ge 0$ for all x. In Figure 2, the area of the shaded region is $U(P,)f - L(P,f)$. From this point of view, 5.2 is a very natural theorem.

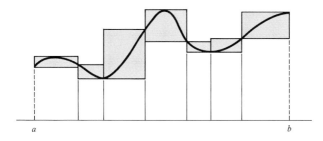

FIGURE 2

The situation that arises here is not uncommon. Theorem 5.2 gives a condition for integrability, but it does not give us any simple means for computing the integral. We encountered the same type of problem in our discussion of sequences.

Let us consider a few examples now. Consider the function $f: [0, 1] \to R$ such that $f(x) = 0$ if x is rational and $f(x) = 1$ if x is irrational. Let P be any partition of $[a, b]$, $P = \{x_0, x_1, \ldots, x_n\}$. Since every interval $[x_{i-1}, x_i]$ contains both rational and irrational points, $M_i(f) = 1$ and $m_i(f) = 0$. Hence, $U(P, f) = 1$ and $L(P, f) = 0$. Since all upper sums are equal to 1 and all lower sums are equal to 0, we have

$$\overline{\int_0^1} f\, dx = 1 \quad \text{and} \quad \underline{\int_0^1} f\, dx = 0,$$

so f is not Riemann-integrable on $[0, 1]$.

Consider now the function $f: [0, 1] \to R$ such that $f(x) = x^2$ for all $x \in [0, 1]$. Choose $\varepsilon > 0$, and let $P = \{x_0, x_1, \ldots, x_n\}$ be any partition of $[0, 1]$ such that

$$\max \{x_i - x_{i-1} : i = 1, \ldots, n\} < \frac{\varepsilon}{2}.$$

Since f is increasing and continuous,

$$M_i(f) = f(x_i) = x_i^2 \quad \text{and} \quad m_i(f) = f(x_{i-1}) = x_{i-1}^2,$$

hence

$$U(P, f) = \sum_{i=1}^n x_i^2(x_i - x_{i-1}) \quad \text{and} \quad L(P, f) = \sum_{i=1}^n x_{i-1}^2(x_i - x_{i-1}).$$

Thus, we have

$$\begin{aligned} U(P, f) - L(P, f) &= \sum_{i=1}^n (x_i^2 - x_{i-1}^2)(x_i - x_{i-1}) \\ &= \sum_{i=1}^n (x_i + x_{i-1})(x_i - x_{i-1})(x_i - x_{i-1}) \\ &< \sum_{i=1}^n 2\frac{\varepsilon}{2}(x_i - x_{i-1}) \\ &= \varepsilon \sum_{i=1}^n (x_i - x_{i-1}) = \varepsilon. \end{aligned}$$

This means that f is Riemann-integrable on $[0, 1]$. Note again that we have no information yet as to the value of $\int_0^1 x^2 dx$. We shall attack that problem soon.

Choose $a < c < b$ and $p \leq r \leq q$. Define $\alpha: [a, b] \to R$ by $\alpha(x) = p$ for $a \leq x < c$, $\alpha(c) = r$ and $\alpha(x) = q$ for $c < x \leq b$. The function α is sometimes referred to as a step function. Let $P = \{x_0, x_1, \ldots, x_n\}$ be any partition of $[a, b]$ with $x_j = c$. If $f : [a, b] \to R$ is bounded, then

$$U(P, f, \alpha) = M_j(f)(\alpha(c) - \alpha(x_{j-1})) + M_{j+1}(f)(\alpha(x_{j+1}) - \alpha(c))$$
$$= M_j(f)(r - p) + M_{j+1}(f)(q - r).$$

Similarly, $L(P, f, \alpha) = m_j(f)(r - p) + m_{j+1}(f)(q - r)$. By 5.2, integrability of f with respect to α hinges on the possibility of finding a partition P such that

$$U(P, f, \alpha) - L(P, f, \alpha) = [M_j(f) - m_j(f)](r - p)$$
$$+ [M_{j+1}(f) - m_{j+1}(f)](q - r)$$

is small. If $p < r < q$, then it is necessary to force $M_j(f) - m_j(f)$ and $M_{j+1}(f) - m_{j+1}(f)$ to be small. The reader is invited to prove that in this case $f \in R(\alpha)$ iff f is continuous at c. If $p = r < q$, then $r - p = 0$, so it is necessary only to have $M_{j+1}(f) - m_{j+1}(f)$ small. In this case, the reader is invited to prove that $f \in R(\alpha)$ iff f is right-continuous at c. Note that in this case, α is left-continuous at c but not right-continuous at c. Now if $p < r = q$, it turns out that $f \in R(\alpha)$ iff f is left-continuous at c. In this case, α is right-continuous at c but not left-continuous at c. Let us now seek to compute $\int_a^b f \, d\alpha$ if $f \in R(\alpha)$. Again, suppose $P = \{x_0, x_1, \ldots, x_n\}$ is a partition of $[a, b]$ with $c = x_j$. Then since $c \in [x_{j-1}, c]$ and $c \in [c, x_{j+1}]$,

$$m_j(f) \leq f(c) \leq M_j(f) \quad \text{and} \quad m_{j+1}(f) \leq f(c) \leq M_{j+1}(f).$$

Thus,

$$L(P, f, \alpha) = m_j(f)(r - p) + m_{j+1}(f)(q - r) \leq f(c)(r - p) + f(c)(q - r)$$
$$= f(c)(q - p) \leq M_j(f)(r - p) + M_{j+1}(f)(q - r) = U(P, f, \alpha).$$

By the definition of $\underline{\int_a^b} f \, d\alpha$ and $\overline{\int_a^b} f \, d\alpha$,

$$\underline{\int_a^b} f \, d\alpha \leq f(c)(q - p) \leq \overline{\int_a^b} f \, d\alpha;$$

hence, since $f \in R(\alpha)$,

$$\int_a^b f \, d\alpha = \underline{\int_a^b} f \, d\alpha = \overline{\int_a^b} f \, d\alpha = f(c)(q - p).$$

Thus, the integral of f with respect to the step function α is found to be the value of f at the jump times the amount of the jump of the function α. It is interesting to note that in each of the three cases, $p < r < q$, $p = r < q$, and $p < r = q$, the integral is the same if it exists. The only role played by r is in determining the integrability of f with respect to α.

Define $f : [0, 1] \to R$ by $f(x) = 0$ if x is irrational and $f(p/q) = 1/q$ where p and q are relatively prime integers with $q > 0$. (We define $f(0) = 1$.) Now since every interval contains irrational points, $L(P,f) = 0$ for all partitions P; hence

$$\underline{\int_a^b} f \, dx = 0.$$

If we can show f is integrable on $[0, 1]$, then we will know

$$\int_a^b f \, dx = \overline{\int_a^b} f \, dx = 0.$$

Choose $0 < \varepsilon < 1$. Since $L(P,f) = 0$ for all partitions P, it suffices to find a partition Q such that $U(Q,f) \le \varepsilon$. Let $\{r_0, \ldots, r_n\}$ be the set of all rationals in $[0, 1]$ such that $f(r_i) \ge \varepsilon/2$, which means all rationals in $[0, 1]$ of the form p/q where p and q are relatively prime and $0 < q \le 2/\varepsilon$. We may assume $0 = r_0 < r_1 < \cdots < r_n = 1$. Let us now proceed to construct a partition P such that $U(P,f) < \varepsilon$. Define $x_0 = r_0 = 0$, and choose x_1 such that

$$0 < x_1 < \frac{r_1}{2} \quad \text{and} \quad x_1 < \frac{\varepsilon}{2(n+1)}.$$

Choose x_2 and x_3 such that

$$x_1 < x_2 < r_1 < x_3 < \frac{r_1 + r_2}{2} \quad \text{and} \quad x_3 - x_2 < \frac{\varepsilon}{2(n+1)}.$$

Continuing in this fashion (by induction), we obtain $x_0 < x_1 < x_2 < \cdots < x_{2n-1}$ such that

$$x_{2k} < r_k < x_{2k+1} \quad \text{and} \quad x_{2k+1} - x_{2k} < \frac{\varepsilon}{2(n+1)}.$$

for $k = 1, 2, \ldots, n-1$. Choose x_{2n} such that

$$x_{2n-1} < x_{2n} < 1 \quad \text{and} \quad 1 - x_{2n} < \frac{\varepsilon}{2(n+1)}.$$

Let $x_{2n+1} = 1$. This process may seem mysterious, but the key to these choices is the desire to guarantee that where the function takes values larger than $\varepsilon/2$, the width of the rectangle is small. Now if we let $P = \{x_0, x_1, \ldots, x_{2n+1}\}$, we have

$$U(P,f) = \sum_{i=1}^{2n+1} M_i(f)(x_i - x_{i-1}) = \sum_{k=0}^{n} M_{2k+1}(f)(x_{2k+1} - x_{2k})$$

$$+ \sum_{k=1}^{n} M_{2k}(f)(x_{2k} - x_{2k-1}) < \sum_{k=0}^{n} (x_{2k+1} - x_{2k})$$

$$+ \sum_{k=1}^{n} \frac{\varepsilon}{2}(x_{2k} - x_{2k-1}) < (n+1)\frac{\varepsilon}{2(n+1)} + \frac{\varepsilon}{2} = \varepsilon.$$

Thus, $f \in R(x)$ on $[0, 1]$ and $\int_0^1 f\,dx = 0$.

In this example, we see a departure from the idea of the integral being the area under a curve. In this case, the function f is non-negative and takes positive values at every rational point but $\int_0^1 f\,dx = 0$.

There are some obvious classes of functions that one might suspect are integrable—the class of continuous functions, for example. Before taking up that problem, let us consider the class of monotone functions.

5.3 THEOREM   If $f : [a, b] \to R$ is monotone and $\alpha : [a, b] \to R$ is increasing and continuous, then $f \in R(\alpha)$ on $[a, b]$.

Proof: Since f is monotone, f is bounded on $[a, b]$. Let us assume f is increasing. The case for f decreasing is similar. Choose $\varepsilon > 0$. There is $k > 0$ such that

$$k(f(b) - f(a)) < \varepsilon.$$

Now α is continuous on $[a, b]$, hence is uniformly continuous on $[a, b]$. Thus, we may choose a partition $P = \{x_0, x_1, \ldots, x_n\}$ such that

$$\alpha(x_i) - \alpha(x_{i-1}) < k$$

for $i = 1, 2, \ldots, n$. Since f is increasing, $M_i(f) = f(x_i)$ and $m_i(f) = f(x_{i-1})$. Now

$$U(P,f) - L(P,f) = \sum_{i=1}^{n} [f(x_i) - f(x_{i-1})][\alpha(x_i) - \alpha(x_{i-1})]$$

$$\leq \sum_{i=1}^{n} [f(x_i) - f(x_{i-1})]k = k[f(b) - f(a)] < \varepsilon.$$

Thus, $f \in R(\alpha)$ on $[a, b]$.

Notice that 5.3 handles the example $f(x) = x^2$ for $x \in [0, 1]$, which we discussed before.

To enlarge the class of integrable functions, let us consider the continuous functions. Let $f: [a, b] \to R$ be continuous and $\alpha: [a, b] \to R$ increasing. Since $[a, b]$ is compact, f is bounded, so we need only consider $U(P, f, \alpha) - L(P, f, \alpha)$ and try to make this difference small. If

$$P = \{x_0, x_1, \ldots, x_n\},$$

then by the continuity of f there are $t_i, s_i \in [x_{i-1}, x_i]$ for $i = 1, 2, \ldots, n$ such that

$$M_i(f) = f(t_i) \quad \text{and} \quad m_i(f) = f(s_i).$$

Now

$$
\begin{aligned}
U(P, f, \alpha) - L(P, f, \alpha) &= \sum_{i=1}^{n} M_i(f)(\alpha(x_i) - \alpha(x_{i-1})) \\
&\quad - \sum_{i=1}^{n} m_i(f)(\alpha(x_i) - \alpha(x_{i-1})) \\
&= \sum_{i=1}^{n} [f(t_i) - f(s_i)](\alpha(x_i) - \alpha(x_{i-1})).
\end{aligned}
$$

If we force $f(t_i) - f(s_i) < \gamma$, then

$$U(P, f, \alpha) - L(P, f, \alpha) < \gamma(\alpha(b) - \alpha(a)).$$

Of course, here is where the continuity of f plays its role. Lest we give away all secrets in advance, let us state and prove the obvious theorem.

5.4 THEOREM   If $f: [a, b] \to R$ is continuous and $\alpha: [a, b] \to R$ increasing, then $f \in R(\alpha)$ on $[a, b]$.

Proof: If $\alpha(b) = \alpha(a)$, then α is constant and $U(P, f, \alpha) = L(P, f, \alpha) = 0$ for all partitions P. Suppose $\alpha(b) - \alpha(a) > 0$. As observed above, f is bounded. Choose $\varepsilon > 0$. Since $[a, b]$ is compact, f is uniformly continuous on $[a, b]$, so there is $\delta > 0$ such that $|x - y| < \delta$, $x, y \in [a, b]$, implies

$$|f(x) - f(y)| < \frac{\varepsilon}{\alpha(b) - \alpha(a)}.$$

Let $P = \{x_0, x_1, \ldots, x_n\}$ be any partition such that $x_i - x_{i-1} < \delta$ for $i = 1, \ldots, n$. There are $t_i, s_i \in [x_{i-1}, x_i]$ such that

$M_i(f) = f(t_i)$ and $m_i(f) = f(s_i)$ for $i = 1, 2, \ldots, n$. Since $x_i - x_{i-1} < \delta$, $|t_i - s_i| < \delta$, and hence

$$0 \leq f(t_i) - f(s_i) < \frac{\varepsilon}{\alpha(b) - \alpha(a)}.$$

Thus, we have

$$U(P, f, \alpha) - L(P, f, \alpha) = \sum_{i=1}^{n} [f(t_i) - f(s_i)](\alpha(x_i) - \alpha(x_{i-1}))$$

$$\leq \sum_{i=1}^{n} \frac{\varepsilon}{\alpha(b) - \alpha(a)} (\alpha(x_i) - \alpha(x_{i-1}))$$

$$= \frac{\varepsilon}{\alpha(b) - \alpha(a)} (\alpha(b) - \alpha(a)) = \varepsilon.$$

Therefore, $f \in R(\alpha)$ on $[a, b]$.

In the discussion at the beginning of the chapter, the approach to the integral involved only upper and lower sums or, for non-negative functions, overestimates and underestimates of the area under the curve. Let us now take a more liberal point of view. Suppose that $f : [a, b] \to R$ is bounded, $\alpha : [a, b] \to R$ is increasing, and $P = \{x_0, x_1, x_2, \ldots, x_n\}$ is a partition of $[a, b]$. For each i among $1, \ldots, n$, choose $t_i \in [x_{i-1}, x_i]$ and form the sum

$$\sum_{i=1}^{n} f(t_i)(\alpha(x_i) - \alpha(x_{i-1})).$$

Now for each i among $1, \ldots, n$,

$$m_i(f) \leq f(t_i) \leq M_i(f);$$

hence

$$L(P, f, \alpha) \leq \sum_{i=1}^{n} f(t_i)(x_i - x_{i-1}) \leq U(P, f, \alpha).$$

Since for integrable functions, $L(P, f, \alpha)$ and $U(P, f, \alpha)$ squeeze in on $\int_a^b f \, d\alpha$, it seems reasonable to suspect that the new sums just considered behave similarly. Indeed, as we have seen, for continuous functions, each upper and lower sum can be written in this way. If this were the case, possibly wise choices for the points t_i might be useful in determining $\int_a^b f \, d\alpha$. Let us illustrate this point with a simple example.

We have seen that the function $f(x) = x^2$ is integrable on the interval $[0, 1]$. Let $P = \{x_0, x_1, \ldots, x_n\}$ be any partition of $[0, 1]$. Consider the function $g(x) = x^3/3$. (Are you surprised by this choice?) Now g is continuous and differentiable on $[0, 1]$ and $g'(x) = f(x)$ for all $x \in [0, 1]$. For each i among $1, \ldots, n$, the mean-value theorem applied to g on $[x_{i-1}, x_i]$ yields $t_i \in [x_{i-1}, x_i]$ such that

$$g(x_i) - g(x_{i-1}) = g'(t_i)(x_i - x_{i-1}) = f(t_i)(x_i - x_{i-1}).$$

Hence,

$$\sum_{i=1}^{n} f(t_i)(x_i - x_{i-1}) = \sum_{i=1}^{n}(g(x_i) - g(x_{i-1})) = g(1) - g(0) = \frac{1}{3}.$$

By our remarks in the preceding paragraph, $L(P, f) \leq \frac{1}{3} \leq U(P, f)$ for all partitions P; hence

$$\underline{\int_a^b} f \, dx \leq \frac{1}{3} \leq \overline{\int_a^b} f \, dx \quad \text{or} \quad \int_a^b x^2 \, dx = \frac{1}{3}.$$

Now this result is not at all surprising, but the basic idea involved will appear later.

Lest we stray too far afield, let us attempt to formulate a condition for integrability involving the type of sum mentioned above. Let P be any partition of $[a, b]$, $P = \{x_0, x_1, \ldots, x_n\}$. Define the *mesh* of P to be the maximum of the lengths $x_i - x_{i-1}, i = 1, \ldots, n$, and denote it by $\mu(P)$. If $t_i \in [x_{i-1}, x_i]$ are chosen for $i = 1, \ldots, n$, P is called a *marked* partition and

$$S(P, f, \alpha) = \sum_{i=1}^{n} f(t_i)(\alpha(x_i) - \alpha(x_{i-1}))$$

is called a *Riemann–Stieltjes* sum for f. There is some ambiguity of notation involved since a partition P may be marked in many ways, but we shall try to handle this problem in a way that avoids any confusion.

5.5 THEOREM   Let $f : [a, b] \to R$ be bounded and α increasing on $[a, b]$. Then $f \in R(\alpha)$ on $[a, b]$ iff there is a real number A such that for each $\varepsilon > 0$, there is a partition P such that for any refinement Q of P, regardless of how marked, $|S(Q, f, \alpha) - A| \leq \varepsilon$. If the latter condition is satisfied, then

$$A = \int_a^b f \, d\alpha.$$

Proof: Suppose $f \in R(\alpha)$ on $[a,b]$. Let $A = \int_a^b f \, d\alpha$, and choose $\varepsilon > 0$. There is a partition P such that $U(P,f,\alpha) - L(P,f,\alpha) \le \varepsilon$. Let Q be any refinement of P marked in any fashion. Then

$$L(P,f,\alpha) \le L(Q,f,\alpha) \le S(Q,f,\alpha) \le U(Q,f,\alpha)$$

$$\le U(P,f,\alpha) \le L(P,f,\alpha) + \varepsilon,$$

and

$$L(Q,f,\alpha) \le \int_a^b f \, d\alpha \le U(Q,f,\alpha).$$

Hence

$$\left| S(Q,f,\alpha) - \int_a^b f \, d\alpha \right| \le \varepsilon.$$

Suppose $f : [a,b] \to R$ is bounded and A is a real number such that for each $\varepsilon > 0$, there is a partition P such that if $P \subseteq Q$, where Q is a partition of $[a,b]$ marked in any fashion, then $|S(Q,f,\alpha) - A| \le \varepsilon$. We shall appeal to 5.2. By previous remarks, we may assume $\alpha(b) - \alpha(a) > 0$. Choose $\varepsilon > 0$. There is a partition $P = \{x_0, x_1, \ldots, x_n\}$ such that

$$|S(P,f,\alpha) - A| < \frac{\varepsilon}{4},$$

regardless of how we choose $t_i \in [x_{i-1}, x_i]$. Recall that

$$M_i(f) = \sup \{f(x) : x \in [x_{i-1}, x_i]\}$$

and

$$m_i(f) = \inf \{f(x) : x \in [x_{i-1}, x_i]\}.$$

Thus, for each i among $1, \ldots, n$, there are $t_i, s_i \in [x_{i-1}, x_i]$ such that

$$M_i(f) - \frac{\varepsilon}{4(\alpha(b) - \alpha(a))} < f(t_i)$$

and

$$f(s_i) < m_i(f) + \frac{\varepsilon}{4(\alpha(b) - \alpha(a))}.$$

Now

$$U(P, f, \alpha) - L(P, f, \alpha) = \sum_{i=1}^{n} M_i(f)(\alpha(x_i) - \alpha(x_{i-1}))$$

$$- \sum_{i=1}^{n} m_i (f)(\alpha(x_i)\alpha(x_{i-1}))$$

$$\leq \sum_{i=1}^{n} \left[f(t_i) + \frac{\varepsilon}{4(\alpha(b) - \alpha(a))} \right](\alpha(x_i) - \alpha(x_{i-1}))$$

$$- \sum_{i=1}^{n} \left[f(s_i) - \frac{\varepsilon}{4(\alpha(b) - \alpha(a))} \right](\alpha(x_i) - \alpha(x_{i-1}))$$

$$= \sum_{i=1}^{n} f(t_i)(\alpha(x_i) - \alpha(x_{i-1})) + \frac{\varepsilon}{4}$$

$$- \sum_{i=1}^{n} f(s_i)(\alpha(x_i) - \alpha(x_{i-1})) + \frac{\varepsilon}{4}$$

$$= \left[\sum_{i=1}^{n} f(t_i)(\alpha(x_i) - \alpha(x_{i-1})) - A \right]$$

$$- \left[\sum_{i=1}^{n} f(s_i)(\alpha(x_i) - \alpha(x_{i-1})) - A \right]$$

$$+ \frac{\varepsilon}{2} \leq \frac{\varepsilon}{4} + \frac{\varepsilon}{4} + \frac{\varepsilon}{2} = \varepsilon.$$

Thus, $f \in R(\alpha)$ on $[a, b]$. It now remains to show that $A = \int_a^b f \, d\alpha$. Choose $\varepsilon > 0$. There is a partition P_1 on $[a, b]$ such that for any refinement Q of P_1, regardless of how marked,

$$|S(Q, f, \alpha) - A| \leq \frac{\varepsilon}{3}.$$

Since $f \in R(\alpha)$, there is a partition P_2 of $[a, b]$ such that

$$U(P_2, f, \alpha) - L(P_2, f, \alpha) \leq \frac{\varepsilon}{3}.$$

Let $Q = P_1 \cup P_2$. Then

$$\left| A - \int_a^b f \, d\alpha \right| \leq |A - S(Q, f, \alpha)| + |S(Q, f, \alpha) - L(Q, f, \alpha)|$$

$$+ \left| L(Q, f, \alpha) - \int_a^b f \, d\alpha \right| \leq \frac{\varepsilon}{3} + \frac{\varepsilon}{3} + \frac{\varepsilon}{3} = \varepsilon$$

since

$$L(Q, f, \alpha) \leq S(Q, f, \alpha) \leq U(Q, f, \alpha) \leq L(Q, f, \alpha) + \frac{\varepsilon}{3}$$

and

$$L(Q, f, \alpha) \le \int_a^b f \, d\alpha \le U(Q, f, \alpha) \le L(Q, f, \alpha) + \frac{\varepsilon}{3}.$$

Since $\varepsilon > 0$ was arbitrary, $A = \int_a^b f \, d\alpha$.

To show that a function is integrable in the examples we have considered, it actually has sufficed to find a partition with sufficiently small mesh. This is not accidental, as can be seen by the next theorem.

5.6 THEOREM   Suppose that $f: [a, b] \to R$ is bounded and $\alpha : [a, b] \to R$ is increasing. Then

(i)   if there is a real number A such that for each $\varepsilon > 0$, there is $\delta > 0$ such that if $\mu(P) < \delta$, then, regardless of how P is marked, $|S(P, f, \alpha) - A| \le \varepsilon$, then $f \in R(\alpha)$ on $[a, b]$ and

$$A = \int_a^b f \, d\alpha;$$

(ii)   if either f is continuous or $f \in R(\alpha)$ on $[a, b]$ and α is continuous, then for any $\varepsilon > 0$, there is $\delta > 0$ such that for any partition P, regardless of how P is marked, $\mu(P) < \delta$ implies

$$\left| S(P, f, \alpha) - \int_a^b f \, d\alpha \right| \le \varepsilon.$$

Before supplying a proof for this theorem, let us give an example to show that some sort of hypothesis is necessary for (ii). Define $\alpha : [0, 2] \to R$ by $\alpha(x) = 0$ for $0 \le x \le 1$ and $\alpha(x) = 2$ for $1 < x \le 2$. Define $f : [0, 2] \to R$ by $f(x) = 16$ for $0 \le x < 1$ and $f(x) = 19$ for $1 \le x \le 2$. Let P be any partition of $[0, 2]$ which contains 1. Then

$$U(P, f, \alpha) = 19 \cdot 2 \quad \text{and} \quad L(P, f, \alpha) = 19 \cdot 2,$$

so $U(P, f, \alpha) - L(P, f, \alpha) = 0$; that is, $f \in R(\alpha)$ on $[a, b]$. Now let $P = \{x_0, x_1, \ldots, x_n\}$ be any partition of $[a, b]$ such that $x_{j-1} < 1 < x_j$. Choose $t_i = x_{i-1}$ for $i = 1, \ldots, n$. Then

$$S(P, f, \alpha) = 16 \cdot 2 = 32 \quad \text{and} \quad \int_a^b f \, d\alpha = 38.$$

Thus, (ii) doesn't hold here since neither f nor α is continuous at 1.

Proof: Suppose that $f: [a,b] \to R$ is bounded, that $\alpha: [a,b] \to R$ is increasing, and that there is a real number A such that for any $\varepsilon > 0$, there is $\delta > 0$ such that for any partition P of $[a,b]$ with $\mu(P) < \delta$, we have $|S(P,f,\alpha) - A| \leq \varepsilon$ regardless of how P is marked. Then if P is any partition of $[a,b]$ with $\mu(P) < \delta$ and Q is a refinement of P, then $\mu(Q) < \delta$, and hence, regardless of how Q is marked, $|S(Q,f,\alpha) - A| \leq \varepsilon$. By 5.5, then, $f \in R(\alpha)$ and $A = \int_a^b f \, d\alpha$.

If $f: [a,b] \to R$ is continuous, then the proof of 5.4 will be adequate for the conclusion of (ii), since for all partitions P,

$$L(P,f,\alpha) \leq S(P,f,\alpha) \leq U(P,f,\alpha)$$

and

$$L(P,f,\alpha) \leq \int_a^b f \, d\alpha \leq U(P,f,\alpha).$$

Suppose now that $f \in R(\alpha)$ on $[a,b]$ and α is continuous. Choose $\varepsilon > 0$. Let $A = \int_a^b f \, d\alpha$ with M a positive real number such that $|f(x)| \leq M$ for all $x \in [a,b]$ and $\varepsilon' = \varepsilon/4$. There is a partition $P = \{x_0, x_1, \ldots, x_n\}$ such that

$$U(P,f,\alpha) - L(P,f,\alpha) < \varepsilon'.$$

Let

$$\varepsilon'' = \frac{\varepsilon}{16Mn}.$$

By the uniform continuity of α, (since $[a,b]$ is compact) there is $\delta > 0$ such that $|x - y| < \delta$ and $x, y \in [a,b]$ implies that $|\alpha(x) - \alpha(y)| < \varepsilon''$. Let $P' = \{z_0, z_1, \ldots, z_r\}$ be any partition of $[a,b]$ such that $\mu(P') < \delta$. Consider any interval $[z_{i-1}, z_i]$, and suppose

$$\{x_j, x_{j+1}, \ldots, x_{j+k}\} \subseteq [z_{i-1}, z_i].$$

Let

$$M_k(f) = \sup\{f(x) : x \in [z_{k-1}, z_k]\},$$
$$m_k(f) = \inf\{f(x) : x \in [z_{k-1}, z_k]\}$$
$$M_k'(f) = \sup\{f(x) : x \in [x_{k-1}, x_k]\},$$

and

$$m_k'(f) = \inf\{f(x) : x \in [x_{k-1}, x_k]\}.$$

Now

$$M_i(f) \le 2M + M_{j+s}'(f)$$

for $s = 1, \ldots, k$,

$$M_i(f) \le 2M + \sup\{f(x) : x \in [z_{i-1}, x_j]\},$$

and

$$M_i(f) \le 2M + \sup\{f(x) : x \in [x_{j+k}, z_i]\}.$$

Similarly,

$$m_i(f) \ge -2M + m_{j+s}'(f)$$

for $s = 1, 2, \ldots, k$,

$$m_i(f) \ge -2M + \inf\{f(x) : x \in [z_{i-1}, x_j]\},$$

and

$$m_i(f) \ge -2M + \inf\{f(x) : x \in [x_{j+k}, z_i]\}.$$

Now

$$U(P', f, \alpha) = \sum_{k=1}^{r} M_k(f)(\alpha(z_k) - \alpha(z_{k-1}))$$
$$\le U(P \cup P', f, \alpha) + 2M(2n)\varepsilon'',$$

and

$$L(P', f, \alpha) = \sum_{k=1}^{r} m_k(f)(\alpha(z_k) - \alpha(z_{k-1}))$$
$$\ge L(P \cup P', f, \alpha) - 2M(2n)\varepsilon''.$$

Choose any $t_i \in [z_{i-1}, z_i]$ for $i = 1, \ldots, r$. Then

$$L(P, f, \alpha) - \frac{\varepsilon}{2} \le L(P, f, \alpha) - 4Mn\varepsilon''$$
$$\le L(P \cup P', f, \alpha) - 4Mn\varepsilon'' \le L(P', f, \alpha) \le A$$

and

$$A \le U(P', f, \alpha) \le U(P \cup P', f, \alpha) + 4Mn\varepsilon''$$

$$\le U(P, f, \alpha) + \frac{\varepsilon}{4} \le L(P, f, \alpha) + \frac{\varepsilon}{2}.$$

Moreover,

$$L(P, f, \alpha) - \frac{\varepsilon}{2} \le L(P', f, \alpha) \le \sum_{i=1}^{n} f(t_i)(\alpha(z_i) - \alpha(z_{i-1}))$$

$$\le U(P, f, \alpha) \le L(P, f, \alpha) + \frac{\varepsilon}{2}.$$

Hence $\left| \sum_{i=1}^{n} f(t_i)(\alpha(z_i) - \alpha(z_{i-1})) - A \right| \le \varepsilon.$

It is very tempting to rephrase 5.6 as follows:
(i)   if $\lim_{\mu(P) \to 0} S(P, f, \alpha)$ exists, then $f \in R(\alpha)$ and

$$\lim_{\mu(P) \to 0} S(P, f, \alpha) = \int_{a}^{b} f \, d\alpha.$$

(ii)   if either f is continuous or $f \in R(\alpha)$ on $[a, b]$ and α is continuous, then

$$\lim_{\mu(P) \to 0} S(P, f, \alpha) = \int_{a}^{b} f \, d\alpha.$$

This is a good naive interpretation of 5.6, although it is not compatible with our concept of limit since $S(P, f, \alpha)$ is not a function of $\mu(P)$. We could readjust the definition of limit to take care of this situation, but it does not seem worth the effort here. The following theorem should help to shed some light on the situation.

5.7 THEOREM   Suppose that $f : [a, b] \to R$ is bounded and $\alpha : [a, b] \to R$ is increasing. Then
(i)   if for every sequence $\{P_n\}_{n=1}^{\infty}$ of marked partitions with $\{\mu(P_n)\}_{n=1}^{\infty}$ converging to zero, we have $\{S(P_n, f, \alpha)\}_{n=1}^{\infty}$ convergent, then $f \in R(\alpha)$ on $[a, b]$ and for all such sequences.

$$\{S(P_n, f, \alpha)\}_{n=1}^{\infty}$$

converges to $\int_{a}^{b} f \, d\alpha.$

(ii)   if either f is continuous or $f \in R(\alpha)$ on $[a, b]$ and α is continuous, then for any sequence $\{P_n\}_{n=1}^{\infty}$ of marked partitions with $\{\mu(P_n)\}_{n=1}^{\infty}$ converging to zero, we have

$$\{S(P_n, f, \alpha)\}_{n=1}^{\infty}$$

converging to $\int_a^b f \, d\alpha$.

The proof of this theorem is left to the reader because of its similarity to 2.1. If the task is difficult for the reader, he has failed to comprehend the strategy of the proof of 2.1.

It is impossible to resist the temptation to use one of these results to prove a very important theorem, the fundamental theorem of integral calculus. This is indeed a rather impressive result in the sense that it gives a method for computing certain integrals and reveals the relationship between integration and differentiation. We have already revealed the secret of the proof to be used here in the discussion preceding 5.5.

5.8 THEOREM   (fundamental theorem of integral calculus) Suppose $f: [a, b] \to R$ is differentiable on $[a, b]$ and $f' \in R(x)$ on $[a, b]$. Then

$$\int_a^b f' \, dx = f(b) - f(a).$$

Proof: Let P be any partition of $[a, b]$, $P = \{x_0, x_1, \ldots, x_n\}$. By the mean-value theorem applied to f on $[x_{i-1}, x_i]$, there is $t_i \in [x_{i-1}, x_i]$ such that

$$f(x_i) - f(x_{i-1}) = f'(t_i)(x_i - x_{i-1}).$$

Thus,

$$\sum_{i=1}^n f'(t_i)(x_i - x_{i-1}) = \sum_{i=1}^n (f(x_i) - f(x_{i-1})) = f(b) - f(a).$$

This means that any partition P of $[a, b]$ may be marked in a way so that $S(P, f') = f(b) - f(a)$. Choose a sequence $\{P_n\}_{n=1}^{\infty}$ of partitions of $[a, b]$, each marked in this fashion and such that $\{\mu(P_n)\}_{n=1}^{\infty}$ converges to zero. Now $f' \in R(x)$ on $[a, b]$ and $\alpha(x) = x$

is continuous; hence, by 5.7, $S(P_n, f')$ converges to $\int_a^b f' \, dx$, but

$$S(P_n, f') = f(b) - f(a)$$

for each n, so $\int_a^b f' \, dx = f(b) - f(a)$.

It should be pointed out that $f' \in R(x)$ is a very important part of the hypothesis of this theorem. For example, the function f defined on $[0, 1]$ by $f(x) = x^2 \sin 1/x^2$ for $x \neq 0$ and $f(0) = 0$ is differentiable on $[0, 1]$, but f' is not Riemann-integrable on $[0, 1]$ since it is unbounded.

It is now appropriate to make some of the usual observations useful in calculating integrals. Since the integral may be considered as a limit of sums in a certain way, the results are derived from similar results for finite sums.

5.9 THEOREM   If $f_1, f_2 : [a, b] \to R$ are bounded, $\alpha : [a, b] \to R$ is increasing, and $f_1, f_2 \in R(\alpha)$ on $[a, b]$, then

(a)   for c_1, c_2 any real numbers, $c_1 f_1 + c_2 f_2 \in R(\alpha)$ on $[a, b]$ and

$$\int_a^b (c_1 f_1 + c_2 f_2) \, d\alpha = c_1 \int_a^b f_1 \, d\alpha + c_2 \int_a^b f_2 \, d\alpha;$$

(b)   if $f_1(x) \leq f_2(x)$ for all $x \in [a, b]$, then

$$\int_a^b f_1(x) \, d\alpha \leq \int_a^b f_2(x) \, d\alpha;$$

(c)   if $m \leq f_1(x) \leq M$ for all $x \in [a, b]$, then

$$m(\alpha(b) - \alpha(a)) \leq \int_a^b f_1 \, d\alpha \leq M(\alpha(b) - \alpha(a));$$

(d)   if $\beta : [a, b] \to R$ is increasing with $f_1 \in R(\beta)$ on $[a, b]$ and c_1 and c_2 are any non-negative real numbers, then

$$f_1 \in R(c_1 \alpha + c_2 \beta)$$

on $[a, b]$ and

$$\int_a^b f_1 \, d(c_1 \alpha + c_2 \beta) = c_1 \int_a^b f_1 \, d\alpha + c_2 \int_a^b f_1 \, d\beta.$$

Proof: (a)   Choose $\varepsilon > 0$. There is $\varepsilon' > 0$ such that

$$(|c_1| + |c_2|)\varepsilon' \le \varepsilon.$$

There are partitions P_1 and P_2 such that for any refinement Q_i of P_i, regardless of how Q_i is marked,

$$\left| S(Q_i, f_i, \alpha) - \int_a^b f_i \, d\alpha \right| \le \varepsilon'.$$

Let $P = P_1 \cup P_2$. If Q is any refinement of P, then Q is a refinement of P_1 and a refinement of P_2, hence

$$\left| S(Q, c_1 f_1 + c_2 f_2, \alpha) - \left[c_1 \int_a^b f_1 \, d\alpha + c_2 \int_a^b f_2 \, d\alpha \right] \right|$$

$$= \left| c_1 S(Q, f_1, \alpha) + c_2 S(Q, f_2, \alpha) - c_1 \int_a^b f_1 \, d\alpha - c_2 \int_a^b f_2 \, d\alpha \right|$$

$$\le |c_1| \left| S(Q, f_1, \alpha) - \int_a^b f_1 \, d\alpha \right| + |c_2| \left| S(Q, f_2, \alpha) - \int_a^b f_2 \, d\alpha \right|$$

$$\le |c_1| \varepsilon' + |c_2| \varepsilon' \le \varepsilon.$$

Hence, by 5.5, $c_1 f_1 + c_2 f_2 \in R(\alpha)$ on $[a, b]$ and

$$\int_a^b (c_1 f_1 + c_2 f_2) \, d\alpha = c_1 \int_a^b f_1 \, d\alpha + c_2 \int_a^b f_2 \, d\alpha.$$

(b)   If $f_1(x) \le f_2(x)$ for all $x \in [a, b]$, then $L(P, f_1, \alpha) \le L(P, f_2, \alpha)$ for all partitions P; hence

$$\int_{\underline{a}}^b f_1 \, d\alpha = \overline{\int_a^b} f_1 \, d\alpha \le \overline{\int_a^b} f_2 \, d\alpha = \int_a^b f_2 \, d\alpha.$$

(c)   If $m \le f_1(x) \le M$ for all $x \in [a, b]$, then for any partition P of $[a, b]$,

$$m[\alpha(b) - \alpha(a)] \le L(P, f_1, \alpha)$$

$$\le \int_a^b f_1 \, d\alpha \le U(P, f_1, \alpha) \le M[\alpha(b) - \alpha(a)].$$

(d)   As in part (a), we shall appeal to 5.5. If c_1, c_2 are non-negative, then $c_1 \alpha + c_2 \beta$ is an increasing function. If

$$P = \{x_0, x_1, \ldots, x_n\}$$

is any partition of $[a, b]$, then

$$S(P, f_1, c_1\alpha + c_2\beta)$$
$$= \sum_{i=1}^{n} f_1(t_i)((c_1\alpha + c_2\beta)(x_i) - (c_1\alpha + c_2\beta)(x_{i-1}))$$
$$= c_1 \sum_{i=1}^{n} f_1(t_i)(\alpha(x_i) - \alpha(x_{i-1})) + c_2 \sum_{i=1}^{n} f_1(t_i)(\beta(x_i) - \beta(x_{i-1}))$$
$$= c_1 S(P, f_1, \alpha) + c_2 S(P, f_1, \beta).$$

Choose $\varepsilon > 0$. There is $\varepsilon' > 0$ such that $(c_1 + c_2)\varepsilon' \leq \varepsilon$. There are partitions P_1 and P_2 of $[a, b]$ such that if Q_i is any refinement of P_i for $i = 1, 2$, then

$$\left| S(Q_1, f_1, \alpha) - \int_a^b f_1 \, d\alpha \right| \leq \varepsilon'$$

and

$$\left| S(Q_2, f_1, \beta) - \int_a^b f_1 \, d\beta \right| \leq \varepsilon'.$$

Let $P = P_1 \cup P_2$ and Q be any refinement of P. Then Q is a refinement of P_1 and a refinement of P_2, hence

$$\left| S(Q, f_1, c_1\alpha + c_2\beta) - \left[c_1 \int_a^b f_1 \, d\alpha + c_2 \int_a^b f_1 \, d\beta \right] \right|$$
$$= \left| c_1 S(Q, f_1, \alpha) + c_2 S(Q, f_1, \beta) - c_1 \int_a^b f_1 \, d\alpha - c_2 \int_a^b f_1 \, d\beta \right|$$
$$\leq c_1 \left| S(Q, f_1, \alpha) - \int_a^b f_1 \, d\alpha \right| + c_2 \left| S(Q, f_1, \beta) - \int_a^b f_1 \, d\beta \right|$$
$$\leq c_1 \varepsilon' + c_2 \varepsilon' \leq \varepsilon.$$

Hence, by 5.5, $f_1 \in R(c_1\alpha + c_2\beta)$ on $[a, b]$ and

$$\int_a^b f_1 \, d(c_1\alpha + c_2\beta) = c_1 \int_a^b f_1 \, d\alpha + c_2 \int_a^b f_1 \, d\beta.$$

Parts (a) and (d) of 5.9 may be considered as distributive laws for the Riemann–Stieltjes integral by comparing the results to similar results for finite sums. Similarly, the next theorem may be thought of as an associative law for integrals.

5.10 THEOREM   Assume that $f: [a, b] \to R$ is bounded and $\alpha : [a, b] \to R$ is increasing. If $a < c < b$, then $f \in R(\alpha)$ on $[a, b]$ iff $f \in R(\alpha)$ on $[a, c]$ and $f \in R(\alpha)$ on $[c, b]$. If $f \in R(\alpha)$ on $[a, b]$, then

$$\int_a^b f \, d\alpha = \int_a^c f \, d\alpha + \int_c^b f \, d\alpha.$$

Proof: Assume $f \in R(\alpha)$ on $[a, c]$ and $f \in R(\alpha)$ on $[c, b]$. Choose $\varepsilon > 0$. There are partitions P_1 and P_2 of $[a, c]$ and $[c, b]$, respectively, such that if Q_1 and Q_2 are refinements of P_1 and P_2, respectively, then

$$\left| S(Q_1, f, \alpha) - \int_a^c f \, d\alpha \right| \leq \frac{\varepsilon}{2} \quad \text{and} \quad \left| S(Q_2, f, \alpha) - \int_c^b f \, d\alpha \right| \leq \frac{\varepsilon}{2}.$$

Let $P = P_1 \cup P_2$. Then P is a partition of $[a, b]$, and if Q is any refinement of P, then $Q_1 = Q \cap [a, c]$ is a refinement of P_1 and $Q_2 = Q \cap [c, b]$ is a refinement of P_2. Thus,

$$\left| S(Q, f, \alpha) - \left[\int_a^c f \, d\alpha + \int_c^b f \, d\alpha \right] \right|$$

$$= \left| S(Q_1, f, \alpha) + S(Q_2, f, \alpha) - \int_a^c f \, d\alpha - \int_c^b f \, d\alpha \right|$$

$$\leq \left| S(Q_1, f, \alpha) - \int_a^c f \, d\alpha \right| + \left| S(Q_2, f, \alpha) - \int_c^b f \, d\alpha \right| \leq \frac{\varepsilon}{2} + \frac{\varepsilon}{2} = \varepsilon.$$

Thus, by 5.5, $f \in R(\alpha)$ on $[a, b]$ and

$$\int_a^b f \, d\alpha = \int_a^c f \, d\alpha + \int_c^b f \, d\alpha.$$

Assume $f \in R(\alpha)$ on $[a, b]$. Choose $\varepsilon > 0$. There is a partition P of $[a, b]$ such that

$$U(P, f, \alpha) - L(P, f, \alpha) < \varepsilon.$$

Let $Q = P \cup \{c\}$ and let $Q_1 = Q \cap [a, c]$ and $Q_2 = Q \cap [c, b]$. Then

$$\varepsilon > U(Q, f, \alpha) - L(Q, f, \alpha)$$

$$= U(Q_1, f, \alpha) + U(Q_2, f, \alpha) - (L(Q_1, f, \alpha) + L(Q_2, f, \alpha))$$

$$= [U(Q_1, f, \alpha) - L(Q_1, f, \alpha)] + [U(Q_2, f, \alpha) - L(Q_2, f, \alpha)].$$

Since $U(Q_1, f, \alpha) - L(Q_1, f, \alpha) > 0$ and $U(Q_2, f, \alpha) - L(Q_2, f, \alpha) > 0$, we may conclude

$$U(Q_1, f, \alpha) - L(Q_1, f, \alpha) < \varepsilon \quad \text{and} \quad U(Q_2, f, \alpha) - L(Q_2, f, \alpha) < \varepsilon.$$

Thus, by 5.2, $f \in R(\alpha)$ on $[a, c]$ and $f \in R(\alpha)$ on $[c, b]$.

We have seen that linear combinations of integrable functions are integrable and now we seek other operations which preserve integrable functions. As has been shown already, continuous functions seem to behave especially well with respect to integration. The next theorem should help to further this opinion.

5.11 THEOREM   Suppose $f : [a, b] \to [c, d]$, $\alpha : [a, b] \to R$ is increasing, $f \in R(\alpha)$ on $[a, b]$, and $\phi : [c, d] \to R$ is continuous. Then $\phi \circ f \in R(\alpha)$ on $[a, b]$.

Proof: Choose $\varepsilon > 0$. Let $K = \sup \{|\phi(t)| : t \in [c, d]\}$, and let $\varepsilon' > 0$ be such that $\varepsilon'[\alpha(b) - \alpha(a) + 2K] \leq \varepsilon$. By uniform continuity of ϕ on $[c, d]$, there is $0 < \delta < \varepsilon'$ such that $s, t \in [c, d]$ and $|s - t| < \delta$ implies $|\phi(s) - \phi(t)| < \varepsilon'$. By the integrability of f with respect to α on $[a, b]$, there is a partition P of $[a, b]$ such that

$$U(P, f, \alpha) - L(P, f, \alpha) \leq \delta^2.$$

Assume $P = \{x_0, x_1, \ldots, x_n\}$, and let

$$A = \{i : M_i(f) - m_i(f) < \delta\}$$

and

$$B = \{i : M_i(f) - m_i(f) \geq \delta\}.$$

Now for $i \in A$, s and $t \in [x_{i-1}, x_i]$, $|f(s) - f(t)| < \delta$, so

$$|\phi(f(s)) - \phi(f(t))| < \varepsilon';$$

that is, $M_i(\phi \circ f) - m_i(\phi \circ f) \leq \varepsilon'$. For $i \in B$,

$$M_i(f) - m_i(f) \geq \delta;$$

hence

$$\delta \sum_{i \in B}(\alpha(x_i) - \alpha(x_{i-1})) \leq \sum_{i \in B}[M_i(f) - m_i(f)][\alpha(x_i) - \alpha(x_{i-1})]$$
$$\leq U(P, f, \alpha) - L(P, f, \alpha) \leq \delta^2.$$

Thus, $\sum_{i \in B}(\alpha(x_i) - \alpha(x_{i-1})) \leq \delta$. It now follows that

$U(P, \phi \circ f, \alpha) - L(P, \phi \circ f, \alpha)$
$$= \sum_{i=1}^{n}[M_i(\phi \circ f) - m_i(\phi \circ f)](\alpha(x_i) - \alpha(x_{i-1}))$$
$$= \sum_{i \in A}^{n}(M_i(\phi \circ f) - m_i(\phi \circ f))(\alpha(x_i) - \alpha(x_{i-1}))$$
$$+ \sum_{i \in B}(M_i(\phi \circ f) - m_i(\phi \circ f))(\alpha(x_i) - \alpha(x_{i-1}))$$
$$\leq \varepsilon'[\alpha(b) - \alpha(a)] + 2K\delta \leq \varepsilon'[\alpha(b) - (a) + 2K] \leq \varepsilon.$$

Thus, by 5.2, $\phi \circ f \in R(\alpha)$ on $[a, b]$.

It is interesting to note that this last theorem does not follow the pattern we have observed before. It is true that the composition of continuous functions is continuous and the composition of differentiable functions is differentiable; one might conjecture that if $f: [a, b] \to [c, d]$ and $g: [c, d] \to R$ are such that $f \in R(x)$ on $[a, b]$ and $g \in R(x)$ on $[c, d]$, then $g \circ f \in R(x)$ on $[a, b]$. To see that this is not the case, we shall consider an example. Define $f: [0, 1] \to R$ by $f(x) = 0$ if x is irrational and $f(x) = 1/q$ if $x = p/q$ with p and q relatively prime non-negative integers, $q \neq 0$. It has already been shown that $f \in R(x)$ on $[0, 1]$. Define $g: [0, 1] \to R$ by $g(x) = 1$ if $0 < x \leq 1$ and $g(0) = 0$. It is left to the reader to show that $g \in R(x)$ on $[a, b]$. Let $h = g \circ f$. Then if x is irrational, $h(x) = 0$, and if x is rational, $h(x) = 1$. As previously observed, h is not integrable on $[0, 1]$.

5.12 THEOREM   If $f: [a, b] \to R$, $g: [a, b] \to R$, $\alpha: [a, b] \to R$ is increasing, and $f, g \in R(\alpha)$ on $[a, b]$, then $fg \in R(\alpha)$ on $[a, b]$ and $|f| \in R(\alpha)$ on $[a, b]$. Also,

$$\left| \int_a^b f \, d\alpha \right| \leq \int_a^b |f| \, d\alpha.$$

Proof: Define $\phi: R \to R$ by $\phi(x) = x^2$. Clearly, ϕ is continuous, so $\phi \circ (f + g) = (f + g)^2 \in R(\alpha)$ on $[a, b]$ by 5.11 and 5.9.

Similarly, $\phi \circ (f - g) = (f - g)^2 \in R(\alpha)$ on $[a, b]$, hence

$$fg = \tfrac{1}{4}((f + g)^2 - (f - g)^2) \in R(\alpha)$$

on $[a, b]$.

We have seen in Chapter 3 that the function $\phi(x) = |x|$ is continuous, hence $\phi \circ f = |f| \in R(\alpha)$ on $[a, b]$. Now $f(x) \le |f|(x)$ and $-f(x) \le |f|(x)$ for all $x \in [a, b]$, so

$$\int_a^b f \, d\alpha \le \int_a^b |f| \, d\alpha \quad \text{and} \quad -\int_a^b f \, d\alpha = \int_a^b -f \, d\alpha \le \int_a^b |f| \, d\alpha.$$

Combining the last two inequalities, we obtain $\left| \int_a^b f \, d\alpha \right| \le \int_a^b |f| \, d\alpha$.

It may be the case that our enthusiasm over Theorems 5.6 and 5.7 forced a premature presentation of the fundamental theorem of integral calculus. Let us now reconsider that result.

THEOREM If $f : [a, b] \to R$ is differentiable on $[a, b]$ and $f' \in R(x)$ on $[a, b]$, then $\int_a^b f' dx = f(b) - f(a)$.

As has already been pointed out, this important theorem reveals the very intimate relation between integration and differentiation. The reader may recall many hours spent in calculating integrals by the use of this theorem. In order to obtain a deeper intuitive feeling for the aspects of these operations, let us take a different point of view. Assume $f : [a, b] \to R$ is differentiable on $[a, b]$. Then a function $f' : [a, b] \to R$ exists, and, as noted in various examples, f' need not be continuous; in fact, f' need not even be Riemann-integrable on $[a, b]$. Thus, the operation of differentiation on a differentiable function yields a function which is less nice in the sense that it need not even be continuous. Viewing integration in some fashion as a process inverse to differentiation, one might expect integration to give "nicer" functions. So far, the integral of a function is just a real number, so we must seek some means to use the integral of a function f to create a new function g. That is the purpose of the next two theorems.

Suppose $f : [a, b] \to R$, $\alpha : [a, b] \to R$ is increasing, and $f \in R(\alpha)$ on $[a, b]$. Then if $a \le c < d \le b$, $f \in R(\alpha)$ on $[c, d]$. If $a \le c \le d \le b$, define for sake of convenience,

$$\int_d^c f \, d\alpha = -\int_c^d f \, d\alpha \quad \text{and} \quad \int_c^c f \, d\alpha = 0.$$

To promote the cause espoused in the paragraph preceding the the preceding paragraph, we shall prove two theorems, the second of which is a generalization of the first. If the reader is impatient with the pace of the text, he may choose to skip 5.13 and pass on to 5.14.

5.13 THEOREM Suppose $f: [a, b] \to R$ is bounded and $f \in R(x)$ on $[a, b]$. Define $F(t) = \int_a^t f(x) \, dx$ for $a \le t \le b$. Then

(1) F is continuous on $[a, b]$;
(2) if f is continuous at x_0, then F is differentiable at x_0 and
     $F'(x_0) = f(x_0)$.

The function F may be referred to as an indefinite integral of f. Note here that the integrability of f implies the continuity of F and that the continuity of f at x_0 implies the differentiability of F at x_0; hence, F is indeed " nicer " than f.

Proof: Choose $M > 0$ such that $|f(x)| \le M$ for all $x \in [a, b]$. Choose $\varepsilon > 0$. Let $\delta = \varepsilon/M$. Thus, if $|x - y| < \delta$, x, $y \in [a, b]$, then

$$|F(x) - F(y)| = \left| \int_a^x f(t) \, dt - \int_a^y f(t) \, dt \right|$$

$$= \left| \int_y^x f(t) \, dt \right| \le |x - y| \, M < \delta M = \varepsilon.$$

Thus, F is continuous on $[a, b]$.

Suppose f is continuous at x_0. Choose $\varepsilon > 0$. There is $\delta > 0$ such that $|x_0 - y| < \delta$ with $y \in [a, b]$ implies $|f(x_0) - f(y)| < \varepsilon/2$. Thus, if $0 < |x_0 - y| < \delta$,

$$\left| \frac{F(x_0) - F(y)}{x_0 - y} - f(x_0) \right| = \left| \frac{1}{x_0 - y} \int_y^{x_0} f(t) \, dt - f(x_0) \right|$$

$$= \frac{1}{|x_0 - y|} \left| \int_y^{x_0} [f(t) - f(x_0)] \, dt \right|$$

$$\le \frac{1}{|x_0 - y|} |x_0 - y| \frac{\varepsilon}{2} = \frac{\varepsilon}{2} < \varepsilon.$$

Therefore, F is differentiable at x_0 and $F'(x_0) = f(x_0)$.

We may use 5.13 to give an easy proof of a slightly weaker version of the fundamental theorem of integral calculus. Suppose $f : [a, b] \to R$ is differentiable and $f' : [a, b] \to R$ is continuous. Then $f' \in R(x)$ and $h(t) = \int_a^t f'(x)\,dx$ is differentiable on $[a, b]$—by 5.13—with $h'(t) = f'(t)$ for all $t \in [a, b]$. Since h and f are both differentiable on $[a, b]$ with $h'(t) = f'(t)$ for all $t \in [a, b]$, there is a constant K such that $h(t) = f(t) + K$ for all $t \in [a, b]$. Now $0 = h(a) = f(a) + K$, hence $K = -f(a)$. Thus,

$$\int_a^b f'(t)\,dt = h(b) = f(b) + K = f(b) - f(a),$$

which is the result of the fundamental theorem of integral calculus.

Before generalizing 5.13, it is appropriate to consider an application of this theorem. Consider the function $f : R \to R$ defined by

$$f(x) = 0 \qquad \text{for } x \leq -1$$

$$f(x) = x + 1 \quad \text{for } -1 \leq x \leq 0$$

$$f(x) = 1 - x \quad \text{for } 0 \leq x \leq 1$$

$$f(x) = 0 \qquad \text{for } x \geq 1.$$

See Figure 3 for a sketch of part of the graph of this function.

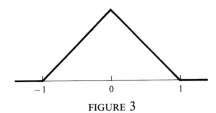

-1 $\quad\quad$ 0 $\quad\quad$ 1

FIGURE 3

At the points $-1, 0$, and 1, this function f fails to have a derivative. We shall seek a function g which is differentiable everywhere and which approximates f, so that there is $\varepsilon > 0$ such that $|f(x) - g(x)| \leq \varepsilon$ for all x. Of interest will be the problem where $\varepsilon > 0$ is specified and then the function g must be produced such that $|f(x) - g(x)| \leq \varepsilon$. Since f is continuous, in fact uniformly continuous, it may be reasonable to try to use 5.13 to produce the function g. Rather than beat about the bush, let us give the function g and then investigate its properties. Choose $\delta > 0$, and define

$$g(t) = \frac{1}{2\delta} \int_{t-\delta}^{t+\delta} f(x)\,dx.$$

Since f is continuous on R, $g(t)$ is well defined for any real number t. From a geometric point of view, $g(t)$ is the "average" value of f over the interval $[t - \delta, t + \delta]$, so if δ is small, $g(t)$ should be close to $f(t)$. It will be left to the reader to verify that g is differentiable on R. Choose $\varepsilon > 0$. By the uniform continuity of f, there is $\delta > 0$ such that $|x - y| \le 2\delta$ implies $|f(x) - f(y)| < \varepsilon$. Thus, for all $t \in R$,

$$|g(t) - f(t)| = \left| \frac{1}{2\delta} \int_{t-\delta}^{t+\delta} f(x)\, dx - f(t) \right|$$

$$= \left| \frac{1}{2\delta} \int_{t-\delta}^{t+\delta} [f(x) - f(t)]\, dx \right| \le \frac{1}{2\delta} [(t + \delta) - (t - \delta)]\varepsilon = \varepsilon.$$

In this particular case, the approximation is even better for certain values of t. Observe that in the cases

(1) $\quad t + \delta \le -1$

(2) $\quad -1 \le t - \delta < t + \delta \le 0$

(3) $\quad 0 \le t - \delta < t + \delta \le 1$

(4) $\quad +1 \le t - \delta$

equality holds, and $g(t) = f(t)$. From the geometric point of view, this is clear since in each of the four cases, $f(t)$ is actually the average value of f over the interval $[t - \delta, t + \delta]$. The reader should do the calculation for some of these cases to see that such is the case.

5.14 THEOREM   Suppose that $f : [a, b] \to R$ is bounded, that $\alpha : [a, b] \to R$ is increasing, and that $f \in R(\alpha)$ on $[a, b]$. For each $t \in [a, b]$, define

$$F(t) = \int_a^t f(x)\, d\alpha(x).$$

Then
 (1)   if α is continuous at x_0, F is continuous at x_0;
 (2)   if f is continuous at x_0 and α is differentiable at x_0 then F is differentiable at x_0 and $F'(x_0) = f(x_0)\alpha'(x_0)$.

Proof: Suppose α is continuous at x_0 and $\varepsilon > 0$. Let $M > 0$ be such that $|f(x)| \le M$ for all $x \in [a, b]$. There is $\delta > 0$ such that if $y \in [a, b]$ and $|x_0 - y| < \delta$, then $|\alpha(y) - \alpha(x_0)| < \varepsilon/M$. Thus for $|x_0 - y| < \delta$,

$$|F(x_0) - F(y)| = \left| \int_y^{x_0} f(t) \, d\alpha(t) \right| \le M |\alpha(y) - \alpha(x_0)| < M \frac{\varepsilon}{M} = \varepsilon.$$

Therefore, F is continuous at x_0.

Assume f is continuous at x_0 and α is differentiable at x_0. Choose $\varepsilon > 0$; then choose $\varepsilon' > 0$ such that

$$[|\alpha'(x_0)| + |f(x_0)|]\varepsilon' + \varepsilon'^2 \le \varepsilon.$$

There is $\delta > 0$ such that if $y \in [a, b]$ and $0 < |y - x_0| < \delta$, then $|f(y) - f(x_0)| < \varepsilon'$ and

$$\left| \frac{\alpha(y) - \alpha(x_0)}{y - x_0} - \alpha'(x_0) \right| < \varepsilon'.$$

Thus, if $y \in [a, b]$ and $0 < |y - x_0| < \delta$, then

$$\left| \frac{F(y) - F(x_0)}{y - x_0} - f(x_0)\alpha'(x_0) \right| = \left| \frac{1}{y - x_0} \int_{x_0}^y f(t) \, d\alpha(t) \right.$$
$$\left. - f(x_0)\alpha'(x_0) \right|$$

$$= \left| \frac{1}{y - x_0} \int_{x_0}^y f(t) \, d\alpha(t) - f(x_0) \frac{\alpha(y) - \alpha(x_0)}{y - x_0} \right.$$
$$\left. + f(x_0) \frac{\alpha(y) - \alpha(x_0)}{y - x_0} - f(x_0)\alpha'(x_0) \right|$$

$$= \left| \frac{1}{y - x_0} \int_{x_0}^y [f(t) - f(x_0)] \, d\alpha(t) + f(x_0) \left[\frac{\alpha(y) - \alpha(x_0)}{y - x_0} - \alpha'(x_0) \right] \right|$$

$$< \left| \frac{\alpha(y) - \alpha(x_0)}{y - x_0} \right| \varepsilon' + |f(x_0)| \varepsilon' \le (|\alpha'(x_0)| + \varepsilon')\varepsilon' + |f(x_0)| \varepsilon' \le \varepsilon.$$

Hence, F is differentiable at x_0, and $F'(x_0) = f(x_0)\alpha'(x_0)$.

Of course, setting $\alpha(x) = x$ on $[a, b]$ gives 5.13 as a special case of 5.14, as advertised.

As pointed out in the discussion of the fundamental theorem of integral calculus, the reader's experience with integration has been largely that of being given a function f on $[a, b]$ to find a differentiable function

g on $[a, b]$ such that $f = g'$. If f is defined on $[a, b]$ and g is a differentiable function on $[a, b]$ such that $g' = f$, then g is called an *anti-derivative* or *primitive* of f. If f is continuous on $[a, b]$, then 5.4 guarantees that $f \in R(x)$ on $[a, b]$, and then 5.13 assures us that f has a primitive, namely $g(t) = \int_a^t f\, dx$. It is not true that every integrable function has a primitive, since our results from Chapter 4 show that if $f = g'$ on $[a, b]$ for some differentiable function g, then f must satisfy certain conditions. For example, the function f, defined by $f(x) = 0$ for $0 \le x < \frac{1}{2}$ and $f(x) = 1$ for $\frac{1}{2} \le x \le 1$, is Riemann integrable on $[0, 1]$ but does not have a primitive since the derivative of a differentiable function, by 4.11, must have the intermediate-value property.

We now wish to give another result relating the two concepts, integration and differentiation. It is especially useful in reducing Riemann–Stieltjes integrals to Riemann integrals.

5.15 THEOREM   Suppose $f: [a, b] \to R$ is bounded, $\alpha : [a, b] \to R$ is increasing and differentiable. If $f \in R(x)$ and $\alpha' \in R(x)$, then $f \in R(\alpha)$, and

$$\int_a^b f\, d\alpha = \int_a^b f\alpha'\, dx.$$

Proof: If $f \in R(x)$ and $\alpha' \in R(x)$, then by 5.12, $f\alpha' \in R(x)$. Choose $\varepsilon > 0$ and choose $M > 0$ such that $|f(x)| \le M$ for all $x \in [a, b]$. Let $\varepsilon' = \varepsilon/(2M + 1)$. Since α is differentiable, hence continuous, and the function $\beta(x) = x$ is continuous, 5.6 is applicable. There is $\delta > 0$ such that if $P = \{x_0, x_1, \ldots, x_n\}$ is any partition of $[a, b]$ such that $\mu(P) < \delta$, then

$$\left| S(P, f\alpha') - \int_a^b f\alpha'\, dx \right| < \varepsilon' \quad \text{and} \quad \left| S(P, \alpha') - \int_a^b \alpha'\, dx \right| < \varepsilon',$$

regardless of how P is marked. Hence, in particular, if t_i, $s_i \in [x_{i-1}, x_i]$, then

$$\left| \sum_{i=1}^n \alpha'(t_i)(x_i - x_{i-1}) - \sum_{i=1}^n \alpha'(s_i)(x_i - x_{i-1}) \right|$$
$$\le \left| \sum_{i=1}^n \alpha'(t_i)(x_i - x_{i-1}) - \int_a^b \alpha'\, dx \right|$$
$$+ \left| \sum_{i=1}^n \alpha'(s_i)(x_i - x_{i-1}) - \int_a^b \alpha'\, dx \right| \le \varepsilon' + \varepsilon' = 2\varepsilon.$$

Note that this inequality holds regardless of how the points t_i and

s_i are chosen in $[x_{i-1}, x_i]$. Thus, if t_i and s_i are chosen in $[x_{i-1}, x_i]$, define $p_i = t_i$ and $q_i = s_i$ if $\alpha'(s_i) \leq \alpha'(t_i)$, and $p_i = s_i$ and $q_i = t_i$ if $\alpha'(t_i) \leq \alpha'(s_i)$. Thus,

$$\sum_{i=1}^{n} |\alpha'(s_i) - \alpha'(t_i)| (x_i - x_{i-1})$$
$$= \left| \sum_{i=1}^{n} (\alpha'(p_i) - \alpha'(q_i))(x_i - x_{i-1}) \right| \leq 2\varepsilon'.$$

Choose $t_i \in [x_{i-1}, x_i]$ for $i = 1, \ldots, n$. By the mean-value theorem, there is $s_i \in [x_{i-1}, x_i]$ such that

$$\alpha(x_i) - \alpha(x_{i-1}) = \alpha'(s_i)(x_i - x_{i-1}).$$

Thus,

$$\left| \sum_{i=1}^{n} f(t_i)(\alpha(x_i) - \alpha(x_{i-1})) - \int_a^b f\alpha' \, dx \right|$$
$$= \left| \sum_{i=1}^{n} f(t_i)\alpha'(s_i)(x_i - x_{i-1}) - \int_a^b f\alpha' \, dx \right|$$
$$= \left| \sum_{i=1}^{n} f(t_i)\alpha'(t_i)(x_i - x_{i-1}) - \int_a^b f\alpha' \, dx \right.$$
$$\left. + \sum_{i=1}^{n} f(t_i)(\alpha'(s_i) - \alpha'(t_i))(x_i - x_{i-1}) \right|$$
$$\leq \left| \sum_{i=1}^{n} f(t_i)\alpha'(t_i)(x_i - x_{i-1}) - \int_a^b f\alpha' \, dx \right|$$
$$+ \left| \sum_{i=1}^{n} f(t_i)(\alpha'(s_i) - \alpha'(t_i))(x_i - x_{i-1}) \right|$$
$$\leq \varepsilon' + M \sum_{i=1}^{n} |\alpha'(s_i) - \alpha'(t_i)| (x_i - x_{i-1}) \leq \varepsilon' + M2\varepsilon'$$
$$= \varepsilon.$$

Therefore, $f \in R(\alpha)$ and $\int_a^b f \, d\alpha = \int_a^b f\alpha' \, dx$.

It is appropriate to use the results presented up to now to compute a Riemann–Stieltjes integral. Define $g(x) = x^3$ for $0 \leq x \leq 1, \alpha(x) = 3x^2$ for $0 \leq x < \frac{1}{2}$, and $\alpha(x) = 3x^2 + 5$ for $\frac{1}{2} \leq x \leq 1$. The continuity of g guarantees that $g \in R(\alpha)$, and the problem is to determine $\int_0^1 g \, d\alpha$. We are unable to apply 5.15 directly, since α is not differentiable, but a trick will remedy this quite easily. Define $\beta(x) = 0$ if $0 \leq x < \frac{1}{2}, \beta(x) = 5$ for $\frac{1}{2} \leq x \leq 1$, and $\gamma(x) = 3x^2$ for $0 \leq x \leq 1$. Then $\alpha = \beta + \gamma$ and β and γ are both increasing with γ differentiable. By 5.9,

$$\int_0^1 x^3 \, d\alpha(x) = \int_0^1 x^3 \, d\beta(x) + \int_0^1 x^3 \, d\gamma(x).$$

Applying 5.15 to $\int_0^1 x^3 \, d\gamma(x)$ yields

$$\int_0^1 x^3 \, d\gamma(x) = \int_0^1 x^3 \gamma'(x) \, dx = \int_0^1 x^3 \cdot 6x \, dx = \int_0^1 6x^4 \, dx.$$

By the fundamental theorem of integral calculus,

$$\int_0^1 6x^4 \, dx = 6 \int_0^1 x^4 \, dx = 6\left[\frac{1}{5} - 0\right] = \frac{6}{5}.$$

The function β is a step function with a jump of 5 at $x = \frac{1}{2}$, and g is continuous at $\frac{1}{2}$, so by our previous discussion,

$$\int_0^1 g(x) \, d\beta(x) = 5g\left(\frac{1}{2}\right) = 5 \cdot \frac{1}{8} = \frac{5}{8}.$$

Thus,

$$\int_0^1 x^3 \, d\alpha(x) = \int_0^1 x^3 \, d\beta(x) + \int_0^1 x^3 \, d\gamma(x) = \frac{5}{8} + \frac{6}{5}.$$

An alternate means of solving this problem will be available after we have at our disposal a theorem concerning integration by parts.

So far, we have restricted our discussion to integrals with α an increasing function. It would seem clear that many of the preceding results could be obtained for decreasing functions since β decreasing implies $-\beta$ increasing. Similarly, one might suspect some results to carry over if α is the sum of two monotone functions, with no insistence that either be increasing. It is now our purpose to investigate such a class of functions, realizing that the preceding discussion gives away the punch line.

DEFINITION   Suppose $f : [a, b] \to R$ and $P = \{x_0, x_1, \ldots, x_n\}$ is any partition of $[a, b]$. Define

$$T(P) = \sum_{i=1}^n |f(x_i) - f(x_{i-1})|.$$

The function f is said to be of *bounded variation on* $[a, b]$ iff there is a real number M such that $T(P) \le M$ for all partitions P of $[a, b]$. We shall merely write "f is of bounded variation" if f is of bounded variation on its domain.

If f is of bounded variation on $[a, b]$, define the *total variation of f over* $[a, b]$ to be $V(f; a, b) = \sup\{T(P) : P \text{ a partition of } [a, b]\}$.

If f is monotone, then for each partition P,

$$T(P) = \sum_{i=1}^{n} |f(x_i) - f(x_{i-1})|$$

collapses to $f(b) - f(a)$ or to $f(a) - f(b)$, depending on whether f is increasing or decreasing, respectively. Thus, if f is monotone on $[a, b]$, then f is of bounded variation on $[a, b]$ and $V(f; a, b) = |f(b) - f(a)|$. Perhaps counterexamples best serve to illustrate this definition, so let us consider a few. Our old friend, $f: [0, 1] \to R$ defined by $f(x) = 0$ if x is irrational and $f(x) = 1$ if x is rational, is certainly not of bounded variation since we can choose a partition $P = \{x_0, x_1, \ldots, x_n\}$ such that x_i is rational for i odd and x_i is irrational for i even, and then $T(P) = n$.

Define $g: [0, 1] \to R$ by $g(x) = x \cos \pi/2x$ for $x \neq 0$ and set $g(0) = 0$. The function g is uniformly continuous on $[0, 1]$ but, as we shall soon see, is not of bounded variation. Let

$$P = \left\{ 0, \frac{1}{2n} \frac{1}{2n-1}, \ldots, \frac{1}{3}, \frac{1}{2}, 1 \right\}.$$

Then

$$T(P) = \frac{1}{n} + \frac{1}{n-1} + \cdots + \frac{1}{2} + 1,$$

which is the nth partial sum of the infinite series $\sum_{n=1}^{\infty} 1/n$. In Chapter 6, a thorough discussion of infinite series will be given, and this particular series will be given due attention. For the moment, let us assume that the student already knows that this series diverges, hence the sum

$$1 + \frac{1}{2} + \frac{1}{3} + \cdots + \frac{1}{n}$$

may be made as large as one pleases by choosing n sufficiently large. Thus, g is not of bounded variation on $[0, 1]$.

Suppose $f: [a, b] \to R$ is differentiable with $|f'(x)| \leq M$ for all $x \in [a, b]$. Then for any $x, y \in [a, b]$, the mean-value theorem implies $|f(x) - f(y)| \leq M |x - y|$. Hence, for any partition $P = \{x_0, x_1, \ldots, x_n\}$ of $[a, b]$,

$$T(P) = \sum_{i=1}^{n} |f(x_i) - f(x_{i-1})| \leq \sum_{i=1}^{n} M |x_i - x_{i-1}| = M(b - a);$$

thus, f is of bounded variation on $[a, b]$ and $V(f; a, b) \leq M(b - a)$.

It is clear that $f: [a, b] \to R$ is of bounded variation if f does not oscillate too wildly, and in particular, f must be bounded.

5.16 THEOREM Suppose $f: [a, b] \to R$ is of bounded variation. Then f is bounded on $[a, b]$.

Proof: Let $x \in [a, b]$ and consider the partition $P = \{a, x, b\}$ of $[a, b]$. Then

$$|f(x) - f(a)| + |f(x) - f(b)| \leq V(f; a, b).$$

Hence,

$$|f(x)| \leq |f(x) - f(b)| + |f(b)|$$
$$+ |f(x) - f(a)| \leq V(f; a, b) + |f(b)|.$$

Thus, $V(f; a, b) + |f(b)|$ serves as a bound for f.

5.17 THEOREM Suppose that $f: [a, b] \to R$ and $g: [a, b] \to R$ are of bounded variation on $[a, b]$. Then $f + g$ and fg are of bounded variation on $[a, b]$.

Proof: Let $P = \{x_0, x_1, \ldots, x_n\}$ be any partition of $[a, b]$. Choose A and B such that $|f(x)| \leq A$ and $|g(x)| \leq B$ for all $x \in [a, b]$. (By 5.16, f and g are bounded on $[a, b]$). Now

$$\sum_{i=1}^{n} |(f + g)(x_i) - (f + g)(x_{i-1})| \leq \sum_{i=1}^{n} |f(x_i) - f(x_{i-1})|$$
$$+ \sum_{i=1}^{n} |g(x_i) - g(x_{i-1})|$$
$$\leq V(f; a, b) + V(g; a, b);$$

hence, $f + g$ is of bounded variation on $[a, b]$. Also

$$\sum_{i=1}^{n} |(fg)(x_i) - (fg)(x_{i-1})| = \sum_{i=1}^{n} |f(x_i)g(x_i) - f(x_{i-1})g(x_{i-1})|$$
$$\leq \sum_{i=1}^{n} |f(x_i)||g(x_i) - g(x_{i-1})|$$
$$+ \sum_{i=1}^{n} |g(x_{i-1})||f(x_i) - f(x_{i-1})|$$
$$\leq A V(g; a, b) + B V(f; a, b);$$

hence fg is of bounded variation on $[a, b]$.

The following corollary follows from 5.17 and the remarks immediately following the definition of bounded variation. Shortly, it will be shown that this corollary has a converse which characterizes all functions of bounded variation.

5.18 COROLLARY   If $f : [a, b] \to R$ and $g : [a, b] \to R$ are monotone, then $f - g$ is of bounded variation.

The master plan has now been revealed. It is our intent to prove that every function of bounded variation may be written as the difference of two monotone functions—in fact, as the difference of two increasing functions. To accomplish this, we shall seek to construct for each function f of bounded variation two increasing functions f_1 and f_2 such that $f = f_1 - f_2$.

5.19 THEOREM   Let $f : [a, b] \to R$ be of bounded variation on $[a, b]$. If $a \le x \le b$, then f is of bounded variation on both $[a, x]$ and $[x, b]$, and

$$V(f; a, b) = V(f; a, x) + V(f; x, b).$$

Proof: Let $P = \{x_0, x_1, \ldots, x_r\}$ be any partition of $[a, x]$, and let $Q = \{x_r, x_{r+1}, \ldots, x_n\}$ be any partition of $[x, b]$. Then $P \cup Q$ is a partition of $[a, b]$, and

$$\sum_{i=1}^{r} |f(x_i) - f(x_{i-1})| + \sum_{i=r+1}^{n} |f(x_i) - f(x_{i-1})| \le V(f; a, b).$$

Thus, f is of bounded variation on $[a, x]$ and on $[x, b]$, and

$$V(f; a, x) + V(f; x, b) \le V(f; a, b).$$

Choose $\varepsilon > 0$. By the definition of $V(f; a, b)$, there is a partition $P = \{x_0, x_1, \ldots, x_n\}$ of $[a, b]$ such that

$$V(f; a, b) - \varepsilon < \sum_{i=1}^{n} |f(x_i) - f(x_{i-1})| \le V(f; a, b);$$

in fact, we may assume $x \in P$; say $x = x_j$. Thus,

$$V(f; a, b) - \varepsilon < \sum_{i=1}^{j} |f(x_i) - f(x_{i-1})| + \sum_{i=j+1}^{n} |f(x_i) - f(x_{i-1})|$$

$$\le V(f; a, x) + V(f; x, b) \le V(f; a, b).$$

Since $\varepsilon > 0$ was arbitrary, $V(f; a, b) = V(f; a, x) + V(f; x, b)$.

Define

$$f(x) = 2x^3 - 9x^2 + 12x + 2$$

for $0 \le x \le 3$. Now $g_1(x) = 2x^3, g_2(x) = -9x^2, g_3(x) = 12x$, and $g_4(x) = 2$ are all monotone on $[0, 3]$; hence, f is of bounded variation on $[0, 3]$. With the aid of 5.19, we shall seek to compute $V(f; 0, 3)$. The function f is a polynomial function, and as such, the behavior of f can be determined by facts from Chapter 4 (familiar facts from differential calculus). For each $x \in [0, 3]$,

$$f'(x) = 6x^2 - 18x + 12 = 6(x^2 - 3x + 2) = 6(x - 2)(x - 1).$$

Thus, for $0 < x < 1, f'(x) > 0$; for $1 < x < 2, f'(x) < 0$; and for $2 < x < 3$, $f'(x) > 0$. We may conclude that f is monotone increasing on $[0, 1]$, monotone decreasing on $[1, 2]$, and monotone increasing on $[2, 3]$. By 5.19 and the results for monotone functions,

$$\begin{aligned}
V(f; 0, 3) &= V(f; 0, 1) + V(f; 1, 2) + V(f; 2, 3) \\
&= |f(1) - f(0)| + |f(2) - f(1)| + |f(2) - f(3)| \\
&= f(1) - f(0) + f(1) - f(2) + f(3) - f(2) \\
&= 7 - 2 + 7 - 6 + 11 - 6 = 11.
\end{aligned}$$

DEFINITION   Let $f : [a, b] \to R$ be of bounded variation. Define $v_f(x) = V(f; a, x)$ for $a \le x \le b$.

5.20 THEOREM   Assume $f : [a, b] \to R$ is of bounded variation. Then

(1) v_f is an increasing function;
(2) $v_f - f$ is an increasing function;
(3) f is continuous at $x_0 \in [a, b]$ iff v_f is continuous at x_0.

Proof: Suppose $a \le x < y \le b$. By 5.19,

$$\begin{aligned}
v_f(y) &= V(f; a, y) = V(f; a, x) + V(f; x, y) \\
&= v_f(x) + V(f; x, y) \ge v_f(x)
\end{aligned}$$

since $V(f; x, y) \ge 0$. Thus, v_f is increasing.

Assume $a \leq x < y \leq b$. Now

$$V(f; x, y) \geq |f(y) - f(x)| \geq f(y) - f(x),$$

so

$$[v_f(y) - f(y)] - [v_f(x) - f(x)] = [v_f(y) - v_f(x)] - [f(y) - f(x)]$$
$$= V(f; x, y) - [f(y) - f(x)] \geq 0;$$

that is, $v_f - f$ is increasing.

Let v_f be continuous at x_0. Then, given $\varepsilon > 0$, there is $\delta > 0$ such that if $|x_0 - y| < \delta$, then $|v_f(x_0) - v_f(y)| < \varepsilon$. If $x_0 \leq y < x_0 + \delta$, then

$$|f(x_0) - f(y)| \leq V(f; x_0, y) = v_f(y) - v_f(x_0) < \varepsilon,$$

and if $x_0 - \delta < y \leq x_0$, then

$$|f(x_0) - f(y)| \leq V(f; y, x_0) = v_f(x_0) - v_f(y) < \varepsilon.$$

So if v_f is continuous at x_0, then f is continuous at x_0.

Choose $\varepsilon > 0$. If f is continuous at x_0, then there is $\delta > 0$ such that $|x_0 - y| < \delta$ implies $|f(x_0) - f(y)| < \varepsilon/2$. There is a partition $P = \{x_0, x_1, \ldots, x_n\}$ of $[x_0, b]$ such that

$$V(f; x_0, b) - \frac{\varepsilon}{2} < \sum_{i=1}^{n} |f(x_i) - f(x_{i-1})|.$$

Let $\delta' = \min\{x_1 - x_0, \delta\}$ and suppose $x_0 \leq y < x_0 + \delta' \leq x_1$. Define $P^* = P \cup \{y\}$, and we shall write $P^* = \{y_0, y_1, \ldots, y_k\}$ where $y = y_1$. Then

$$V(f; x_0, b) - \frac{\varepsilon}{2} < \sum_{i=1}^{n} |f(y_i) - f(y_{i-1})|$$

$$= |f(x_0) - f(y_1)| + \sum_{i=2}^{n} |f(y_i) - f(y_{i-1})| \leq \frac{\varepsilon}{2} + V(f; y, b).$$

Now if $x_0 \leq y < x_0 + \delta'$, then

(1) $\qquad V(f; y, b) \leq V(f; x_0, b) \leq \varepsilon + V(f; y, b).$

In like fashion, there is a partition $Q = \{z_0, z_1, \ldots, z_m\}$ of $[a, x_0]$ such that

$$V(f; a, x_0) - \frac{\varepsilon}{2} < \sum_{i=1}^{m} |f(z_i) - f(z_{i-1})|.$$

Choose $\delta'' = \min\{z_m - z_{m-1}, \delta'\}$, and suppose $x_0 - \delta'' < y \le x_0$. Letting $Q^* = Q \cup \{y\}$, we shall write $Q^* = \{w_0, w_1, \ldots, w_s\}$, where $w_s = x_0$ and $w_{s-1} = y$. Then

$$V(f; a, x_0) - \frac{\varepsilon}{2} \le \sum_{i=1}^{s}|f(w_i) - f(w_{i-1})|$$

$$= \sum_{i=1}^{s-1}|f(w_i) - f(w_{i-1})| + |f(x_0 - f(y)| \le V(f; a, y) + \frac{\varepsilon}{2}.$$

Thus, if $x_0 - \delta'' < y \le x_0$, then

(2) $V(f; a, y) \le V(f; a, x_0) \le V(f; a, y) + \varepsilon.$

By 5.19, $v_f(x) = V(f; a, b) - V(f; x, b)$. If $x_0 - \delta'' < y \le x_0$, then by (2),

$$v_f(x_0) - \varepsilon = V(f; a, x_0) - \varepsilon \le V(f; a, y) = v_f(y) \le v_f(x_0).$$

If $x_0 \le y < x_0 + \delta$, then by (1),

$$v_f(x_0) \le v_f(y) = V(f; a, b) - V(f; y, b)$$
$$\le V(f; a, b) - V(f; x_0, b) + \varepsilon$$
$$= v_f(x_0) + \varepsilon.$$

Thus, v_f is continuous at x_0.

Since $f = v_f - (v_f - f)$, we may now summarize 5.19 and 5.20 as follows: the function $f: [a, b] \to R$ is of bounded variation iff f may be written as the difference of two increasing functions. Note that there are many ways of accomplishing this decomposition now that at least one is available. For instance, if g is any increasing function and f is of bounded variation, then

$$f = v_f + g - (v_f - f + g),$$

where $v_f + g$ is increasing, and $v_f - f + g$ is also increasing. As shown by 5.20, f and v_f have the property that f is continuous at x_0 iff v_f is continuous at x_0. In some sense, the decomposition of f indicated above, that of $f = v_f - (v_f - f)$, is the most desirable one. We intend now to consider integrating functions with respect to functions of bounded variation rather than with respect to increasing functions.

Suppose $\alpha : [a, b] \to R$ is of bounded variation and $f : [a, b] \to R$ is bounded. Now there are increasing functions $\beta : [a, b] \to R$ and $\gamma : [a, b] \to R$ such that $\alpha = \beta - \gamma$. It seems reasonable to define f to be integrable with respect to α iff $f \in R(\beta)$ and $f \in R(\gamma)$ and to define

$$\int_a^b f(x)\, d\alpha(x) = \int_a^b f(x)\, d\beta(x) - \int_a^b f(x)\, d\gamma(x).$$

The only questions which must be settled hinge on the fact that there are many different ways of writing α as the difference of two increasing functions. First of all, let us show that this definition of the integral will be independent of the decomposition of α, assuming all the integrals involved exist.

5.21 THEOREM   Suppose that $\alpha_1, \alpha_2, \beta_1, \beta_2$ are increasing functions on $[a, b]$, that $f \in R(\alpha_1) \cap R(\alpha_2) \cap R(\beta_1) \cap R(\beta_2)$, and that $\alpha_1 - \beta_1 = \alpha_2 - \beta_2$. Then

$$\int_a^b f\, d\alpha_1 - \int_a^b f\, d\beta_1 = \int_a^b f\, d\alpha_2 - \int_a^b f\, d\beta_2 .$$

Proof: Since $f \in R(\alpha_1)$ and $f \in R(\beta_2)$, then $f \in R(\alpha_1 + \beta_2)$ and

$$\int f\, d(\alpha_1 + \beta_2) = \int f\, d\alpha_1 + \int f\, d\beta_2 .$$

Similarly, if $f \in R(\alpha_2)$ and $f \in R(\beta_1)$, then $f \in R(\alpha_2 + \beta_1)$ and

$$\int f\, d(\alpha_2 + \beta_1) = \int f\, d\alpha_2 + \int f\, d\beta_1 .$$

Now $\alpha_1 - \beta_1 = \alpha_2 - \beta_2$; hence, $\alpha_1 + \beta_2 = \alpha_2 + \beta_1$. Thus,

$$\int f\, d\alpha_2 + \int f\, d\beta_1 = \int f\, d(\alpha_2 + \beta_1) = \int f\, d(\alpha_1 + \beta_2)$$

$$= \int f\, d\alpha_1 + \int f\, d\beta_2 .$$

Therefore, $\int f\, d\alpha_1 - \int f\, d\beta_1 = \int f\, d\alpha_2 - \int f\, d\beta_2 .$

It now remains to decide on a suitable definition of integrability. Since there are many ways of decomposing a function of bounded variation into the difference of two increasing functions, it seems foolish to insist that $f \in R(\beta)$ and $f \in R(\gamma)$ for all increasing functions such that $\alpha = \beta - \gamma$. Instead, we shall merely ask that this holds for at least one such decomposition.

DEFINITION   Let $f : [a, b] \to R$ be bounded and $\alpha : [a, b] \to R$ be of bounded variation. If there are increasing functions β and γ such that $\alpha = \beta - \gamma, f \in R(\beta)$, and $f \in R(\gamma)$, then we say that f is *integrable with respect to α* on $[a, b]$, written $f \in R(\alpha)$, and we define

$$\int_a^b f\,d\alpha = \int_a^b f\,d\beta - \int_a^b f\,d\gamma.$$

If α is increasing, then we write $\alpha = \alpha - 0$ and see that this new definition of integrability is actually an extension of the previous one presented, since $f \in R(0)$ for any bounded real-valued function f. It was the purpose of 5.21 to show that $\int_a^b f\,d\alpha$ is independent of β and γ subject only to $\alpha = \beta - \gamma$, with β and γ increasing and $f \in R(\beta) \cap R(\gamma)$. In a situation such as this where there may be some question about how a concept should be defined, perhaps a word of explanation supporting the decision should be given. If α is of bounded variation on $[a, b]$ and $f : [a, b] \to R$ is bounded, then, to show $f \in R(\alpha)$ and to compute $\int_a^b f\,d\alpha$, it suffices to find increasing functions β and γ such that $f \in R(\beta)$ and $f \in R(\gamma)$ and $\alpha = \beta - \gamma$. As observed earlier, $\alpha = v_\alpha - (v_\alpha - \alpha)$ is a decomposition of α as the difference of two increasing functions. We shall see shortly that if $f \in R(\alpha)$, i.e., if there are increasing functions β and γ such that $\alpha = \beta - \gamma$ and $f \in R(\beta) \cap R(\gamma)$, then $f \in R(v_\alpha)$ and $f \in R(v_\alpha - \alpha)$. One might argue that it would be preferable to define $f \in R(\alpha)$ iff $f \in R(v_\alpha)$ and $f \in R(v_\alpha - \alpha)$, thus avoiding much of the labor involved in proving the next theorem. The advantage of having the results of 5.22 will be apparent later.

5.22 THEOREM   Suppose that $f : [a, b] \to R$ is bounded and $\alpha : [a, b] \to R$ is of bounded variation. Then (i)–(iii) below are equivalent:

   (i) $f \in R(\alpha)$ on $[a, b]$;
   (ii) $f \in R(v_\alpha) \cap R(v_\alpha - \alpha)$ on $[a, b]$;
   (iii) there is a real number A such that for each $\varepsilon > 0$ there is a partition P of $[a, b]$ such that if Q is any refinement of P, regardless of how marked, $|S(Q, f, \alpha) - A| < \varepsilon$.

In case (iii) holds, then $A = \int_a^b f\,d\alpha$.

Proof: Assume (i). Then there are increasing functions β and γ such that $\alpha = \beta - \gamma$ and $f \in R(\beta) \cap R(\gamma)$. Choose $\varepsilon > 0$. By 5.5, there are partitions P_1 and P_2 of $[a, b]$ such that if Q_1 and Q_2 are refinements of P_1 and P_2, respectively, then

$$\left| S(Q_1, f, \beta) - \int_a^b f \, d\beta \right| \leq \frac{\varepsilon}{2}$$

and

$$\left| S(Q_2, f, \gamma) - \int_a^b f \, d\gamma \right| \leq \frac{\varepsilon}{2}.$$

Let $P = P_1 \cup P_2$ and let

$$A = \int_a^b f \, d\alpha = \int_a^b f \, d\beta - \int_a^b f \, d\gamma.$$

Now if Q is a refinement of P, then Q is a refinement of both P_1 and P_2; hence, regardless of how Q is marked,

$$|S(Q, f, \alpha) - A| = |S(Q, f, \beta) - S(Q, f, \gamma) - A|$$

$$\leq \left| S(Q, f, \beta) - \int_a^b f \, d\beta \right| + \left| \int_a^b f \, d\gamma - S(Q, f, \gamma) \right| \leq \frac{\varepsilon}{2} + \frac{\varepsilon}{2} = \varepsilon.$$

Thus, (i) implies (iii).

Assume (iii) holds. If $v_\alpha(b) = 0$, then $v_\alpha(x) = 0$ for all $x \in [a, b]$ and $f \in R(v_\alpha)$. Suppose $v_\alpha(b) \neq 0$. Choose $M > 0$ such that $|f(x)| \leq M$ for all $x \in [a, b]$. Choose $\varepsilon > 0$. There is a partition $P = \{x_0, x_1, \ldots, x_n\}$ of $[a, b]$ such that

$$v_\alpha(b) - \frac{\varepsilon}{6M} < \sum_{i=1}^n |\alpha(x_i) - \alpha(x_{i-1})|.$$

We may further assume that regardless of how P is marked, $|S(P, f, \alpha) - A| < \varepsilon/6$. Thus, in particular, if we choose $s_k, s_k' \in [x_{k-1}, x_k]$, then

$$\left| \sum_{k=1}^n f(s_k)(\alpha(x_k) - \alpha(x_{k-1})) - \sum_{k=1}^n f(s_k')(\alpha(x_k) - \alpha(x_{k-1})) \right|$$

$$\leq \left| \sum_{k=1}^n f(s_k)(\alpha(x_k) - \alpha(x_{k-1})) - A \right|$$

$$+ \left| A - \sum_{k=1}^n f(s_k')(\alpha(x_k) - \alpha(x_{k-1})) \right|$$

$$\leq \frac{\varepsilon}{6} + \frac{\varepsilon}{6} = \frac{\varepsilon}{3}.$$

Let

$$A(P) = \{k : \alpha(x_k) - \alpha(x_{k-1}) \geq 0\}$$

and

$$B(P) = \{k : \alpha(x_k) - \alpha(x_{k-1}) < 0\}.$$

For $k \in A(P)$, choose $t_k, t_k' \in [x_{k-1}, x_k]$ such that

$$f(t_k) - f(t_k') > M_k(f) - m_k(f) - \frac{\varepsilon}{3v_\alpha(b)},$$

and for $k \in B(P)$, choose $t_k, t_k' \in [x_{k-1}, x_k]$ such that

$$f(t_k') - f(t_k) > M_k(f) - m_k(f) - \frac{\varepsilon}{3v_\alpha(b)},$$

Then

$$
\begin{aligned}
U(P,f,v_\alpha) - L(P,f,v_\alpha) &= \sum_{k=1}^{n} [M_k(f) - m_k(f)][v_\alpha(x_k) - v_\alpha(x_{k-1})] \\
&= \sum_{k=1}^{n} [M_k(f) - m_k(f)][v_\alpha(x_k) - v_\alpha(x_{k-1}) - |\alpha(x_k) - \alpha(x_{k-1})| \\
&\quad + |\alpha(x_k) - \alpha(x_{k-1})|] \\
&= \sum_{k=1}^{n} [M_k(f) - m_k(f)][v_\alpha(x_k) - v_\alpha(x_{k-1}) - |\alpha(x_k) - \alpha(x_{k-1})|] \\
&\quad + \sum_{k=1}^{n} [M_k(f) - m_k(f)]\,|\alpha(x_k) - \alpha(x_{k-1})| \\
&\leq 2M[v_\alpha(b) - \sum_{k=1}^{n} |\alpha(x_k) - \alpha(x_{k-1})|] \\
&\quad + \sum_{k=1}^{n} [M_k(f) - m_k(f)]\,|\alpha(x_k) - \alpha(x_{k-1})| \\
&\quad (\text{since } v_\alpha(x_k) - v_\alpha(x_{k-1}) \geq |\alpha(x_k) - \alpha(x_{k-1})|) \\
&\leq 2M \frac{\varepsilon}{6M} + \sum_{k \in A(P)} [f(t_k) - f(t_k')][\alpha(x_k) - \alpha(x_{k-1})] \\
&\quad + \sum_{k \in B(P)} [f(t_k) - f(t_k')][\alpha(x_k) - \alpha(x_{k-1})] \\
&\quad + \sum_{k=1}^{n} \frac{\varepsilon}{3v_\alpha(b)}\,|\alpha(x_k) - \alpha(x_{k-1})| \\
&\leq \frac{\varepsilon}{3} + \sum_{k=1}^{n} [f(t_k) - f(t_k')][\alpha(x_k) - \alpha(x_{k-1})] + \frac{\varepsilon}{3} \leq \frac{\varepsilon}{3} + \frac{\varepsilon}{3} + \frac{\varepsilon}{3} \\
&= \varepsilon.
\end{aligned}
$$

Thus, $f \in R(v_\alpha)$.

It now remains to prove that $f \in R(v_\alpha - \alpha)$. Choose $\varepsilon > 0$. There is a partition P such that for any refinement Q of P, regardless of how marked, the inequality $|S(Q, f, \alpha) - A| < \varepsilon/2$ holds. Similarly, there is a partition P' such that for any refinement Q' of P', regardless of how marked,

$$\left| S(Q', f, v_\alpha) - \int f \, dv_\alpha \right| \le \frac{\varepsilon}{2}.$$

Let $P'' = P' \cup P$. If Q'' is any refinement of P'', then

$$\left| S(Q'', f, v_\alpha - \alpha) - \int_a^b f \, dv_\alpha + A \right|$$

$$\le \left| S(Q'', f, v_\alpha) - \int_a^b f \, dv_\alpha \right| + |S(Q'', f, \alpha) - A| \le \frac{\varepsilon}{2} + \frac{\varepsilon}{2} = \varepsilon.$$

Thus, by 5.5, $f \in R(v_\alpha - \alpha)$. Therefore, (iii) implies (ii).

It is a result of the definition of $R(\alpha)$ that (ii) implies (i), so the proof is complete.

Now it seems clear that many of the previous results for increasing functions carry over for functions of bounded variation. The following theorem will serve to summarize some of these results. We shall prove prove parts a, b, and c only, leaving the proof of part d to the reader.

5.23 THEOREM   Suppose that $f : [a, b] \to R$ and $g : [a, b] \to R$ are bounded, that $\alpha : [a, b] \to R$ and $\beta : [a, b] \to R$ are of bounded variation, and that $f, g \in R(\alpha) \cap R(\beta)$. Then
   (a)   for all real numbers s and t, $sf + tg \in R(\alpha)$ and

$$\int_a^b (sf + tg) \, d\alpha = s \int_a^b f \, d\alpha + t \int_a^b g \, d\alpha;$$

   (b)   for all real numbers s and t, $f \in R(s\alpha + t\beta)$ and

$$\int_a^b f \, d(s\alpha + t\beta) = s \int_a^b f \, d\alpha + t \int_a^b f \, d\beta;$$

   (c) $|f| \in R(v_\alpha)$ and $\left| \int_a^b f \, d\alpha \right| \le \int_a^b |f| \, d_\alpha v;$
   (d) $fg \in R(\alpha)$.

Proof: (a)   Suppose $f, g \in R(\alpha)$ and that s and t are real numbers. By 5.22,

$$f, g \in R(v_\alpha) \cap R(v_\alpha - \alpha).$$

Thus, by 5.9,

$$sf + tg \in R(v_\alpha) \cap R(v_\alpha - \alpha);$$

that is, $sf + tg \in R(\alpha)$ and

$$\int_a^b (sf + tg)\, d\alpha = \int_a^b (sf + tg)\, dv_\alpha - \int_a^b (sf + tg)\, d(v_\alpha - \alpha)$$

$$= s \int_a^b f\, dv_\alpha + t \int_a^b g\, dv_\alpha - s \int_a^b f\, d(v_\alpha - \alpha) - t \int_a^b g\, d(v_\alpha - \alpha)$$

$$= s \int_a^b f\, d\alpha + t \int_a^b g\, d\alpha.$$

(b)   If $f \in R(\alpha) \cap R(\beta)$, then there are increasing functions $\alpha_1, \alpha_2, \beta_1, \beta_2$ such that

$$f \in R(\alpha_1) \cap R(\alpha_2) \cap R(\beta_1) \cap R(\beta_2)$$

and

$$\alpha = \alpha_1 - \alpha_2, \beta = \beta_1 - \beta_2.$$

By 5.9, $f \in R(\alpha_1 + \beta_1)$, $f \in R(\alpha_2 + \beta_2)$,

$$\int_a^b f\, d(\alpha_1 + \beta_1) = \int_a^b f\, d\alpha_1 + \int_a^b f\, d\beta_1,$$

and

$$\int_a^b f\, d(\alpha_2 + \beta_2) = \int_a^b f\, d\alpha_2 + \int_a^b f\, d\beta_2.$$

Now $\alpha + \beta = (\alpha_1 + \beta_1) - (\alpha_2 + \beta_2)$, hence $f \in R(\alpha + \beta)$ and

$$\int_a^b f\, d(\alpha + \beta) = \int_a^b f\, d(\alpha_1 + \beta_1) - \int_a^b f\, d(\alpha_2 + \alpha_2)$$

$$= \int_a^b f\, d\alpha_1 + \int_a^b f\, d\beta_1 - \int_a^b f\, d\alpha_2 - \int_a^b f\, d\beta_2$$

$$= \int_a^b f\, d\alpha + \int_a^b f\, d\beta.$$

It now remains only to show that $f \in R(\alpha)$ implies $f \in R(s\alpha)$ and $\int_a^b f\, d(s\alpha) = s \int_a^b f\, d\alpha$. As above, assume α_1, α_2 are increasing with $f \in R(\alpha_1) \cap R(\alpha_2)$ and $\alpha = \alpha_1 - \alpha_2$. If $s \geq 0$, then $s\alpha_1$ and $s\alpha_2$ are increasing, $f \in R(s\alpha_1) \cap R(s\alpha_2)$ by 5.9, and

$$\int_a^b f\, d(s\alpha_i) = s \int_a^b f\, d\alpha_i$$

for $i = 1, 2$. If $s < 0$, then $-s\alpha_1$ and $-s\alpha_2$ are increasing,

$$f \in R(-s\alpha_1) \cap R(-s\alpha_2)$$

by 5.9, and

$$\int_a^b f\, d(-s\alpha_i) = -s \int_a^b f\, d\alpha_i.$$

Now $s\alpha = s\alpha_1 - s\alpha_2 = -s\alpha_2 - (-s\alpha_1)$. Hence, in either case, $s \geq 0$ or $s < 0$, $f \in R(s\alpha)$, and

$$\int_a^b f\, d(s\alpha) = s \int_a^b f\, d\alpha.$$

(c)   Suppose $f \in R(\alpha)$ on $[a, b]$. Then by 5.23,

$$f \in R(v_\alpha) \cap R(v_\alpha - \alpha);$$

hence,

$$|f| \in R(v_\alpha) \cap R(v_\alpha - \alpha)$$

by 5.12, so that $|f| \in R(\alpha)$. Let $P = \{x_0, x_1, \ldots, x_n\}$ be any partition of $[a, b]$. Then, if $t_i \in [x_{i-1}, x_i]$ for $i = 1, \ldots, n$,

$$\left| \sum_{i=1}^n f(t_i)(\alpha(x_i) - \alpha(x_{i-1})) \right| \leq \sum_{i=1}^n |f(t_i)| \, [v_\alpha(x_i) - v_\alpha(x_{i-1})].$$

Thus, by 5.22, $\left| \int_a^b f\, d\alpha \right| \leq \int_a^b |f|\, dv_\alpha$.

The reasons for proving Theorem 5.22 now become apparent. If $f \in R(\alpha)$ and $g \in R(\alpha)$, then there are increasing functions $\alpha_1, \alpha_2, \alpha_3, \alpha_4$ such that $\alpha = \alpha_1 - \alpha_2 = \alpha_3 - \alpha_4$ and

$$f \in R(\alpha_1) \cap R(\alpha_2), \qquad g \in R(\alpha_3) \cap R(\alpha_4).$$

Without using 5.22, it is not clear that one may choose $\alpha_1 = \alpha_3$ and $\alpha_2 = \alpha_4$ in order to conclude that $f + g \in R(\alpha)$. If one were to define $f \in R(\alpha)$ iff $f \in R(v_\alpha)$ and $f \in R(v_\alpha - \alpha)$, then (a) would be easy to prove, but (b) would pose a problem. In the proof of Theorem 5.17, it was shown that $V(\alpha + \beta; a, b) \leq V(\alpha; a, b) + V(\beta; a, b)$. It is convenient in proving (b) not to be forced to use $v_\alpha, v_\alpha - \alpha$ and $v_\beta, v_\beta - \beta$, since then one would have to show that $v_{\alpha+\beta} = v_\alpha + v_\beta$. Unfortunately, $v_{\alpha+\beta} \neq v_\alpha + v_\beta$ for appropriate choices of α and β. The reader is invited to construct such an example.

Theorem 5.10 now may be extended to functions of bounded variation. Again, the proof is left to the reader.

5.24 THEOREM   Suppose $f: [a, b] \to R$ is bounded, $\alpha : [a, b] \to R$ is of bounded variation, and $a < c < b$. Then $f \in R(\alpha)$ on $[a, b]$ iff $f \in R(\alpha)$ on $[a, c]$ and $f \in R(\alpha)$ on $[c, b]$. If $f \in R(\alpha)$ then

$$\int_a^b f\,d\alpha = \int_a^c f\,d\alpha + \int_c^b f\,d\alpha.$$

The next theorem should be familiar to the reader. It is often referred to as the " partial integration formula " or " integration by parts."

5.25 THEOREM   Suppose that $\alpha : [a, b] \to R$ and $\beta : [a, b] \to R$ are of bounded variation and that $\alpha \in R(\beta)$. Then $\beta \in R(\alpha)$ and

$$\int_a^b \alpha\,d\beta = \alpha(b)\beta(b) - \alpha(a)\beta(a) - \int_a^b \beta\,d\alpha.$$

Proof: Choose $\varepsilon > 0$. There is a partition P of $[a, b]$ such that if Q is any refinement of P, regardless of how Q is marked,

$$\left| S(Q, \alpha, \beta) - \int_a^b \alpha\,d\beta \right| < \varepsilon.$$

Suppose $Q = \{x_0, x_1, \ldots, x_n\}$ is a refinement of P and $t_k \in [x_{k-1}, x_k]$ is chosen for $k = 1, 2, \ldots, n$. Then

$$\tilde{Q} = Q \cup \{t_1, \ldots, t_n\}$$

is a partition of $[a, b]$, which is a refinement of P, Now

$$\alpha(b)\beta(b) - \alpha(a)\beta(a) = \sum_{k=1}^n \alpha(x_k)\beta(x_k) - \sum_{k=1}^n \alpha(x_{k-1})\beta(x_{k-1}),$$

and

$$S(Q, \beta, \alpha) = \sum_{k=1}^n \beta(t_k)[\alpha(x_k) - \alpha(x_{k-1})];$$

hence

$$\alpha(b)\beta(b) - \alpha(a)\beta(a) - S(Q, \beta, \alpha)$$
$$= \sum_{k=1}^n [\alpha(x_k)\beta(x_k) - \alpha(x_{k-1})\beta(x_{k-1})] - \sum \beta(t_k)[\alpha(x_k) - \alpha(x_{k-1})]$$
$$= \sum_{k=1}^n \alpha(x_k)[\beta(x_k) - \beta(t_k)] + \sum_{k=1}^n \alpha(x_{k-1})[\beta(t_k) - \beta(x_{k-1})]$$
$$= S(\tilde{Q}, \alpha, \beta).$$

Thus,

$$\left| S(Q, \beta, \alpha) - \left[\alpha(b)\beta(b) - \alpha(a)\beta(a) - \int_a^b \alpha \, d\beta \right] \right|$$

$$= \left| \int_a^b \alpha \, d\beta - S(\tilde{Q}, \alpha, \beta) \right| < \varepsilon.$$

So by 5.22, $\beta \in R(\alpha)$ and

$$\int_a^b \alpha \, d\beta = \alpha(b)\beta(b) - \alpha(a)\beta(a) - \int_a^b \beta \, d\alpha.$$

Let us consider a problem we have solved before and attack it with integration by parts. Define $g(x) = x^3$ for $0 \le x \le 1$ and $\alpha(x) = 3x^2$ for $0 \le x < \frac{1}{2}$ and $\alpha(x) = 3x^2 + 5$ for $\frac{1}{2} \le x \le 1$. The continuity of g guarantees that $g \in R(\alpha)$ on $[0, 1]$; the problem remains to determine $\int_0^1 g \, d\alpha$. Since both α and g are increasing, both are of bounded variation, and we may apply 5.26. Thus, $\alpha \in R(g)$ and

$$\int_0^1 g \, d\alpha = \alpha(1)g(1) - \alpha(0)g(0) - \int_0^1 \alpha \, dg.$$

Now g is differentiable on $[0, 1]$, and $g' \in R(x)$ since g' is continuous; hence, 5.15 applies, and we have

$$\int_0^1 \alpha \, dg = \int_0^1 \alpha g' \, dx = \int_0^1 3x^2 \alpha \, dx.$$

We shall leave the computation of this integral as an exercise to the reader.

The next two theorems are in a sense analogues of the mean-value theorem for derivatives.

5.26 FIRST MEAN-VALUE THEOREM   If $f : [a, b] \to R$ is continuous and $\alpha : [a, b] \to R$ is increasing, then there is $c \in [a, b]$ such that

$$\int_a^b f \, d\alpha = f(c)[\alpha(b) - \alpha(a)].$$

Proof: Let $m = \inf \{ f(x) : x \in [a, b] \}$ and

$$M = \sup \{ f(x) : x \in [a, b] \}.$$

By 5.9,

$$m[\alpha(b) - \alpha(a)] \leq \int_a^b f \, d\alpha \leq M[\alpha(b) - \alpha(a)];$$

hence there is a real number λ such that $m \leq \lambda \leq M$ and

$$\lambda[\alpha(b) - \alpha(a)] = \int_a^b f \, d\alpha.$$

Now f is continuous on $[a, b]$, and hence by 3.12, there is $c \in [a, b]$ such that $f(c) = \lambda$. Therefore,

$$f(c)[\alpha(b) - \alpha(a)] = \int_a^b f \, d\alpha.$$

5.27 SECOND MEAN-VALUE THEOREM   Suppose

$$f : [a, b] \to R$$

is increasing and $\alpha : [a, b] \to R$ is continuous and of bounded variation on $[a, b]$. Then there is $c \in [a, b]$ such that

$$\int_a^b f \, d\alpha = f(a)[\alpha(c) - \alpha(a)] + f(b)[\alpha(b) - \alpha(c)].$$

Proof: Theorem 5.20 and the continuity of α guarantees that v_α and $v_\alpha - \alpha$ are continuous; hence, by 5.3,

$$f \in R(v_\alpha) \quad \text{and} \quad f \in R(v_\alpha - \alpha).$$

Therefore, $f \in R(\alpha)$. By 5.26, $\alpha \in R(f)$ and

$$\int_a^b f \, d\alpha = f(b)\alpha(b) - f(a)\alpha(a) - \int_a^b \alpha \, df.$$

We may now apply the first mean-value theorem to $\int_a^b \alpha \, df$ to conclude that there is $c \in [a, b]$ such that

$$\alpha(c)[f(b) - f(a)] = \int_a^b \alpha \, df.$$

Thus, we have

$$\int_a^b f \, d\alpha = f(b)\alpha(b) - f(a)\alpha(a) - \alpha(c)[f(b) - f(a)]$$

$$= f(b)[\alpha(b) - \alpha(c)] + f(a)[\alpha(c) - \alpha(a)].$$

The next theorem is stated in slightly different form than usual. After stating the theorem and giving the proof, we shall justify this deviation from the standard.

5.28 CHANGE OF VARIABLES THEOREM   Suppose

$$\phi : [a, b] \to R$$

is increasing and 1–1 and that

$$\phi([a, b]) = [\phi(a), \phi(b)].$$

Let $f : [a, b] \to R$ be bounded. Then $f \in R(x)$ on $[a, b]$ iff

$$f \circ \phi^{-1} \in R(\phi^{-1})$$

on $[\phi(a), \phi(b)]$, and

$$\int_a^b f(x)\, dx = \int_{\phi(a)}^{\phi(b)} f \circ \phi^{-1}\, d\phi^{-1}.$$

Proof: First of all, note that $\phi^{-1} : [\phi(a), \phi(b)] \to [a, b]$ is increasing, is 1–1, and

$$\phi^{-1}([\phi(a), \phi(b)]) = [a, b].$$

Suppose $f \in R(x)$ on $[a, b]$. Choose $\varepsilon > 0$. There is a partition P of $[a, b]$ such that for any refinement Q of P, regardless of how marked,

$$\left| S(Q, f) - \int_a^b f(x)\, dx \right| < \varepsilon.$$

If $P = \{x_0, x_1, \ldots, x_n\}$, then $\tilde{P} = \{\phi(x_0), \phi(x_1), \ldots, \phi(x_n)\}$ is a partition of $[\phi(a), \phi(b)]$, since ϕ is increasing and 1–1, and $\phi([a, b]) = [\phi(a), \phi(b)]$. Let $\tilde{Q} = \{z_0, z_1, \ldots, z_m\}$ be any refinement of $\tilde{P}$, and choose $w_i \in [z_{i-1}, z_i]$ for $i = 1, \ldots, m$. Then

$$Q = \{\phi^{-1}(z_0), \ldots, \phi^{-1}(z_m)\}$$

is a refinement of P, and

$$\phi^{-1}(w_i) \in [\phi^{-1}(z_{i-1}), \phi^{-1}(z_i)].$$

Thus, we have

$$\left| S(\tilde{Q}, f \circ \phi^{-1}, \phi^{-1}) - \int_a^b f(x)\,dx \right|$$

$$= \left| \sum_{i=1}^m (f \circ \phi^{-1})(w_i)(\phi^{-1}(z_i) - \phi^{-1}(z_{i-1})) - \int_a^b f(x)\,dx \right|$$

$$= \left| \sum_{i=1}^m f(\phi^{-1}(w_i))(\phi^{-1}(z_i) - \phi^{-1}(z_{i-1})) - \int_a^b f(x)\,dx \right|$$

$$= \left| S(Q, f) - \int_a^b f(x)\,dx \right| < \varepsilon.$$

Thus, $f \circ \phi^{-1} \in R(\phi^{-1})$ on $[\phi(a), \phi(b)]$, and

$$\int_a^b f(x)\,dx = \int_{\phi(a)}^{\phi(b)} f \circ \phi^{-1}\,d\phi^{-1}.$$

Suppose now that $f \circ \phi^{-1} \in R(\phi^{-1})$ on $[\phi(a), \phi(b)]$. Choose $\varepsilon > 0$. There is a partition $\tilde{P}$ of $[\phi(a), \phi(b)]$ such that if $\tilde{Q}$ is any refinement of $\tilde{P}$, regardless of how marked,

$$\left| S(\tilde{Q}, f \circ \phi^{-1}, \phi^{-1}) - \int_{\phi(a)}^{\phi(b)} f \circ \phi^{-1}\,d\phi^{-1} \right| < \varepsilon.$$

If $\tilde{P} = \{y_0, y_1, \ldots, y_n\}$, then $P = \{\phi^{-1}(y_0), \ldots, \phi^{-1}(y_n)\}$ is a partition of $[a, b]$, by an argument already presented. Let Q be any refinement of P, $Q = \{u_0, u_1, \ldots, u_m\}$, and suppose $s_i \in [u_{i-1}, u_i]$ is chosen for $i = 1, \ldots, m$. Then $\tilde{Q} = \{\phi(u_0), \ldots, \phi(u_m)\}$ is a refinement of $\tilde{P}$ and

$$\phi(s_i) \in [\phi(u_{i-1}), \phi(u_i)].$$

Thus, we have

$$\left| S(Q, f) - \int_{\phi(a)}^{\phi(b)} f \circ \phi^{-1}\,d\phi^{-1} \right|$$

$$= \left| \sum_{i=1}^n f(s_i)(u_i - u_{i-1}) - \int_{\phi(a)}^{\phi(b)} f \circ \phi^{-1}\,d\phi^{-1} \right|$$

$$= \left| \sum_{i=1}^n (f \circ \phi^{-1})(\phi(s_i))(\phi^{-1}(\phi(u_i)) - \phi^{-1}(\phi(u_{i-1}))) \right.$$

$$\left. - \int_{\phi(a)}^{\phi(b)} f \circ \phi^{-1}\,d\phi^{-1} \right|$$

$$= \left| S(\tilde{Q}, f \circ \phi^{-1}, \phi^{-1}) - \int_{\phi(a)}^{\phi(b)} f \circ \phi^{-1}\,d\phi^{-1} \right| < \varepsilon.$$

Thus, $f \in R(x)$ on $[a, b]$, and

$$\int_a^b f(x)\,dx = \int_{\phi(a)}^{\phi(b)} f \circ \phi^{-1}\,d\phi^{-1}.$$

Normally, the function ϕ is assumed to be 1–1, increasing, and continuous. It is clear from the proof that the key fact is that there is a 1–1 correspondence $P \leftrightarrow \tilde{P}$ between partitions $P = \{x_0, x_1, \ldots, x_n\}$ of $[a, b]$ and $\tilde{P} = \{\phi(x_0), \ldots, \phi(x_n)\}$ of $[\phi(a), \phi(b)]$. One need not assume that ϕ is 1–1, increasing, and continuous—merely that ϕ is 1–1, increasing, and that $\phi([a, b]) = [\phi(a), \phi(b)]$, as we assumed in Theorem 5.28. However, we should point out that the hypotheses given imply that ϕ is continuous so that we have not proved a stronger theorem than the one usually presented, but just a different version of that theorem.

EXERCISES

1. Suppose $f : [a, b] \rightarrow R$ is bounded and that $f \in R(\alpha)$ for every increasing function $\alpha : [a, b] \rightarrow R$. Prove that f is continuous.

2. Assuming that $f : [a, b] \rightarrow R$ is continuous and $f(x) \geq 0$ for all $x \in [a, b]$, prove that $\int_a^b f(x)\, dx = 0$ implies that $f(x) = 0$ for all $x \in [a, b]$.

3. Prove 5.7.

4. Suppose $g : [a, b] \rightarrow R$ is continuous except at $x_1, \ldots, x_n \in [a, b]$. Prove that $g \in R(x)$ on $[a, b]$.

5. Let $f : R \rightarrow R$ be continuous and $\delta > 0$. Define
$$g(t) = \int_{t-\delta}^{t+\delta} f(x)\, dx$$
for all $t \in R$. Prove that g is differentiable and compute g'.

6. Assume $f : [a, b] \rightarrow R$ is continuous, $f(x) \geq 0$ for all $x \in [a, b]$, and $M = \sup\{f(x) : x \in [a, b]\}$. Show that
$$\left\{ \left[\int_a^b [f(x)]^n\, dx \right]^{1/n} \right\}_{n=1}^{\infty}$$
converges to M.

7. Define $h(x) = x^2$ for $0 \leq x < 1$ and $h(x) = x^3 + 1$ for $1 \leq x \leq 2$. Define $g(x) = x^2 - 2x$ for $0 \leq x \leq 2$. Compute $\int_0^2 g\, dh$.

8. Suppose f is continuous on $[0, 1]$. Define $g_n(x) = f(x^n)$ for $n = 1, 2, \ldots$. Prove $\left\{ \int_0^1 g_n(x)\, dx \right\}_{n=1}^{\infty}$ converges to $f(0)$.

9. Let
$$g(x) = \begin{cases} -x, & 0 \leq x < 1 \\ 3, & x = 1 \\ 1 + x, & 1 < x \leq 2 \end{cases} \quad \text{and} \quad h(x) = x^2 - 2x.$$
(a) Compute $V(g; 0, 2)$.   (b) Compute $\int_0^2 h(x)\, dg(x)$.

10. Suppose $\phi : [a, b] \rightarrow R$ is 1–1, is increasing, and is such that $\phi([a, b]) = [\phi(a), \phi(b)]$. Prove that ϕ is continuous.

11. Give an example of two functions α and β of bounded variation such that $v_\alpha + v_\beta \neq v_{\alpha+\beta}$.

12. Give an example of a function α of bounded variation such that at some point α is not differentiable but v_α is differentiable at that point.

13. Consider the function $f : [0,1] \to R$ such that $f(x) = 0$ if x is irrational and $f(x) = 1/q$ if $x = p/q$ where p and q are relatively prime positive integers. Define $f(0) = 1$. Is f of bounded variation on $[0,1]$? What is the result if $f(p/q) = 1/q^2$? (Hint: Review a few facts about infinite series before considering this problem.)

14. Suppose $f : R \to R$ is continuous and has period p, so that $f(x + p) = f(x)$ for all $x \in R$. Show that $\int_x^{x+p} f(t)\, dt$ is independent of x, in that for all x, y,

$$\int_x^{x+p} f(t)\, dt = \int_y^{y+p} f(t)\, dt.$$

Show, then, that $\int_0^p [f(x + a) - f(x)]\, dx = 0$ for any real number a. Conclude that for any real number a, there is x such that $f(x + a) = f(x)$.

15. Prove that if $f \in R(x)$ on $[0,1]$ and $a_n = 1/n \sum_{k=1}^n f(k/n)$ for $n = 1, 2, \ldots$, then $\{a_n\}_{n=1}^\infty$ converges to $\int_0^1 f(t)\, dt$.

16. Define $\gamma_n = 1 + \frac{1}{2} + \frac{1}{3} + \cdots + 1/n - \int_1^n dt/t$. Prove that $\{\gamma_n\}_{n=1}^\infty$ converges.

17. A set $A \subseteq [0,1]$ is dense in $[0,1]$ iff every open interval which intersects $[0,1]$ contains a point of A. Suppose $f : [0,1] \to R$ is integrable and $f(x) = 0$ for all $x \in A$ with A dense in $[0,1]$. Prove that $\int_0^1 f(x)\, dx = 0$.

18. Use 5.28 to show that

$$\int_1^{xy} \frac{dt}{t} = \int_1^y \frac{dt}{t} + \int_1^x \frac{dt}{t}$$

for all $x, y > 0$.

19. Prove the following variation on 5.28: Suppose $f : [a, b] \to R$ is continuous and $g : [c, d] \to [a, b]$ is differentiable with g' continuous. Assume $g(c) = a$, $g(d) = b$. Prove that

$$\int_a^b f(t)\, dt = \int_c^d f(g(t))g'(t)\, dt.$$

(Hint: Set

$$F(x) = \int_a^x f(t)\, dt \text{ and } G(x) = \int_c^x f(g(t))g'(t)\, dt,$$

and prove that $G = F \circ g$.)

20. Assume $g \in R(x)$ on $[a, b]$ and define $f(x) = \int_a^x g(t)\, dt$ for all $x \in [a, b]$. Show that $v_f(x) = \int_a^x |g(t)|\, dt$ for all $x \in [a, b]$.

CHAPTER 6

INFINITE SERIES

The majority of students of mathematics who have completed calculus feel competent in the techniques of differentiation and integration, though they may panic at the mere mention of infinite series. However, the notions of convergence and divergence of infinite series are actually quite easy to assimilate if properly presented. Since the question of convergence of an infinite series depends upon the convergence of a certain sequence, a brief review of sequences, in Chapter 1, may help prepare the reader for what is to come.

Finite sums of real numbers are familiar objects; our purpose in this chapter is to determine when we should assign a real number to a string of symbols such as $a_1 + a_2 + a_3 + \cdots$. The approach is the usual one—that of looking at the partial sums of this "infinite sum."

> **DEFINITION** An *infinite series* is a pair $(\{a_n\}_{n=1}^{\infty}, \{S_n\}_{n=1}^{\infty})$ where $\{a_n\}_{n=1}^{\infty}$ is a sequence of real numbers, and for $n = 1, 2, \ldots, S_n = \sum_{k=1}^{n} a_k$.

In keeping with more customary notation, we may denote the infinite series $(\{a_n\}_{n=1}^{\infty}, \{S_n\}_{n=1}^{\infty})$ by $\sum_{n=1}^{\infty} a_n$ or by $a_1 + a_2 + \cdots + a_n + \cdots$. The number a_n is called the *nth term* of the series, and S_n is called the *nth partial sum* of the series. It is often convenient to index the terms of an infinite series beginning with an integer other than 1. As our discussion unfolds, it will be clear that questions of convergence are independent of whether we index the terms beginning with $n = 1$ or $n = p$ for some other integer p.

The infinite series $(\{a_n\}_{n=1}^{\infty}, \{S_n\}_{n=1}^{\infty})$ *converges* if the sequence $\{S_n\}_{n=1}^{\infty}$ converges. If $\{S_n\}_{n=1}^{\infty}$ converges to S, we write

$$\sum_{n=1}^{\infty} a_n = S;$$

the number S is called the *sum* of the infinite series $\sum_{n=1}^{\infty} a_n$. Perhaps we should apologize for using $\sum_{n=1}^{\infty} a_n$ as a name for the infinite series and also as a name for the real number that is the limit of the sequence $\{S_n\}_{n=1}^{\infty}$. However, this abuse conforms to convention, which we do not defend but merely bow to. If the sequence $\{S_n\}_{n=1}^{\infty}$ does not converge, we say that the infinite series $\sum_{n=1}^{\infty} a_n$ *diverges*; note that in this case, we do not use $\sum_{n=1}^{\infty} a_n$ to denote a real number.

Let us first consider an infinite series $\sum_{n=1}^{\infty} a_n$ where $a_n = 0$ for $n \geq N + 1$. Then for $n \geq N, S_n = S_N$, hence $\{S_n\}_{n=1}^{\infty}$ converges to $S_N = a_1 + a_2 + \cdots + a_N$. In this case, the infinite series is in reality a finite sum, a fact that should certainly be no surprise to the reader. Suppose now that $a_n > 0$ for all n; then $\{S_n\}_{n=1}^{\infty}$ is increasing. Hence, in order for $\sum_{n=1}^{\infty} a_n$ to converge, it is necessary that $\{S_n\}_{n=1}^{\infty}$ be bounded. Now $S_{n+1} = S_n + a_n$ for each n, so for $\{S_n\}_{n=1}^{\infty}$ to be bounded, it is necessary that the terms a_n get small "fast enough" as n gets large. To illustrate what we mean by "fast enough," we shall consider several examples.

Consider the infinite series $\sum_{n=1}^{\infty} \log(1 + 1/n)$. (We shall assume the usual properties of the function $\log x$.) Now

$$S_n = \log 2 + \log \frac{3}{2} + \log \frac{4}{3} + \cdots + \log \frac{n+1}{n} = \log(n+1).$$

The sequence $\{S_n\}_{n=1}^{\infty}$ is unbounded and, hence, not convergent. Note that $\{(n+1)/n\}_{n=1}^{\infty}$ converges to 1, so by the continuity of the log function,

$$\left\{ \log \frac{n+1}{n} \right\}_{n=1}^{\infty}$$

converges to $\log 1 = 0$. In this case, the nth term of the series gets small as n gets large, but not "fast enough." Consider now the infinite series $\sum_{n=1}^{\infty} 1/(n(n+1))$. For each n,

$$S_n = \frac{1}{2} + \frac{1}{2 \cdot 3} + \frac{1}{3 \cdot 4} + \cdots + \frac{1}{n(n+1)} = 1 - \frac{1}{n+1}$$

since for all k,

$$\frac{1}{k(k+1)} = \frac{1}{k} - \frac{1}{k+1}.$$

Clearly $\{S_n\}_{n=1}^{\infty}$ converges to 1, and we write

$$\sum_{n=1}^{\infty} \frac{1}{n(n+1)} = 1.$$

In this case, the nth term of the sequence tends to zero "fast enough." Unfortunately, there are no simple criteria for determining whether or not a series $\sum_{n=1}^{\infty} a_n$ converges merely by considering the nth term of the series. In this chapter, we present some of standard methods of determining convergence of infinite series.

Suppose now that $\sum_{n=1}^{\infty} a_n$ is convergent, which means that $\{S_n\}_{n=1}^{\infty}$ is convergent. By our previous discussion of sequences, $\{S_n\}_{n=1}^{\infty}$ is convergent iff it is Cauchy.

6.1 THEOREM The infinite series $\sum_{n=1}^{\infty} a_n$ converges iff for each $\varepsilon > 0$, there is N such that if $n \geq N$ and $p \geq 0$, then

$$|a_n + a_{n+1} + \cdots + a_{n+p}| < \varepsilon.$$

Proof: Suppose $\sum_{n=1}^{\infty} a_n$ converges. Then the sequence $\{S_n\}_{n=1}^{\infty}$ converges and, hence, is Cauchy. Choose $\varepsilon > 0$. There is N such that $m, n \geq N$ implies that $|S_m - S_n| < \varepsilon$. Now if $n \geq N + 1$ and $p \geq 0$, then $n - 1 \geq N$ and $n + p \geq N$; hence,

$$|a_n + a_{n+1} + \cdots + a_{n+p}| = |S_{n+p} - S_{n-1}| < \varepsilon.$$

Assume the condition holds, and choose $\varepsilon > 0$. There is N such that for $n \geq N$ and $p \geq 0$, $|a_n + a_{n+1} + \cdots + a_{n+p}| < \varepsilon$. Choose $r \geq n \geq N$. Then

$$|S_r - S_n| = |a_{n+1} + \cdots + a_r| < \varepsilon.$$

Hence, $\{S_n\}_{n=1}^{\infty}$ is Cauchy and the series converges.

Let us pause to ponder the content of 6.1. First of all, the convergence or divergence of an infinite series is independent of whether we index the terms beginning with $n = 1$ or with $n = p$ for some other integer p. Secondly, the convergence is unaffected by changing finitely many terms of the series, although if the series converges, the limit of the partial sums may be altered. Now if $\sum_{n=1}^{\infty} a_n$ converges and k is a positive integer, then $\sum_{n=k}^{\infty} a_n$ converges; in fact, given $\varepsilon > 0$, there is N such that

$$|a_N + a_{N+1} + \cdots + a_{N+p}| < \varepsilon$$

for all $p \geq 0$, but

$$a_N + a_{N+1} + \cdots + a_m = T_m$$

is the mth partial sum for the convergent infinite series $\sum_{n=N}^{\infty} a_n$; hence, $\left|\sum_{n=N}^{\infty} a_n\right| \leq \varepsilon$.

6.2 COROLLARY If $\sum_{n=1}^{\infty} a_n$ converges, then $\{a_n\}_{n=1}^{\infty}$ converges to zero.

Proof: Choose $\varepsilon > 0$. By 6.1, there is N such that, for $n \geq N$ and $p \geq 0$, we have $|a_n + a_{n+1} + \cdots + a_{n+p}| < \varepsilon$. In particular, for $p = 0$, $|a_n| < \varepsilon$. Hence, $\{a_n\}_{n=1}^{\infty}$ converges to zero.

It is with mixed emotions that we present 6.2. This result is very useful, since it allows one to observe quite easily that certain series diverge —namely. those series $\sum_{n=1}^{\infty} a_n$ where $\{a_n\}_{n=1}^{\infty}$ does not converge to zero. Unfortunately, this result is frequently misused, for many students assume that the converse is true—namely, that if $\{a_n\}_{n=1}^{\infty}$ converges to zero, then $\sum_{n=1}^{\infty} a_n$ converges. This converse is definitely false, as we have already seen by considering

$$\sum_{n=1}^{\infty} \log\left(\frac{n+1}{n}\right).$$

Here

$$\left\{\log\left(\frac{n+1}{n}\right)\right\}_{n=1}^{\infty}$$

converges to zero, but the series

$$\sum_{n=1}^{\infty} \log\left(\frac{n+1}{n}\right)$$

diverges. To emphasize this fact, we present the following example, which will also be of use later.

Consider the infinite series $\sum_{n=1}^{\infty} 1/n$, often referred to as the *harmonic series*. Since $1/n > 0$ for each n, the sequence $\{S_n\}_{n=1}^{\infty}$ is increasing, and we shall show it is unbounded. If $n = 2^k$, then

$$S_n = 1 + \frac{1}{2} + \frac{1}{3} + \cdots + \frac{1}{2^k}$$

$$= 1 + \frac{1}{2} + \left(\frac{1}{3} + \frac{1}{4}\right) + \left(\frac{1}{5} + \frac{1}{6} + \frac{1}{7} + \frac{1}{8}\right) + \cdots + \left(\frac{1}{2^{k-1}+1} + \cdots + \frac{1}{2^k}\right)$$

$$\geq 1 + \frac{1}{2} + 2\left(\frac{1}{4}\right) + 4\left(\frac{1}{8}\right) + \cdots + 2^{k-1}\left(\frac{1}{2^k}\right) = 1 + \frac{k}{2}.$$

Thus, $\{S_n\}_{n=1}^{\infty}$ is unbounded, so $\sum_{n=1}^{\infty} 1/n$ is divergent.

In the study of infinite series, it is useful to have a great many examples at hand. Such examples help to develop the intuition and, as will be seen later, may sometimes be used in testing infinite series for convergence. Before continuing further, we shall present one more classic example. The infinite series $\sum_{n=0}^{\infty} r^n$ is called the *geometric series* with ratio r. For $n \geq 0$,

$$S_n = 1 + r + r^2 + \cdots + r^n = \frac{1 - r^{n+1}}{1 - r}$$

for all $r \neq 1$. Now $\{r^{n+1}\}_{n=1}^{\infty}$ converges iff $-1 < r \leq 1$; and if $|r| < 1$, $\{r^{n+1}\}_{n=1}^{\infty}$ converges to 0. For $r = 1$, $S_n = 1 + 1 + \cdots + 1 = n + 1$; hence, $\{S_n\}_{n=1}^{\infty}$ is not convergent. To summarize, $\sum_{n=0}^{\infty} r^n$ converges to $1/(1 - r)$ for $|r| < 1$ and diverges for $|r| \geq 1$.

So far, in most of the examples we have considered, the terms of the infinite series were non-negative. Let us consider now the infinite series

$$\sum_{n=1}^{\infty} (-1)^n \frac{1}{n}.$$

Shortly it will be shown that this series converges; in fact, this will follow from the alternating series test, which the reader may recall from elementary calculus. It has been remarked earlier that if $a_n \geq 0$ for all n, the infinite series $\sum_{n=1}^{\infty} a_n$ converges if the nth terms tend to zero "fast enough." Now $\sum_{n=1}^{\infty} 1/n$ is divergent; hence $\{1/n\}_{n=1}^{\infty}$ does not converge to zero "fast enough." However, $\sum_{n=1}^{\infty} (-1)^n 1/n$ does converge, so it is clear that the convergence depends somehow on the fact that the terms alternate in sign. We shall now give a definition which we shall use to investigate this behavior further.

DEFINITION   An infinite series $\sum_{n=1}^{\infty} a_n$ *converges absolutely* iff $\sum_{n=1}^{\infty} |a_n|$ converges. If $\sum_{n=1}^{\infty} a_n$ converges but $\sum_{n=1}^{\infty} |a_n|$ diverges, then $\sum_{n=1}^{\infty} a_n$ is said to *converge conditionally*.

Thus, $\sum_{n=1}^{\infty} (-1)^n 1/n$ converges conditionally. The series

$$\sum_{n=1}^{\infty} (-1)^n \frac{1}{n(n + 1)}$$

converges absolutely since we have already demonstrated that

$$\sum_{n=1}^{\infty} \frac{1}{n(n + 1)}$$

converges. It is automatic that every absolutely convergent infinite series is convergent.

6.3 THEOREM Suppose $\sum_{n=1}^{\infty} a_n$ is absolutely convergent. Then $\sum_{n=1}^{\infty} a_n$ is convergent.

Proof: Choose $\varepsilon > 0$. Now since $\sum_{n=1}^{\infty} a_n$ is absolutely convergent, $\sum_{n=1}^{\infty} |a_n|$ converges. Thus, there is N such that $n \geq N$ and $p \geq 0$ implies that

$$||a_n| + \cdots + |a_{n+p}|| < \varepsilon.$$

But $|a_n + a_{n+1} + \cdots + a_{n+p}| \leq |a_n| + \cdots + |a_{n+p}| < \varepsilon$; hence by 6.1, $\sum_{n=1}^{\infty} a_n$ converges.

Some of the distinctions between absolute convergence and conditional convergence shall be brought out as our tale unfolds.

At the risk of being repetitious, we remind the reader again that an infinite series $\sum_{n=1}^{\infty} a_n$ of non-negative terms converges if the terms get small "fast enough." Thus, the infinite series $\sum_{n=1}^{\infty} a_n$ converges absolutely if the sequence $\{|a_n|\}_{n=1}^{\infty}$ converges to zero "fast enough." This notion of "fast enough" is quite vague, and we shall do our best to make this notion more meaningful to the reader. To this end, consider two infinite series $\sum_{n=1}^{\infty} a_n$ and $\sum_{n=1}^{\infty} b_n$, where $a_n \geq 0$ and $b_n \geq 0$ for all n. If $\sum_{n=1}^{\infty} b_n$ converges, then the sequence $\{b_n\}_{n=1}^{\infty}$ converges to zero "fast enough." Suppose now that there is N such that for $n \geq N, 0 \leq a_n \leq b_n$. Then it seems plausible to conjecture that $\{a_n\}_{n=1}^{\infty}$ converges to zero as fast as $\{b_n\}_{n=1}^{\infty}$, which is "fast enough." These remarks yield the basis for Theorem 6.4, the "comparison test." In other words, we shall try to determine convergence or divergence of a series by comparing it to one whose behavior is already known. Since the comparison must take place between infinite series of non-negative numbers, the comparison test will only yield information concerning absolute convergence. The success of this test is dependent upon the user's stock of examples. Therefore, it is important to begin to build this stock as one studies infinite series. The observant reader will note that the comparison test is indeed the basis for the limit-comparison, ratio, and root tests to be presented later. In the latter two cases, the series to be examined are compared to the geometric series $\sum_{n=0}^{\infty} r^n$.

6.4 THEOREM (Comparison Test) Suppose $\sum_{n=1}^{\infty} a_n$ and $\sum_{n=1}^{\infty} b_n$ are infinite series with $b_n \geq 0$ for all n. Then

(1) If $\sum_{n=1}^{\infty} b_n$ converges and there is N_0 such that $n \geq N_0$ implies $|a_n| \leq b_n$, then $\sum_{n=1}^{\infty} a_n$ converges absolutely.

(2) If $\sum_{n=1}^{\infty} b_n$ diverges and there is N_0 such that $n \geq N_0$ implies $b_n \leq |a_n|$, then $\sum_{n=1}^{\infty} |a_n|$ diverges.

(See Exercise 6 for a generalization of this test.)

Proof: Suppose the hypotheses of (1) hold. Thus, $\sum_{n=1}^{\infty} b_n$ converges and there is N_0 such that $n \geq N_0$ implies $|a_n| \leq b_n$. Since $\sum_{n=1}^{\infty} b_n$ converges, given $\varepsilon > 0$, there is N such that $n \geq N$ and $p \geq 0$ imply that $b_n + b_{n+1} + \cdots + b_{n+p} < \varepsilon$. Let

$$N_1 = \max \{N, N_0\}.$$

Then if $n \geq N_1$ and $p \geq 0$,

$$|a_n| + \cdots + |a_{n+p}| \leq b_n + b_{n+1} + \cdots + b_{n+p} < \varepsilon.$$

Thus, $\sum_{n=1}^{\infty} |a_n|$ converges, and $\sum_{n=1}^{\infty} a_n$ converges absolutely.

The proof of (2) can be obtained most easily by using the result just obtained. If $\sum_{n=1}^{\infty} |a_n|$ converges and there is N_0 such that $n \geq N_0$ implies $|b_n| = b_n \leq |a_n|$, then since $|a_n| \geq 0$, the result of (1) guarantees that $\sum_{n=1}^{\infty} b_n$ converges, contrary to assumption. Thus, (2) holds.

Let us give several examples to illustrate 6.4. Consider the series

$$\sum_{n=1}^{\infty} \frac{1}{(n + 1)^2}.$$

We shall choose to compare this series with the series

$$\sum_{n=1}^{\infty} \frac{1}{n(n + 1)},$$

because this is one of the few examples we know much about and because for all n,

$$\frac{1}{(n + 1)^2} \leq \frac{1}{n(n + 1)}.$$

Hence, by 6.4,

$$\sum_{n=1}^{\infty} \frac{1}{(n+1)^2}$$

converges since

$$\sum_{n=1}^{\infty} \frac{1}{n(n+1)}$$

converges. Note that since $1/(n+1)^2 \geq 0$ for all n, convergence is the same as absolute convergence.

Consider now the infinite series $\sum_{n=1}^{\infty} (-1)^n / \sqrt{n}$. For all $n \geq 1$,

$$\left| \frac{(-1)^n}{\sqrt{n}} \right| = \frac{1}{\sqrt{n}} \geq \frac{1}{n}$$

and $\sum_{n=1}^{\infty} 1/n$ diverges. Hence,

$$\sum_{n=1}^{\infty} \frac{(-1)^n}{\sqrt{n}}$$

does not converge absolutely; but, as we shall see later, it does converge conditionally.

The following theorem is an immediate consequence of the corresponding result for sequences, and the proof is left to the reader.

6.5 THEOREM   Suppose $\sum_{n=1}^{\infty} a_n$ and $\sum_{n=1}^{\infty} b_n$ converge and that α and β are real numbers. Then $\sum_{n=1}^{\infty} (\alpha a_n + \beta b_n)$ converges and

$$\sum_{n=1}^{\infty} (\alpha a_n + \beta b_n) = \alpha \sum_{n=1}^{\infty} a_n + \beta \sum_{n=1}^{\infty} b_n .$$

With 6.4 and 6.5 at our disposal, we can now examine in greater detail the distinction between absolute and conditional convergence. As one might well suspect, if $\sum_{n=1}^{\infty} a_n$ converges conditionally, the sequence $\{|a_n|\}_{n=1}^{\infty}$ does not converge to zero fast enough, but because the terms a_n are not of constant sign, enough cancellation takes place to cause the sequence of partial sums to converge. We seek now to examine this behavior more closely.

DEFINITION   Let $\{a_n\}_{n=1}^{\infty}$ be any sequence of real numbers. For each n, define $a_n^+ = a_n$ if $a_n \geq 0$ and $a_n^+ = 0$ if $a_n < 0$. Define $a_n^- = a_n$ if $a_n < 0$ and $a_n^- = 0$ if $a_n \geq 0$. Thus, if

$$\{a_n\}_{n=1}^{\infty} = \left\{1, -\frac{1}{2}, \frac{1}{3}, -\frac{1}{4}, \frac{1}{5}, -\frac{1}{6}, \ldots\right\},$$

then

$$\{a_n^+\}_{n=1}^{\infty} = \left\{1, 0, \frac{1}{3}, 0, \frac{1}{5}, \ldots\right\}$$

and

$$\{a_n^-\}_{n=1}^{\infty} = \left\{0, -\frac{1}{2}, 0, -\frac{1}{4}, 0, -\frac{1}{6}, \ldots\right\}.$$

In any case, $a_n = a_n^+ + a_n^-$ for all n.

Suppose now that $\sum_{n=1}^{\infty} a_n$ converges absolutely. Then for each n,

$$|a_n^+| \leq |a_n| \quad \text{and} \quad |a_n^-| \leq |a_n|;$$

hence, $\sum_{n=1}^{\infty} a_n^+$ and $\sum_{n=1}^{\infty} a_n^-$ converge absolutely. Conversely, if $\sum_{n=1}^{\infty} a_n^+$ and $\sum_{n=1}^{\infty}(-a_n^-)$ converge (actually, this is absolute convergence since both are series of non-negative terms), then, since $|a_n| = a_n^+ - a_n^-$,

$$\sum_{n=1}^{\infty} |a_n|$$

converges by 6.5. We summarize this in the following theorem.

6.6 THEOREM   The infinite series $\sum_{n=1}^{\infty} a_n$ converges absolutely iff the series $\sum_{n=1}^{\infty} a_n^+$ and $\sum_{n=1}^{\infty} a_n^-$ converge. If $\sum_{n=1}^{\infty} a_n^+$ converges with sum A^+ and $\sum_{n=1}^{\infty} a_n^-$ converges with sum A^-, then the sum of $\sum_{n=1}^{\infty} a_n$ is $A^+ + A^-$, and the sum of $\sum_{n=1}^{\infty} |a_n|$ is $A^+ - A^-$.

Proof: See remarks preceding this theorem.

To recap our results, if a series $\sum_{n=1}^{\infty} a_n$ converges conditionally, then at least one of the two series, $\sum_{n=1}^{\infty} a_n^+$ or $\sum_{n=1}^{\infty} a_n^-$, diverges. Since we may write

$$a_n^+ = a_n - a_n^- \quad \text{and} \quad a_n^- = a_n - a_n^+,$$

we see that if $\sum_{n=1}^{\infty} a_n$ converges conditionally, then both $\sum_{n=1}^{\infty} a_n^{+}$ and $\sum_{n=1}^{\infty} a_n^{-}$ must diverge. Since $a_n^{+} \geq 0$, the partial sums of $\sum_{n=1}^{\infty} a_n^{+}$ form an increasing sequence unbounded from above, and since $a_n^{-} \leq 0$, the partial sums of $\sum_{n=1}^{\infty} a_n^{-}$ must form a decreasing sequence unbounded from below. When we consider rearrangements of series, we shall have recourse to this result. If we denote the nth partial sum of

$$\sum_{n=1}^{\infty} a_n, \qquad \sum_{n=1}^{\infty} a_n^{+}, \quad \text{and} \quad \sum_{n=1}^{\infty} a_n^{-}$$

by S_n, S_n^{+}, and S_n^{-}, respectively, then

$$\{S_n\}_{n=1}^{\infty} = \{S_n^{+} + S_n^{-}\}_{n=1}^{\infty}$$

converges, whereas $\{S_n^{+}\}_{n=1}^{\infty}$ and $\{S_n^{-}\}_{n=1}^{\infty}$ do not. The manner in which the cancellation takes place in the series $\sum_{n=1}^{\infty} a_n$ may be very complicated, and our techniques for recognizing conditionally convergent series will unfortunately be applicable only to certain special types.

The next few results are intended to populate, as painlessly as possible, our stock of examples of convergent infinite series.

6.7 THEOREM Suppose $\{a_n\}_{n=1}^{\infty}$ is a sequence of non-negative terms such that $a_n \geq a_{n+1}$ for all n. Then $\sum_{n=1}^{\infty} a_n$ converges iff $\sum_{k=0}^{\infty} 2^k a_{2^k}$ converges.

Proof: Define

$$S_n = a_1 + a_2 + \cdots + a_n$$

and

$$T_k = a_1 + 2a_2 + 4a_4 + \cdots + 2^k a_{2^k}.$$

S_n is the nth partial sum of $\sum_{n=1}^{\infty} a_n$, and T_k is the kth partial sum of $\sum_{k=0}^{\infty} 2^k a_{2^k}$. Now if $n \leq 2^k$,

$$S_n = a_1 + a_2 + \cdots + a_n$$
$$\leq a_1 + (a_2 + a_3) + (a_4 + a_5 + a_6 + a_7) + \cdots + (a_{2^k} + \cdots + a_{2^{k+1}-1})$$
$$\leq a_1 + 2a_2 + 4a_4 + \cdots + 2^k a_{2^k} = T_k$$

since $a_n \geq a_{n+1}$ for all n.

On the other hand, if $n \geq 2^k$, then

$$S_n = a_1 + a_2 + \cdots + a_n$$

$$\geq a_1 + a_2 + (a_3 + a_4) + \cdots + (a_{2^{k-1}+1} + \cdots + a_{2^k})$$

$$\geq \frac{1}{2}a_1 + a_2 + 2a_4 + \cdots + 2^{k-1}a_{2^k} = \frac{1}{2}T_k,$$

so that $2S_n \geq T_k$.

Now if $\sum_{n=1}^{\infty} a_n$ converges, then the sequence $\{S_n\}_{n=1}^{\infty}$ is increasing and it converges to $S = \sup S_n$. Since $2^k \geq 0$ for all k, it suffices to show that $\{T_k\}_{k=1}^{\infty}$ is bounded in order to prove that $\sum_{k=0}^{\infty} 2^k a_{2^k}$ converges. Choose k. Then there is n such that $n \geq 2^k$; hence $T_k \leq 2S_n \leq 2S$. Thus, $\{T_k\}_{k=1}^{\infty}$ is bounded, and hence $\sum_{k=0}^{\infty} 2^k a_{2^k}$ is convergent.

Suppose now that $\sum_{k=0}^{\infty} 2^k a_{2^k}$ is convergent. Then $\{T_k\}_{k=1}^{\infty}$ converges to $T = \sup T_k$. As before, it suffices to show that $\{S_n\}_{n=1}^{\infty}$ is bounded in order to prove that $\sum_{n=1}^{\infty} a_n$ converges. Choose n. There is k such that $2^k \geq n$. Then $S_n \leq T_k \leq T$. Thus, $\{S_n\}_{n=1}^{\infty}$ is bounded and hence $\sum_{n=1}^{\infty} a_n$ converges.

The infinite series of the form $\sum_{n=1}^{\infty} 1/n^p$, p a real number, are called p-series. Theorem 6.7 allows us to classify these quite easily.

6.8 THEOREM $\sum_{n=1}^{\infty} 1/n^p$ converges iff $p > 1$.

Proof: If $p \leq 0$, then $\{1/n^p\}_{n=1}^{\infty}$ does not converge to zero, so $\sum_{n=1}^{\infty} 1/n^p$ diverges. If $p > 0$, then $1/n^p - 1/(n+1)^p > 0$ for all n, and 6.7 may be utilized. Thus, $\sum_{n=1}^{\infty} 1/n^p$ converges iff

$$\sum_{k=0}^{\infty} \frac{2^k}{(2^k)^p}$$

converges. But

$$\frac{2^k}{(2^k)^p} = (2^{1-p})^k,$$

and the series $\sum_{k=0}^{\infty} (2^{1-p})^k$ is a geometric series which converges iff $2^{1-p} < 1$, or, in other words, iff $p > 1$.

6.9 THEOREM   Let $\sum_{n=1}^{\infty} a_n$ be an infinite series of nonzero terms. Then

(1) if there is a real number q such that $0 < q < 1$ and a positive integer N such that $n \geq N$ implies

$$\left| \frac{a_{n+1}}{a_n} \right| \leq q,$$

then $\sum_{n=1}^{\infty} a_n$ converges absolutely.

(2) If there is N_0 such that $n \geq N_0$ implies

$$\left| \frac{a_{n+1}}{a_n} \right| \geq 1,$$

then $\sum_{n=1}^{\infty} a_n$ diverges.

Proof: Suppose the hypothesis of (1) holds. Then

$$|a_{N+1}| \leq q\,|a_N|,$$

$$|a_{N+2}| \leq q\,|a_{N+1}| \leq q^2 |a_N|, \ldots, |a_{N+r}| \leq q^r |a_N|.$$

Thus, for $n \geq N$, $|a_n| \leq q^n |a_N| q^{-N}$. Since $0 < q < 1$, $\sum_{n=0}^{\infty} q^n$ converges, so by 6.4,

$$\sum_{n=1}^{\infty} |a_N| q^{-N} q^n$$

converges. Thus, by the comparison test, $\sum_{n=1}^{\infty} a_n$ converges absolutely.

Suppose the hypothesis of (2) holds. Since $|a_n| > 0$ for all n and $|a_{n+1}/a_n| \geq 1$ for $n \geq N_0$, we have $|a_n| \leq |a_{n+1}|$ for $n \geq N_0$; hence, $\{a_n\}_{n=1}^{\infty}$ does not converge to zero. Thus, $\sum_{n=1}^{\infty} a_n$ does not converge.

If $\sum_{n=1}^{\infty} a_n$ is an infinite series of nonzero terms such that the sequence $\{|a_{n+1}/a_n|\}_{n=1}^{\infty}$ is convergent, the next theorem follows from 6.9. This is the form in which the "ratio test" usually occurs in calculus books.

6.10 THEOREM   Suppose $\sum_{n=1}^{\infty} a_n$ is an infinite series of nonzero terms such that the sequence $\{|a_{n+1}/a_n|\}_{n=1}^{\infty}$ converges to L. Then,

(1) if $L < 1$, the series converges absolutely;
(2) if $L > 1$, the series diverges;
(3) if $L = 1$, no conclusion concerning convergence can be made.

Proof: Suppose $L < 1$. Then $L < (L + 1)/2 < 1$, and since

$$\left\{ \left| \frac{a_{n+1}}{a_n} \right| \right\}_{n=1}^{\infty}$$

converges to L, then there is N such that $n \geq N$ implies that

$$\left| \frac{a_{n+1}}{a_n} \right| < \frac{L + 1}{2}.$$

Hence, by 6.9, $\sum_{n=1}^{\infty} a_n$ converges absolutely.
If $L > 1$, then there is N such that $n \geq N$ implies

$$\left| \frac{a_{n+1}}{a_n} \right| \geq 1;$$

hence, by 6.9, $\sum_{n=1}^{\infty} a_n$ diverges.

In order to verify that we gain no information when $L = 1$, we shall give an example of a convergent series for which $L = 1$ and a divergent series for which $L = 1$. Consider first the infinite series $\sum_{n=1}^{\infty} 1/n^2$. By 6.8, this series converges and

$$\left\{ \frac{\dfrac{1}{(n + 1)^2}}{\dfrac{1}{n^2}} \right\}_{n=1}^{\infty} = \left\{ \frac{n^2}{(n + 1)^2} \right\}_{n=1}^{\infty}$$

converges to 1. The series $\sum_{n=1}^{\infty} n$ obviously diverges, but again, $\{(n + 1)/n\}_{n=1}^{\infty}$ converges to 1.
Theorem 6.10 fails to give any information if

$$\left\{ \left| \frac{a_{n+1}}{a_n} \right| \right\}_{n=1}^{\infty}$$

fails to converge. In this case, one may have recourse to 6.9, but that may also fail to shed any light on the situation. To illustrate this point, consider the infinite series $\sum_{n=1}^{\infty} a_n$ where $a_n = 1/3^n$ for n odd and $a_n = 1/2^n$ for n even. For n odd,

$$\frac{a_{n+1}}{a_n} = \frac{3^n}{2^n};$$

and for n even,

$$\frac{a_{n+1}}{a_n} = \frac{2^n}{3^n}.$$

Here the sequence $\{a_{n+1}/a_n\}_{n=1}^{\infty}$ has a subsequence which converges to zero and a subsequence which is unbounded, so neither 6.9 nor 6.10 applies. The comparison test may be used to verify that this series converges. The "root test," which comes next, is more conclusive than the ratio test in that if the root test gives no information concerning the convergence of a series, then neither does the ratio test. However, as we shall see by some examples, the root test may be harder to use in some cases. If this were not true, there would be no reason to present the ratio test.

6.11 THEOREM   Suppose $\sum_{n=1}^{\infty} a_n$ is an infinite series. Then
(1) if there is a real number q such that $0 \leq q < 1$ and N such
     that $\sqrt[n]{|a_n|} \leq q$ for $n \geq N$, then $\sum_{n=1}^{\infty} a_n$ converges absolutely;
(2) if for infinitely many n, $\sqrt[n]{|a_n|} \geq 1$, then $\sum_{n=1}^{\infty} a_n$ diverges.

Proof: Suppose there is a real number q such that $0 \leq q < 1$ and a positive integer N such that for $n \geq N$, $\sqrt[n]{|a_n|} \leq q$. Then for $n \geq N$, $|a_n| \leq q^n$. Since $0 < q < 1$, $\sum_{n=1}^{\infty} q^n$ converges; hence, by the comparison test, $\sum_{n=1}^{\infty} a_n$ converges absolutely.

Suppose now that $\sqrt[n]{|a_n|} \geq 1$ for infinitely many n. Then for infinitely many n, $|a_n| \geq 1$, so $\{a_n\}_{n=1}^{\infty}$ does not converge to zero, and $\sum_{n=1}^{\infty} a_n$ does not converge.

Let us now attempt to apply the root test to the earlier example—that is, $\sum_{n=1}^{\infty} a_n$ where $a_n = 1/2^n$ for n even and $a_n = 1/3^n$ for n odd. Now $\sqrt[n]{a_n} = \frac{1}{2}$ for n even and $\sqrt[n]{a_n} = \frac{1}{3}$ for n odd. Thus, for all n, $\sqrt[n]{a_n} \leq \frac{1}{2}$; hence, by 6.11, the series converges absolutely.

Let us pause to consider a few examples to make use of the root and ratio tests.

Consider the series

$$\sum_{n=1}^{\infty} \frac{2^n n!}{n^n}.$$

If we attempt to apply the root test, we are faced with considering the sequence whose nth term is

$$\sqrt[n]{\frac{2^n n!}{n^n}} = \frac{2}{n} \sqrt[n]{n!}.$$

Rather than pursue this task further, let us try the ratio test. Now

$$\frac{a_{n+1}}{a_n} = \frac{2^{n+1}(n+1)!}{(n+1)^{n+1}} \frac{n^n}{2^n n!} = \frac{2}{\left(\dfrac{n+1}{n}\right)^n} = \frac{2}{\left(1 + \dfrac{1}{n}\right)^n}.$$

In Chapter 1, we observed that the sequence

$$\left\{\left(1 + \frac{1}{n}\right)^n\right\}_{n=1}^{\infty}$$

converges with limit $e, 2 < e < 3$. Thus,

$$\left\{\frac{2}{\left(1 + \dfrac{1}{n}\right)^n}\right\}_{n=1}^{\infty}$$

converges with limit $2/e < 1$. Therefore, by the ratio test, this series converges.

Let $\{a_n\}_{n=0}^{\infty}$ be any sequence of real numbers such that $|a_n| \le n$. Consider $-1 < r < 1$ and the infinite series $\sum_{n=0}^{\infty} a_n r^n$. Since little is assumed about the sequence $\{a_n\}_{n=0}^{\infty}$, it seems useless to attempt the ratio test. Let us rather attempt to use the root test. Now

$$\sqrt[n]{|a_n| r^n} = \sqrt[n]{|a_n|} |r|.$$

The sequence $\sqrt[n]{|a_n|}$ may fail to converge, so we appeal to 6.11. For each $n, |a_n| \le n$; hence

$$\sqrt[n]{|a_n|} \le \sqrt[n]{n}.$$

The sequence $\{\sqrt[n]{n}\}_{n=1}^{\infty}$ converges to 1; hence, since $-1 < r < 1$, $\{|r|\sqrt[n]{n}\}_{n=1}^{\infty}$ converges to $|r| < 1$. Let

$$q = \frac{|r| + 1}{2}.$$

Then $|r| < q < 1$, so there is a positive integer N such that $n \geq N$ implies that

$$\sqrt[n]{|a_n|}\,|r| \leq \sqrt[n]{n}\,|r| \leq q.$$

Thus, by 6.11, $\sum_{n=0}^{\infty} a_n r^n$ converges absolutely. If the reader will review the manner of attack, he should observe that we have proved that $\sum_{n=0}^{\infty} nr^n$ converges absolutely for $-1 < r < 1$ and then used the comparison test to show that $\sum_{n=0}^{\infty} a_n r^n$ converges absolutely for $-1 < r < 1$ if $|a_n| \leq n$.

In summary, the root test has wider scope than the ratio test, although in practice, it may be more difficult to use. Neither is subtle with regard to divergence, since one deduces divergence from the fact that $\{a_n\}_{n=1}^{\infty}$ fails to converge to zero. Neither test will serve to identify series which converge conditionally. The next few theorems are of some use in studying such series.

6.12 THEOREM   Suppose $\{a_n\}_{n=0}^{\infty}$ and $\{b_n\}_{n=0}^{\infty}$ are two sequences of real numbers. Define $A_n = \sum_{k=0}^{n} a_k$ for $n \geq 0$ and $A_{-1} = 0$. Then if $0 \leq p \leq q$,

$$\sum_{n=p}^{q} a_n b_n = \sum_{n=p}^{q-1} A_n(b_n - b_{n+1}) + A_q b_q - A_{p-1} b_p.$$

Proof: For $n = 1, 2, \ldots, a_n = A_n - A_{n-1}$, hence

$$\sum_{n=p}^{q} a_n b_n = \sum_{n=p}^{q} (A_n - A_{n-1}) b_n$$
$$= \sum_{n=p}^{q} A_n b_n - \sum_{n=p-1}^{q-1} A_n b_{n+1}$$
$$= \sum_{n=p}^{q-1} A_n(b_n - b_{n+1}) + A_q b_q - A_{p-1} b_p.$$

6.13 THEOREM   Assume $\{a_n\}_{n=0}^{\infty}$ and $\{b_n\}_{n=0}^{\infty}$ are sequences of real numbers such that

   (1)   the partial sums of $\sum_{n=0}^{\infty} a_n$ are bounded;

   (2) $b_0 \geq b_1 \geq b_2 \geq \ldots$;

   (3) $\{b_n\}_{n=0}^{\infty}$ converges to zero.

Then $\sum_{n=1}^{\infty} a_n b_n$ converges.

Proof: As in 6.12, define $A_n = \sum_{k=0}^{n} a_k$ for $n \geq 0$ and $A_{-1} = 0$. By
(1), $\{A_n\}_{n=1}^{\infty}$ is a bounded sequence; hence there is $M > 0$ such that
$|A_n| \leq M$ for all n. Choose $\varepsilon > 0$. Since $\{b_n\}_{n=1}^{\infty}$ converges to zero,
there is N such that $n \geq N$ implies $|b_n| < \varepsilon/2M$. Recall now that
$b_n \geq 0$ for all n and $b_n - b_{n+1} \geq 0$ for all n. Hence, if $N \leq p \leq q$,

$$\left| \sum_{n=p}^{q} a_n b_n \right| = \left| \sum_{n=p}^{q-1} A_n (b_n - b_{n+1}) + A_q b_q - A_{p-1} b_p \right|$$

$$\leq \sum_{n=p}^{q-1} |A_n|(b_n - b_{n+1}) + |A_q| b_q + |A_{p-1}| b_p$$

$$\leq M \left[\sum_{n=p}^{q-1} (b_n - b_{n+1}) + b_q + b_p \right]$$

$$= M2b_p < M \frac{2\varepsilon}{2M} = \varepsilon.$$

Thus, by 6.1, $\sum_{n=0}^{\infty} a_n b_n$ converges.

As an immediate consequence of 6.13, we have the "alternating
series test."

6.14 THEOREM   Suppose $\{b_n\}_{n=0}^{\infty}$ is a sequence of real numbers
such that
   (1) $\{b_n\}_{n=0}^{\infty}$ converges to zero;
   (2) $b_0 \geq b_1 \geq b_2 \geq \ldots$.
Then $\sum_{n=0}^{\infty} (-1)^n b_n$ converges.

Proof: Set $a_n = (-1)^n$ for all n. Then

$$A_n = \sum_{k=0}^{n} a_k = 1$$

if n is even and $A_n = 0$ if n is odd. Thus, $\{A_n\}_{n=0}^{\infty}$ is bounded, and
we may invoke 6.13 to conclude that

$$\sum_{n=0}^{\infty} a_n b_n = \sum_{n=0}^{\infty} (-1)^n b_n$$

converges.

In light of Theorem 6.5, one may be tempted to conclude that
convergent infinite series may be handled in much the same manner as
finite sums. We have postponed the discussion of this problem until now,

because an understanding of the distinction between absolute and conditional convergence helps solve the problems to be considered. We have seen that two convergent series may be added term by term, and the resulting series converges to the sum of the two series. Let us now consider multiplication of two infinite series involving what is called the "Cauchy product," which is motivated by multiplication of finite sums.

> **DEFINITION**   Let $\sum_{n=0}^{\infty} a_n$ and $\sum_{n=0}^{\infty} b_n$ be two infinite series. For each n, define
>
> $$c_n = \sum_{k=0}^{n} a_k b_{n-k}.$$
>
> The infinite series $\sum_{n=0}^{\infty} c_n$ is called the "*Cauchy product*" of the two series $\sum_{n=0}^{\infty} a_n$ and $\sum_{n=0}^{\infty} b_n$.

This definition may perhaps be best motivated as follows. Suppose that

$$p(x) = \sum_{m=0}^{s} a_m x^m \quad \text{and} \quad q(x) = \sum_{m=0}^{r} b_m x^m$$

are polynomials. Define $a_m = 0$ for $m > s$ and $b_m = 0$ for $m > r$. Then the pointwise product pq is a polynomial and

$$
\begin{aligned}
p(x)q(x) &= (a_0 + a_1 x + \cdots + a_s x^s)(b_0 + b_1 x + \cdots + b_r x^r) \\
&= a_0 b_0 + (a_0 b_1 + a_1 b_0)x + \cdots + (a_0 b_n + a_1 b_{n-1} + \cdots + a_n b_0)x^n \\
&\quad + \cdots + a_s b_r x^{s+r} \\
&= c_0 + c_1 x + \cdots + c_n x^n + \cdots + c_{s+r} x^{s+r}
\end{aligned}
$$

where $c_n = \sum_{k=0}^{n} a_k b_{n-k}$. In particular, for $x = 1$,

$$(a_0 + a_1 + \cdots + a_s) \cdot (b_0 + b_1 + \cdots + b_r) = c_0 + c_1 + \cdots + c_{s+r}.$$

The result that one might hope for now is that the Cauchy product of two convergent series is convergent and converges to the product of the sums of the two series. More precisely, if $\sum_{n=1}^{\infty} a_n$ and $\sum_{n=1}^{\infty} b_n$ converge to A and B, respectively, then $\sum_{n=1}^{\infty} c_n$ converges to $A \cdot B$. It turns out that this is false. In the next few paragraphs, we shall explore these questions and prove the main result.

Consider the series

$$\sum_{n=0}^{\infty} \frac{(-1)^n}{\sqrt{n+1}}.$$

By the alternating series test, this series converges. We shall now consider the Cauchy product $\sum_{n=0}^{\infty} c_n$ of this series with itself. Now

$$c_n = (-1)^n \sum_{k=0}^{n} \frac{1}{\sqrt{(n-k+1)(k+1)}}.$$

For $n \geq k$,

$$(n-k+1)(k+1) = \left(\frac{n}{2}+1\right)^2 - \left(\frac{n}{2}-k\right)^2 \leq \left(\frac{n}{2}+1\right)^2;$$

hence,

$$\frac{1}{\sqrt{(n-k+1)(k+1)}} \geq \frac{1}{\frac{n}{2}+1} = \frac{2}{n+2}.$$

Thus,

$$|c_n| \geq \sum_{k=0}^{n} \frac{2}{n+2} = \frac{2(n+1)}{n+2}$$

and $\{c_n\}_{n=0}^{\infty}$ does not converge to zero, and $\sum_{n=0}^{\infty} c_n$ fails to converge. As we shall see by the next theorem, $\sum_{n=0}^{\infty} c_n$ fails to converge because

$$\sum_{n=0}^{\infty} \frac{(-1)^n}{\sqrt{n+1}}$$

converges conditionally.

6.15 THEOREM Suppose $\sum_{n=0}^{\infty} a_n$ converges absolutely and $\sum_{n=0}^{\infty} b_n$ converges with

$$\sum_{n=0}^{\infty} a_n = A \quad \text{and} \quad \sum_{n=0}^{\infty} b_n = B.$$

Define

$$c_n = \sum_{k=0}^{n} a_k b_{n-k}.$$

Then $\sum_{n=0}^{\infty} c_n$ converges to AB.

Proof: Define

$$A_n = \sum_{k=0}^{n} a_k, \qquad B_n = \sum_{k=0}^{n} b_k,$$

$$C_n = \sum_{k=0}^{n} c_k, \quad \text{and} \quad \beta_n = B_n - B.$$

We wish to prove that $\{C_n\}_{n=1}^{\infty}$ converges to AB. Now for each n,

$$C_n = c_0 + c_1 + c_2 + \cdots + c_n$$

$$= a_0 b_0 + (a_0 b_1 + a_1 b_0) + \cdots + (a_0 b_n + a_1 b_{n-1} + \cdots + a_n b_0)$$

$$= a_0 B_n + a_1 B_{n-1} + \cdots + a_n B_0$$

$$= a_0(B + \beta_n) + a_1(B + \beta_{n-1}) + \cdots + a_n(B + \beta_0).$$

Define $\gamma_n = a_0 \beta_n + a_1 \beta_{n-1} + \cdots + a_n \beta_0$. Since $\{A_n\}_{n=0}^{\infty}$ converges to A, the theorem will be proved if we can show that $\{\gamma_n\}_{n=0}^{\infty}$ converges to zero.

Choose $\varepsilon > 0$. Let $K = \sum_{n=0}^{\infty} |a_n|$ and $M = \sup_{n \geq 0} |\beta_n|$. There is N such that $n \geq N$ implies that

$$|\beta_n| = |B_n - B| < \frac{\varepsilon}{2K}$$

and that for $q \geq N$,

$$\sum_{p=N+1}^{q} |a_p| < \frac{\varepsilon}{2M}.$$

Thus, for $n \geq 2N$,

$$|\gamma_n| = |a_0 \beta_n + a_1 \beta_{n-1} + \cdots + a_n \beta_0| \leq \sum_{k=0}^{n} |a_k \beta_{n-k}|$$

$$= \sum_{k=0}^{N} |a_k \beta_{n-k}| + \sum_{k=N+1}^{n} |a_k \beta_{n-k}|$$

$$\leq \frac{\varepsilon}{2K} \sum_{k=0}^{N} |a_k| + M \sum_{k=N+1}^{n} |a_k| < \frac{\varepsilon}{2K} K + M \frac{\varepsilon}{2M} = \varepsilon.$$

A related theorem in which no absolute convergence is assumed is needed to round out the picture. We shall state it without proof.

6.16 THEOREM   Suppose $\sum_{n=0}^{\infty} a_n$ and $\sum_{n=0}^{\infty} b_n$ converge to A and B, respectively. Define

$$c_n = \sum_{k=0}^{n} a_k b_{n-k}.$$

If $\sum_{n=0}^{\infty} c_n$ converges to C, then $C = A \cdot B$.

For finite sums, the order in which the terms are arranged has no effect upon the sum. We shall now concern ourselves with the similar situation for infinite series.

DEFINITION   Let $\sum_{n=0}^{\infty} a_n$ be an infinite series. If T is any 1–1 function from $\{0, 1, 2, \ldots\}$ onto $\{0, 1, 2, \ldots\}$, then the infinite series $\sum_{n=0}^{\infty} a_{T(n)}$ is called a *rearrangement* of $\sum_{n=0}^{\infty} a_n$.

Of course, we are now concerned with questions about the convergence of the rearrangements of a convergent infinite series and what the sums of such rearrangements might be. Our experience up to now leads us to suspect that all is well with absolutely convergent series, so let us look at a conditionally convergent series. Consider the conditionally convergent series

$$\sum_{n=1}^{\infty} (-1)^{n+1} \frac{1}{n}$$

and denote its sum by S. (S happens to be approximately .693; see Exercise 14.)

$$\sum_{n=1}^{\infty} (-1)^{n+1} \frac{1}{2n}$$

then converges to $S/2$. We now consider a new series $\sum_{n=1}^{\infty} a_n$ where $a_n = 0$ if n is odd and

$$a_n = \frac{(-1)^{(n+2)/2}}{n}$$

if n is even. $\sum_{n=1}^{\infty} a_n$ converges to $S/2$, since all we have done is insert a zero into the series $\sum_{n=1}^{\infty} (-1)^{n+1} 1/2n$ between each pair of terms. To see that this is the case, let S_n be the nth partial sum of $\sum_{n=1}^{\infty} (-1)^{n+1} 1/2n$, and let A_n be the nth partial sum of $\sum_{n=1}^{\infty} a_n$. Then $A_1 = 0, A_{2n} = S_n = A_{2n+1}$ for all $n \geq 1$, hence $\{A_n\}_{n=1}^{\infty}$ converges to the same limit as $\{S_n\}_{n=1}^{\infty}$, which is $S/2$. Now adding

$$\sum_{n=1}^{\infty} (-1)^{n+1} \frac{1}{n} \quad \text{and} \quad \sum_{n=1}^{\infty} a_n,$$

we obtain a series which converges to $3S/2$. Deleting the zeros from this resulting series, it is easy to see that it is a rearrangement of $\sum_{n=1}^{\infty} (-1)^{n+1} 1/n$. To clarify this situation, let us write out a few terms of each series in question.

$$\sum_{n=1}^{\infty} (-1)^{n+1} \frac{1}{n} = 1 - \frac{1}{2} + \frac{1}{3} - \frac{1}{4} + \frac{1}{5} - \frac{1}{6} + \frac{1}{7} - \frac{1}{8} + \cdots$$

$$\sum_{n=1}^{\infty} a_n = 0 + \frac{1}{2} + 0 - \frac{1}{4} + 0 + \frac{1}{6} + 0 - \frac{1}{8} + 0 \cdots$$

$$\sum_{n=1}^{\infty} \left[(-1)^{n+1} \frac{1}{n} + a_n \right] = 1 + 0 + \frac{1}{3} - \frac{1}{2} + \frac{1}{5} + 0 + \frac{1}{7} - \frac{1}{4} + \cdots$$

$$= 1 + \frac{1}{3} - \frac{1}{2} + \frac{1}{5} + \frac{1}{7} - \frac{1}{4} + \cdots$$

Thus, we have found a rearrangement of $\sum_{n=1}^{\infty} (-1)^{n+1}/n$ which converges to a different limit. Of course,

$$\sum_{n=1}^{\infty} \frac{(-1)^{n+1}}{n}$$

is only conditionally convergent. Let us now attack the problem for absolutely convergent series. If a series converges absolutely, it is easy to see that any rearrangement will converge absolutely, since all one needs to do to verify convergence for series with non-negative terms is to show that the partial sums are bounded. We seek to solve the more difficult problem of showing that all rearrangements converge to the same limit.

6.17 THEOREM   Let $\sum_{n=1}^{\infty} a_n$ be an absolutely convergent series converging to A and $\sum_{n=1}^{\infty} a_{T(n)}$ any rearrangement of $\sum_{n=1}^{\infty} a_n$. Then

$$\sum_{n=1}^{\infty} a_{T(n)}$$

converges to A.

Proof: For each n, let

$$S_n = \sum_{k=1}^{n} a_k \quad \text{and} \quad S_n^{~1} = \sum_{k=1}^{n} a_{T(k)}.$$

Now $\{S_n\}_{n=1}^{\infty}$ converges to A. We seek to prove that $\{S_k^{~1}\}_{k=1}^{\infty}$ also converges to A. Choose $\varepsilon > 0$. There is N such that for $n \geq N$,

$$|S_n - A| = \left|\sum_{k=n+1}^{\infty} a_k\right| \leq \sum_{k=n+1}^{\infty} |a_k| < \frac{\varepsilon}{2}$$

(since $\sum_{n=1}^{\infty} a_n$ converges absolutely). Now T is a 1–1 function mapping $\{1, 2, \ldots\}$ onto $\{1, 2, \ldots\}$; hence, there is $K \geq N$ such that $\{1, 2, 3, \ldots N\} \subseteq \{T(1), T(2), \ldots, T(K)\}$. Assume $n \geq K$. Then

$$|S_n^{~1} - A| \leq |S_n^{~1} - S_N| + |S_N - A| < \left|\sum_{k=1}^{n} a_{T(k)} - \sum_{k=1}^{N} a_k\right| + \frac{\varepsilon}{2}$$

$$\leq \sum_{k=N+1}^{\infty} |a_k| + \frac{\varepsilon}{2} < \frac{\varepsilon}{2} + \frac{\varepsilon}{2}.$$

Thus, $\{S_n^{~1}\}_{n=1}^{\infty}$ converges to A, and the theorem is proved.

Theorem 6.17 has a converse in the following sense. If $\sum_{n=1}^{\infty} a_n$ has the property that every rearrangement converges to the same sum, then $\sum_{n=1}^{\infty} a_n$ is absolutely convergent. In fact, if a series $\sum_{n=1}^{\infty} a_n$ converges conditionally, then for any real numbers α and β, one may rearrange the terms of the series such that one subsequence of the partial sums of the rearrangement converges to α, and another subsequence of the partial sums converges to β. We shall not prove this theorem here. The proof depends on the facts that $\{a_n\}_{n=1}^{\infty}$ converges to zero and the partial sums of $\sum_{n=1}^{\infty} a_n^{+}$ and $\sum_{n=1}^{\infty} a_n^{-}$ are unbounded.

We are now going to consider a special type of infinite series called *power series*. Since the reader has encountered this topic in the study of calculus, many of our results will not be new. However, armed with a firm grasp of the basic facts about infinite series, we should be prepared to gain a much fuller understanding of the inner workings of power series.

DEFINITION   Let $\{a_n\}_{n=0}^{\infty}$ be a sequence of real numbers. For each real number x, we may consider the infinite series

$$\sum_{n=0}^{\infty} a_n x^n.$$

We shall refer to this collection of infinite series as the *power series* generated by $\{a_n\}_{n=0}^{\infty}$ or, more briefly, as the power series $\sum_{n=0}^{\infty} a_n x^n$.

Given a power series $\sum_{n=0}^{\infty} a_n x^n$, we find that for some values of x, it converges (for $x = 0$, for example), while for some other values of x, it may diverge. Our first considerations will be to find the set of points where a given power series converges and determine the general nature of that set.

Let us consider several familiar examples. We have already seen that $\sum_{n=0}^{\infty} x^n$ converges for $-1 < x < 1$ and diverges elsewhere. On the set $(-1, 1)$,

$$\sum_{n=0}^{\infty} x^n = \frac{1}{1-x}.$$

This is, of course, the power series generated by the sequence $\{a_n\}_{n=0}^{\infty}$, with $a_n = 1$ for all n. The power series $\sum_{n=0}^{\infty} x^n/(n!)$ is also familiar; it converges to e^x for all real x. (We shall prove this later.)

Intuitively, an infinite series will converge if the nth term tends to zero "fast enough." Thus, one is led to suspect that if $\sum_{n=0}^{\infty} a_n x^n$ converges and $|y| < x$, then maybe $\sum_{n=0}^{\infty} a_n y^n$ converges. However, our past experiences with conditionally convergent series should cause us to proceed with caution.

6.18 THEOREM Let $\sum_{n=0}^{\infty} a_n x^n$ be a power series which converges for $x = x_0$ and diverges for $x = x_1$. Then
(1) $\sum_{n=0}^{\infty} a_n x^n$ converges absolutely for $|x| < |x_0|$; and
(2) $\sum_{n=0}^{\infty} a_n x^n$ diverges for $|x| > |x_1|$.

Proof: Assume $\sum_{n=0}^{\infty} a_n x_0{}^n$ converges and $|x| < |x_0|$ with $x_0 \neq 0$. Since $\sum_{n=0}^{\infty} a_n x_0{}^n$ converges, the sequence $\{a_n x_0{}^n\}_{n=0}^{\infty}$ converges to zero, hence is bounded; that is, there is $M \in R$ such that $|a_n x^n| \leq M$ for all n. For all n,

$$|a_n x^n| = |a_n x_0{}^n| \cdot \left| \frac{x}{x_0} \right|^n \leq M \left| \frac{x}{x_0} \right|^n.$$

Since

$$\left|\frac{x}{x_0}\right| < 1,$$

the series

$$\sum_{n=0}^{\infty} M \left|\frac{x}{x_0}\right|^n$$

converges, and hence, by the comparison test, $\sum_{n=0}^{\infty} a_n x^n$ converges absolutely.

If $|x| > |x_1|$ and $\sum_{n=0}^{\infty} a_n x^n$ converges, then by (1), $\sum_{n=0}^{\infty} a_n x_1^n$ converges absolutely, contrary to assumption. Hence, $\sum_{n=0}^{\infty} a_n x^n$ diverges.

Let us summarize these results. Suppose $\sum_{n=0}^{\infty} a_n x^n$ is a power series and let $C = \{x : \sum_{n=0}^{\infty} a_n x^n \text{ converges}\}$. The possibilities for C are listed below:

(i) $C = R$, in which case $\sum_{n=0}^{\infty} a_n x^n$ converges for all $x \in R$.

(ii) $C = \{0\}$, in which case $\sum_{n=0}^{\infty} a_n x^n$ diverges for all $x \neq 0$.

(iii)   There is $r > 0$ such that $(-r, r) \subset C \subset [-r, r]$, in which case $\sum_{n=0}^{\infty} a_n x^n$ converges absolutely for $|x| < r$ and diverges for $|x| > r$.

Cases (i) and (ii) are self-explanatory. We should justify (iii). Suppose $C \neq \{0\}$ and $C \neq R$. Since $C \neq R$, there is $x_1 \in R$ such that $\sum_{n=0}^{\infty} a_n x_1^n$ diverges. Hence, by 6.18, for each $x \in C$, $|x| \leq |x_1|$. Therefore, C is bounded; let $r = \sup C$. If $|x| > r$, then $x \notin C$, so $\sum_{n=0}^{\infty} a_n x^n$ diverges. If $|x| < r$, then there is a member p of C such that $|x| < p \leq r$ since $r = \sup C$. Thus, by 6.19, $\sum_{n=0}^{\infty} a_n x^n$ converges absolutely, since $\sum_{n=0}^{\infty} a_n p^n$ converges. Since $C \neq \{0\}$, there is $x \in C$ such that $x \neq 0$; hence, $r \geq |x| > 0$. Note that we cannot assert what happens at r or at $-r$.

Consider again the power series $\sum_{n=0}^{\infty} x^n/(n!)$. For each n,

$$\frac{x^{n+1}}{(n+1)!} \cdot \frac{n!}{x^n} = \frac{x}{n+1};$$

hence, by the ratio test, this series converges for all x, as stated earlier. Similarly, the ratio test may be used to show that $\sum_{n=0}^{\infty} n! x^n$ converges only for $x = 0$. The geometric series $\sum_{n=0}^{\infty} x^n$ converges for $-1 < x < 1$ and diverges for $|x| \geq 1$. The power series $\sum_{n=0}^{\infty} x^n/n$ converges for $-1 \leq x < 1$ and diverges for both $|x| > 1$ and $x = 1$.

If $\sum_{n=0}^{\infty} a_n x^n$ is a power series, then the set of points at which the series converges is either the set of all real numbers, $\{0\}$, or an interval of positive finite length centered at zero which may contain all, none, or one of its end points. We choose to consider $\{0\}$ as an interval of zero radius and R as an interval of infinite radius. With this convention, we feel free to speak of the *interval of convergence* of a power series. In particular, $\sum_{n=0}^{\infty} a_n x^n$ converges absolutely at any point of its interval of convergence which is not an end point of that interval. In case the interval of convergence is R, the series converges absolutely at each point; and in case $(-r,r) \subset C \subset [-r,r]$, where C is the interval of convergence, then the series converges absolutely at x for $x \in (-r,r)$. As shown by our examples, the behavior at the end points is unpredictable.

If $\sum_{n=0}^{\infty} a_n x^n$ has an interval of convergence C which is different from R and $\{0\}$, then there is a unique real number r such that

$$(-r,r) \subset C \subset [-r,r].$$

This number r is called the *radius of convergence* of the power series. We now seek a way to determine r. Since we have already used the ratio test in one case, let's see what we can deduce from this test.

Suppose $\sum_{n=0}^{\infty} a_n x^n$ is a power series with $a_n \neq 0$ for all n and $x \neq 0$. Consider the ratio

$$\left| \frac{a_{n+1} x^{n+1}}{a_n x^n} \right| = \left| \frac{a_{n+1}}{a_n} \right| \cdot |x|.$$

For the ratio test, we may refer to either 6.9 or 6.10. For the simplest case, let us assume that the sequence

$$\left\{ \left| \frac{a_{n+1}}{a_n} \right| \right\}_{n=1}^{\infty}$$

converges to $L \neq 0$. Then the sequence

$$\left\{ \left| \frac{a_{n+1} x^{n+1}}{a_n x^n} \right| \right\}_{n=1}^{\infty}$$

converges for $x \cdot L$. Hence, $\sum_{n=0}^{\infty} a_n x^n$ converges for $|x| \cdot L < 1$, or for $|x| < 1/L$, and diverges for $|x| \cdot L > 1$, or for $|x| > 1/L$. Thus, the radius of convergence is $1/L$ if $L \neq 0$. If $L = 0$, then $|x| \cdot L = 0 < 1$ for all x, so the series converges for all x. We summarize these results as follows:

6.19 THEOREM   Suppose $\sum_{n=0}^{\infty} a_n x^n$ is a power series with $a_n \neq 0$ for all n such that

$$\left\{ \left| \frac{a_{n+1}}{a_n} \right| \right\}_{n=0}^{\infty}$$

converges to L. Then
(1)   if $L = 0$, the series converges for all x;
(2)   if $L \neq 0$, $1/L$ is the radius of convergence.

Theorem 6.19 has the obvious advantage of being easy to apply when it is applicable. However, when

$$\left\{ \left| \frac{a_{n+1}}{a_n} \right| \right\}_{n=0}^{\infty}$$

fails to converge, 6.19 yields no information. At this point, we still have recourse to 6.9.

6.20 THEOREM   Let $\sum_{n=0}^{\infty} a_n x^n$ be a power series with $a_n \neq 0$ for all n. Then
(1)   if there are real numbers $q \neq 0$ and N such that $n \geq N$ implies that

$$\left| \frac{a_{n+1}}{a_n} \right| \leq q,$$

then $\sum_{n=0}^{\infty} a_n x^n$ converges absolutely for $|x| < 1/q$;
(2)   if there are real numbers $p > 0$ and N such that for all $n \geq N$,

$$\left| \frac{a_{n+1}}{a_n} \right| \geq p,$$

then $\sum_{n=0}^{\infty} a_n x^n$ diverges for $|x| > 1/p$.

Proof: Suppose the condition of (1) holds and $|x| < 1/q$. Then by (1) of 6.9, $\sum_{n=0}^{\infty} a_n x^n$ converges absolutely.
Suppose now the condition of (2) holds and $|x| > 1/p$. Then by (2) of 6.9, $\sum_{n=0}^{\infty} a_n x^n$ diverges.

Theorem 6.20 tells us that the radius of convergence r satisfies $1/q \leq r \leq 1/p$ for all p and q that satisfy the hypotheses of this theorem. If

$$\left\{ \left| \frac{a_{n+1}}{a_n} \right| \right\}_{n=1}^{\infty}$$

converges to $L \neq 0$, then p may be chosen to be any number less than L and q any number greater than L, hence this yields again the fact that $1/L \leq r \leq 1/L$, which means $r = 1/L$.

Theorem 6.20 is an inefficient device for finding the radius of convergence of a power series since it is conclusive only if

$$\left\{ \left| \frac{a_{n+1}}{a_n} \right| \right\}_{n=0}^{\infty}$$

converges, in which case one should apply 6.19. Let us consider the power series $\sum_{n=0}^{\infty} a_n x^n$ where $a_n = 2$ for n odd and $a_n = 3$ for n even. In this case,

$$\frac{a_{n+1}}{a_n} = \frac{2}{3}$$

if n is even, and

$$\frac{a_{n+1}}{a_n} = \frac{3}{2}$$

if n is odd. Thus, 6.20 tells us only that the radius of convergence is less than or equal to $\frac{3}{2}$ and greater than or equal to $\frac{2}{3}$. In this case, it is easy to see that the radius of convergence is equal to 1. If we let $a_n = 2^{-n}$ for n even and $a_n = 3^{-n}$ for n odd, then

$$\frac{a_{n+1}}{a_n} = \left(\frac{2}{3} \right)^n$$

for n even and

$$\frac{a_{n+1}}{a_n} = \left(\frac{3}{2} \right)^n$$

for n odd. For this power series, there are no real numbers q that satisfy (1) of 6.20 and no real numbers p that satisfy (2) of 6.20, so 6.20 is useless. We invite the reader to show that the radius of convergence of this power series is 2.

Perhaps the root test may yield better results, although we suspect it may be more difficult to apply. Let us experiment briefly before we formulate a theorem. If there is a real number q and a positive integer N such that $n \geq N$ implies that $\sqrt[n]{|a_n|} \leq q$, then

$$\sqrt[n]{|a_n x^n|} = \sqrt[n]{|a_n|} \cdot |x| \leq q \cdot |x|;$$

hence, by 6.11, the series $\sum_{n=0}^{\infty} a_n x^n$ converges absolutely for $|x| < 1/q$ if $q \neq 0$ and for all x if $q = 0$. Thus, the radius of convergence r satisfies $r \geq 1/q$ if $q \neq 0$. Since there may be many possible choices for q, we would like to prove a more conclusive theorem. Our concern centers about the possible candidates for q.

Let $\sum_{n=0}^{\infty} a_n x^n$ be a power series, and define $A = \{q:$ there is N such that $n \geq N$ implies that $\sqrt[n]{|a_n|} \leq q\}$. Clearly, zero is a lower bound for A, and, if the sequence $\{\sqrt[n]{|a_n|}\}_{n=1}^{\infty}$ is bounded, then A is not empty. Let us suppose A is nonempty, and define $b = \inf A$. Since the radius of convergence r of the power series $\sum_{n=0}^{\infty} a_n x^n$ satisfies $r \geq 1/q$ for all $q \in A$, then if $b \neq 0$, we might suspect that $r \geq 1/b$, and in fact, we hope $r = 1/b$. To prove this, we need to know some of the properties of b; in fact, this notion might be worth considering in a more general setting.

Suppose $\{b_n\}_{n=1}^{\infty}$ is any bounded sequence of real numbers, and define $A = \{q:$ for some N, $n \geq N$ implies that $b_n \leq q\}$. Since $\{b_n\}_{n=1}^{\infty}$ is bounded, A is nonvoid and also bounded. Let $b = \inf A$. Consider any real numbers x and y such that $x < b < y$. There is $q \in A$ such that $b \leq q < y$ since $b = \inf A$, so there is N such that $n \geq N$ implies $b_n \leq q < y$. Since $x < b, x \notin A$, then for infinitely many $n, b_n > x$. Thus, we have infinitely many members of the sequence greater than x while only finitely many are larger than y. Since x and y are any real numbers satisfying $x < b < y$, we are led to suspect that there is a subsequence of $\{b_n\}_{n=1}^{\infty}$ which converges to b. Moreover, no number larger than b has this property. We are now ready for a theorem.

6.21 THEOREM   Let $\{b_n\}_{n=1}^{\infty}$ be a bounded sequence of real numbers, and define $A = \{p:$ there is a subsequence of $\{b_n\}_{n=1}^{\infty}$ converging to $p\}$ and $B = \{q:$ there is N such that for $n \geq N$, $b_n \leq q\}$. Then the following are equivalent:
   (1) $b = \inf B$.
   (2) $b = \sup A$ and $b \in A$.

(3)   For each $\varepsilon > 0$, there is N such that $n \geq N$ implies that $b_n < b + \varepsilon$ and for each M, there is $m \geq M$ such that $b_m > b - \varepsilon$.

Proof: Assume 1 holds. Choose $\varepsilon > 0$. Then $b + \varepsilon$ is not a lower bound for B and $b - \varepsilon \notin B$ since $b - \varepsilon < b$. Thus, there is $q \in B$ such that $b \leq q < b + \varepsilon$; hence, there is N such that $n \geq N$ implies that $b_n \leq q < b + \varepsilon$. Since $b - \varepsilon$ is not in B, there must be infinitely many terms of the sequence which satisfy $b_n > b - \varepsilon$. Consequently, (1) implies (3).

Assume (3) holds. Then for $\varepsilon_k = 1/k$, with k any positive integer, there is N_k such that $n \geq N_k$ implies

$$b_n < b + \varepsilon_k,$$

and there is $n_k \geq N_k$ such that $b - \varepsilon_k < b_{n_k}$. Thus,

$$|b_{n_k} - b| < \frac{1}{k}$$

for each k, so $\{b_{n_k}\}_{k=1}^{\infty}$ converges to b and $b \in A$. Consider any $x > b$. There is N such that $n \geq N$ implies that

$$b_n < \frac{x + b}{2} < x,$$

so there is a neighborhood of x which contains only finitely many terms of the sequence $\{b_n\}_{n=1}^{\infty}$. This means that no subsequence of $\{b_n\}_{n=1}^{\infty}$ can converge to x, or $x \notin A$. Thus, we have $b \in A$ and for all $x \in A, x \leq b$. We have shown that (3) implies (2).

Assume (2) holds. We have proved that (1) implies (3) and (3) implies (2); to finish the proof, we need only prove that (2) implies (1). Suppose $q \in B$. Then there is N such that $n \geq N$ implies $b_n \leq q$. Since there are but finitely many terms of the sequence $\{b_n\}_{n=1}^{\infty}$ which are larger than q, there can be no subsequence of $\{b_n\}_{n=1}^{\infty}$ converging to any x larger than q. This means that $b \leq q$ since $b \in A$. Therefore, b is a lower bound for B; it remains to be shown that b is the greatest lower bound of B. Suppose $b < a$ and that a is a lower bound for B. Then $(a + b)/2$ does not belong to B, and so we may choose a sequence of positive integers $\{n_k\}_{k=1}^{\infty}$ such that $n_1 < n_2 < \cdots$ and such that $b_{n_k} > (a + b)/2$. Since the sequence $\{b_{n_k}\}_{k=1}^{\infty}$ is bounded, it has a convergent subsequence, and the limit of that subsequence, which we will call L, must be greater than or equal to $(a + b)/2$. This convergent subsequence is also a subsequence of the sequence $\{b_n\}_{n=1}^{\infty}$; hence, $L \in A$. But we had assumed $b = \sup A$ and $b < (a + b)/2 \le L$. Thus, any real number $a > b$ cannot be a lower bound for B. We conclude that $b = \inf B$. Therefore, (2) implies (1).

Let us make a few observations about Theorem 6.21. First of all, the boundedness of $\{b_n\}_{n=1}^{\infty}$ implies that B is nonvoid and bounded, so there is a unique real number b satisfying (1) and hence (2) and (3). Condition (1) is important here in that this description of b was the motivating factor in the investigation of the properties of b. Condition (2) describes b as the largest subsequential limit of the sequence, and the theorem guarantees that there is a largest subsequential limit if the sequence is bounded. Moreover, if $\{b_n\}_{n=1}^{\infty}$ converges, then it converges to b. It seems natural that one might be able to prove a similar theorem concerning $\inf \{p:$ some subsequence of $\{b_n\}_{n=1}^{\infty}$ converges to $p\}$. See the exercises for some interesting challenges along these lines.

DEFINITION   Let $\{b_n\}_{n=1}^{\infty}$ be a sequence of real numbers, and define $B = \{p:$ there is a subsequence of $\{b_n\}_{n=1}^{\infty}$ converging to $p\}$. If B is not void and if B has an upper bound, define

$$\limsup_{n \to \infty} b_n = \sup B.$$

If B is not void and if B has a lower bound, define

$$\liminf_{n \to \infty} b_n = \inf B.$$

Consider the sequence $\{b_n\}_{n=1}^{\infty}$, where $b_n = (-1)^n$. Then

$$\limsup_{n \to \infty} b_n = 1 \quad \text{and} \quad \liminf_{n \to \infty} b_n = -1.$$

If $b_n = n$ for each n, B is void; hence, we define neither $\limsup_{n \to \infty} b_n$ nor $\liminf_{n \to \infty} b_n$. If $b_n = n$ for n even and $b_n = 1 - 1/n$ for n odd, then $\liminf_{n \to \infty} b_n = 1$, whereas $\limsup_{n \to \infty} b_n$ is not defined. We have proved that the set of all rational numbers is countable, so we may arrange the rational numbers in $(0, 1)$ in a sequence $\{r_n\}_{n=1}^{\infty}$. We urge the reader to prove that in this case

$$B = [0, 1], \quad \lim\inf_{n \to \infty} r_n = 0, \quad \text{and} \quad \lim\sup_{n \to \infty} r_n = 1.$$

We now return to the problem that led us to this latest diversion.

6.22 THEOREM   Let $\sum_{n=0}^{\infty} a_n x^n$ be a power series:

(1)   If the sequence $\{\sqrt[n]{|a_n|}\}_{n=0}^{\infty}$ is unbounded, $\sum_{n=0}^{\infty} a_n x^n$ converges only for $x = 0$.

(2)   If the sequence $\{\sqrt[n]{|a_n|}\}_{n=0}^{\infty}$ converges to zero, then $\sum_{n=0}^{\infty} a_n x^n$ converges for all x.

(3)   If the sequence $\{\sqrt[n]{|a_n|}\}_{n=0}^{\infty}$ is bounded and

$$a = \lim\sup_{n \to \infty} \sqrt[n]{|a_n|} \neq 0,$$

then $1/a$ is the radius of convergence.

Proof: (1)   Choose $x \neq 0$. For each N, there is $n \geq N$ such that

$$\sqrt[n]{|a_n|} > \frac{1}{|x|}.$$

Hence, $|a_n x^n| > 1$ for some $n \geq N$. In particular, $\{a_n x^n\}_{n=0}^{\infty}$ does not converge to zero for $x \neq 0$, hence $\sum_{n=0}^{\infty} a_n x^n$ diverges for $x \neq 0$.

(2)   Suppose $\{\sqrt[n]{|a_n|}\}_{n=0}^{\infty}$ converges to zero and $x \neq 0$. Define $\varepsilon = 1/|2x|$. There is N such that $n \geq N$ implies that

$$\sqrt[n]{|a_n|} < \varepsilon = \frac{1}{|2x|}.$$

Thus, for $n \geq N$,

$$|a_n x^n| < \varepsilon^n x^n = \left(\frac{1}{2}\right)^n.$$

Therefore, by the comparison test, $\sum_{n=0}^{\infty} a_n x^n$ converges for all x.

(3)   Suppose that

$$a = \lim\sup_{n \to \infty} \sqrt[n]{|a_n|} \neq 0.$$

Consider any $x \neq 0$ such that $|x| < 1/a$. Then $a < 1/|x|$, and, by 1 of 6.21, there are real numbers q and N such that $a \leq q < 1/x$, and for $n \geq N$, $\sqrt[n]{|a_n|} \leq q < 1/x$. Hence, for $n \geq N$,

$$\sqrt[n]{|a_n x^n|} \leq q |x| < 1.$$

Therefore, by 6.11, $\sum_{n=0}^{\infty} a_n x^n$ converges absolutely. To show that $1/a$ is actually the radius of convergence, we must show that the power series $\sum_{n=0}^{\infty} a_n x^n$ diverges for $|x| > 1/a$. Suppose $|x| > 1/a$. Then $a > 1/|x|$, and hence, by (3) of 6.21, there are infinitely many n such that

$$\sqrt[n]{|a_n|} > \frac{1}{|x|}.$$

So for infinitely many n, $|a_n x^n| > 1$, and hence $\{a_n x^n\}_{n=1}^{\infty}$ does converge to zero. Thus, for $|x| > 1/a$, the series $\sum_{n=0}^{\infty} a_n x^n$ diverges.

We have as an immediate corollary to 6.22, a slightly different statement of 6.11.

6.23 THEOREM   Let $\sum_{n=0}^{\infty} a_n$ be an infinite series. Then
   (1)   if $\{\sqrt[n]{|a_n|}\}_{n=0}^{\infty}$ is unbounded, the series diverges.
   (2)   if $\{\sqrt[n]{|a_n|}\}_{n=0}^{\infty}$ is bounded, then $\sum_{n=0}^{\infty} a_n$ converges absolutely if

$$\limsup_{n \to \infty} \sqrt[n]{|a_n|} < 1$$

   and diverges if

$$\limsup_{n \to \infty} \sqrt[n]{|a_n|} > 1.$$

Proof: The series $\sum_{n=0}^{\infty} a_n$ converges if and only if the power series $\sum_{n=0}^{\infty} a_n x^n$ converges at $x = 1$. The theorem then follows directly from 6.23.

The impatient reader may now wish to go back and restate 6.20 and 6.9 in terms of the new concepts just introduced. He will find it quite instructive.

Let us reconsider an example mentioned earlier. Define $a_n = 2^{-n}$ for n odd and $a_n = 3^{-n}$ for n even. Then

$$\sqrt[n]{|a_n|} = \frac{1}{2}$$

for n odd and

$$\sqrt[n]{|a_n|} = \frac{1}{3}$$

for n even. Hence, $\{\sqrt[n]{|a_n|}\}_{n=1}^{\infty}$ has precisely two subsequential limits, $\frac{1}{2}$ and $\frac{1}{3}$. Since the larger of the two is $\limsup_{n\to\infty} \sqrt[n]{|a_n|}$, the radius of convergence is 2, as claimed earlier.

We now take up a slightly different aspect of power series. Recall that for all n and $-1 < x < 1$,

$$1 + x + x^2 + \cdots + x^n = \frac{1 - x^{n+1}}{1 - x}.$$

Since $\{x^{n+1}\}_{n=1}^{\infty}$ converges to zero for $-1 < x < 1$, the power series $\sum_{n=0}^{\infty} x^n$ converges to $1/(1 - x)$ for $-1 < x < 1$. We shall now inquire what conditions on a function f will guarantee that there is a power series $\sum_{n=0}^{\infty} a_n x^n$ such that for all x in some interval, $\sum_{n=0}^{\infty} a_n x^n$ converges to $f(x)$. Since the point zero is not magic in this discussion, we shall now extend our previous results by a few simple remarks. The function $g(x) = 1/x$ is not well behaved at zero, but we may still write

$$g(x) = \frac{1}{x} = \frac{-1}{1 - (x + 1)} = -\sum_{n=0}^{\infty} (x + 1)^n$$

for $|x + 1| < 1$ or $-2 < x < 0$. By the same sort of device, we may also write

$$g(x) = \frac{\dfrac{1}{5}}{1 - \left[-\dfrac{(x - 5)}{5} \right]} = \sum_{n=0}^{\infty} \frac{(-1)^n}{5^{n+1}} (x - 5)^n$$

for $|(x - 5)/5| < 1$, or for $0 < x < 10$. If a power series $\sum_{n=0}^{\infty} a_n y^n$ converges for $-r < y < r$, then the power series $\sum_{n=0}^{\infty} a_n (x - a)^n$ converges for

$-r < x - a < r$ and, hence, for $a - r < x < a + r$. Thus, the set of points where $\sum_{n=0}^{\infty} a_n(x - a)^n$ converges is either $\{a\}$, the set of all real numbers, or an interval of positive length centered at a. (The same remarks as before hold concerning the end points.)

Suppose $f: [a, b] \rightarrow R$ is differentiable on (a, b) and continuous on $[a, b]$. Then by the mean-value theorem,

$$f(b) = f(a) + f'(c)(b - a)$$

for some $c \in (a, b)$. The next result, Taylor's theorem, is an extension of the mean-value theorem.

6.24 THEOREM (Taylor's theorem).   Suppose that $f: [a, b] \rightarrow R$ is n-times differentiable on $[a, b]$ and that $f^{(n)}$ is continuous on $[a, b]$ and differentiable on (a, b). Assume $x_0 \in [a, b]$. Then for each $x \in [a, b]$ with $x \neq x_0$, there is c between x and x_0 such that

$$f(x) = f(x_0) + \sum_{k=1}^{n} \frac{f^{(k)}(x_0)}{k!} (x - x_0)^k + \frac{f^{(n+1)}(c)}{(n + 1)!} (x - x_0)^{n+1}.$$

Proof: Define

$$F(t) = f(t) + \sum_{k=0}^{n} \frac{f^{(k)}(t)}{k!} (x - t)^k + M(x - t)^{n+1},$$

where M is chosen so that $F(x_0) = f(x)$. This is possible since $x - x_0 \neq 0$. Now F is continuous on $[a, b]$ and differentiable on (a, b), and

$$F(x) = f(x) = F(x_0);$$

hence, by Rolle's theorem, there is c between x and x_0 such that

$$0 = F'(c) = \frac{f^{(n+1)}(c)}{n!} (x - c)^n - (n + 1)M(x - c)^n.$$

Thus,

$$M = \frac{f^{(n+1)}(c)}{(n + 1)!}.$$

Hence,

$$f(x) = F(x_0)$$

$$= f(x_0) + \sum_{k=0}^{n} \frac{f^{(k)}(x_0)}{k!} (x - x_0)^k + \frac{f^{(n+1)}(c)}{(n+1)!} (x - x_0)^{n+1},$$

as the theorem states.

Assume the hypotheses of 6.24 and fix $x_0 \in [a, b]$. Define

$$p(x) = f(x_0) + \sum_{k=0}^{n} \frac{f^{(k)}(x_0)}{k!} (x - x_0)^k.$$

Now p is a polynomial of degree less than or equal to n and Taylor's formula gives us a means of approximating the error when we approximate f by the polynomial p. There are other forms for this remainder $f - p$, and we refer the reader to the exercises for one such example (cf. Exercise 27).

Let us illustrate Taylor's theorem with a rather easy example. We again assume knowledge of the function $f(x) = e^x$. Now f is differentiable everywhere and $f'(x) = e^x = f(x)$. Hence, f has continuous derivatives of all orders; namely $f^{(n)} = f$ for all n. Then for each x and each M, there is c_n between x and 0 such that

$$e^x = f(x) = f(0) + \sum_{k=0}^{n} \frac{f^{(k)}(0)}{k!} x^k + \frac{f^{(n+1)}(c_n)}{(n+1)} x^{n+1}$$

$$= 1 + \sum_{k=1}^{n} \frac{x^k}{k!} + e^{c_n} \frac{x^{n+1}}{(n+1)!}.$$

Since f is increasing, $e^{-|x|} \le e^c \le e^{|x|}$ for all c between x and 0. Thus,

$$\left\{ e^{c_n} \frac{x^{n+1}}{(n+1)!} \right\}_{n=1}^{\infty}$$

converges to zero, and so

$$\left\{ 1 + \sum_{k=1}^{n} \frac{x^k}{k!} \right\}_{n=1}^{\infty}$$

converges to e^x. As x was arbitrary, we have

$$\sum_{k=0}^{n} \frac{x^k}{k!} = e^x$$

for all x.

Assuming the basic facts about the functions $g(x) = \sin x$ and $h(x) = \cos x$, we know that g is differentiable everywhere, $g'(x) = \cos x$, which is also differentiable everywhere and $g''(x) = -\sin x = -g(x)$. Thus, g has continuous derivatives of all orders, and $|g^{(n)}(x)| \leq 1$ for all n and all x. As in the preceding example, this guarantees that

$$\sum_{n=0}^{\infty} \frac{g^{(n)}(0)}{n!} x^n$$

converges to $\sin x$ for all real x. Since $\cos 0 = 1$ and $\sin 0 = 0$, we have

$$\sin x = \sum_{n=0}^{\infty} \frac{(-1)^n}{(2n + 1)!} x^{2n+1}$$

for all x. A similar line of reasoning allows us to conclude that

$$\cos x = \sum_{n=0}^{\infty} \frac{(-1)^n}{(2n)!} x^{2n}$$

for all x.

The interested reader is referred to Appendix II for more on power series and the convergence of sequences of functions.

EXERCISES

1. Let $\{a_n\}_{n=1}^{\infty}$ be a sequence of real numbers. Prove that

$$\sum_{n=1}^{\infty} (a_n - a_{n+1})$$

converges iff $\{a_n\}_{n=1}^{\infty}$ converges. If $\sum_{n=1}^{\infty} (a_n - a_{n+1})$ converges, what is the sum?

2. Prove that $\{nx^n\}_{n=1}^{\infty}$ converges to zero for $|x| < 1$.

3. Suppose $\sum_{n=1}^{\infty} a_n$ converges absolutely and $\{b_n\}_{n=1}^{\infty}$ is bounded. Prove that $\sum_{n=1}^{\infty} a_n b_n$ converges absolutely.

4. If $\sum_{n=1}^{\infty} a_n$ converges absolutely, prove that $\sum_{n=1}^{\infty} a_n^2$ converges. Is the converse true? Is the statement true if $\sum_{n=1}^{\infty} a_n$ converges conditionally?

5. Let $\sum_{n=1}^{\infty} a_n$ converge. Let $\{n_k\}_{k=1}^{\infty}$ be a subsequence of the sequence of positive integers. For each k, define

$$b_k = a_{n_{k-1}+1} + \cdots + a_{n_k}.$$

Prove that $\sum_{k=1}^{\infty} b_k$ converges and that

$$\sum_{k=1}^{\infty} b_k = \sum_{n=1}^{\infty} a_n.$$

6. (Limit comparison test) Prove the following generalization of 6.4. Suppose $\sum_{n=0}^{\infty} a_n$ and $\sum_{n=0}^{\infty} b_n$ are series of positive terms such that

$$\left\{\frac{a_n}{b_n}\right\}_{n=1}^{\infty}$$

converges to $L \neq 0$. Then $\sum_{n=0}^{\infty} a_n$ and $\sum_{n=0}^{\infty} b_n$ either both diverge or both converge. What can be concluded if $L = 0$?

7. If $\{a_n\}_{n=1}^{\infty}$ is a sequence of positive real numbers such that

$$\left\{\frac{a_{n+1}}{a_n}\right\}_{n=1}^{\infty}$$

converges to L, prove that $\{\sqrt[n]{a_n}\}_{n=1}^{\infty}$ converges to L.

8. Prove that

$$\left\{\frac{\sqrt[n]{n!}}{n}\right\}_{n=1}^{\infty}$$

converges, and find the limit.

9. Prove that the Cauchy product of two absolutely convergent series is absolutely convergent.

10. For each positive integer n, define

$$\gamma_n = 1 + \frac{1}{2} + \cdots + \frac{1}{n} - \log n.$$

Prove that $\{\gamma_n\}_{n=1}^{\infty}$ converges. (Use the fact that $\log x = \int_1^x dt/t$ for $x > 0$.)

11. Determine those values of p for which

$$\sum_{n=2}^{\infty} \frac{1}{n(\log n)^p}$$

converges.

12. Give an example of an infinite series for which 6.9 yields results but 6.10 does not.

13. If $\sum_{n=1}^{\infty} a_n$ converges and $\{b_n\}_{n=1}^{\infty}$ is monotone and bounded, prove that $\sum_{n=1}^{\infty} a_n b_n$ converges.

14. Suppose $\{a_n\}_{n=1}^{\infty}$ is a sequence of positive real numbers converging to zero such that $a_n \geq a_{n+1}$ for all n. Then by the alternating series test, $\sum_{n=1}^{\infty} (-1)^n a_n$ converges; call the sum S. Let S_n be the nth partial sum of $\sum_{n=1}^{\infty} (-1)^n a_n$. Prove that $|S_n - S| \leq a_{n+1}$.

15. Let $\sum_{n=1}^{\infty} a_n$ be an infinite series and $\{n_k\}_{k=1}^{\infty}$ a subsequence of the sequence of positive integers. Prove that if $\sum_{n=1}^{\infty} a_n$ converges absolutely, then $\sum_{k=1}^{\infty} a_{n_k}$, converges absolutely. What can be concluded if $\sum_{n=1}^{\infty} a_n$ converges conditionally?

16. Prove that $\sum_{k=1}^{\infty} \sin kx/k$ converges. (Hint: Use 6.13.)

17. Construct a rearrangement of $\sum_{n=1}^{\infty} (-1)^n(1/n)$ which converges to zero.

18. Test the following series for convergence:

    (a) $\sum_{n=1}^{\infty} n^p p^n$, $p > 0$ (b) $\sum_{n=1}^{\infty} (\sqrt[n]{n} - 1)^n$

    (c) $\sum_{n=1}^{\infty} n^{-1-1/n}$ (d) $\sum_{n=2}^{\infty} 1/(p^n - q^n)$, $0 < q < p$.

19. Determine the interval of convergence of the power series

$$\sum_{n=1}^{\infty} \frac{1}{n^p} x^n$$

for different values of p.

20. Determine the radius of convergence of the power series

$$\sum_{n=1}^{\infty} \frac{2^n n!}{n^n} x^n.$$

21. Show that the power series $\sum_{n=0}^{\infty} a_n x^n$ and $\sum_{n=1}^{\infty} n a_n x^{n-1}$ either both converge for all x, both converge only for $x = 0$, or both have the same finite nonzero radius of convergence.

22. Let $\{a_n\}_{n=1}^{\infty}$ be a sequence of real numbers and let $A = \{p$: there is a subsequence of $\{a_n\}_{n=1}^{\infty}$ converging to $p\}$. Suppose A is nonvoid and bounded from below. Define $a = \inf A$. Prove that $a \in A$ and that for each $\varepsilon > 0$, there is N such that for all $n \geq N$, $a - \varepsilon < a_n$ and there are infinitely many m such that $a_m < a + \varepsilon$.

23. State and prove theorems similar to 6.9 and 6.20 in terms of

$$\liminf_{n \to \infty} \left| \frac{a_{n+1}}{a_n} \right| \quad \text{and} \quad \limsup_{n \to \infty} \left| \frac{a_{n+1}}{a_n} \right|.$$

24. Find $\liminf_{n \to \infty} a_n$ and $\limsup_{n \to \infty} a_n$ for the sequence $\{a_n\}_{n=1}^{\infty}$ defined by

$$a_n = (-1)^n \frac{n}{(1+n)^n}.$$

25. Suppose $\sum_{n=0}^{\infty} a_n x^n$ has r as its radius of convergence. Find the radius of convergence of the power series

$$\sum_{n=0}^{\infty} a_n^k x^n \quad \text{and} \quad \sum_{n=0}^{\infty} a_n x^{kn},$$

where k is a fixed positive integer. What is the radius of convergence of $\sum_{n=0}^{\infty} a_n x^{n^2}$?

26. Suppose $\sum_{n=0}^{\infty} a_n$ diverges and that $\{a_n\}_{n=0}^{\infty}$ is bounded. Prove that the radius of convergence of $\sum_{n=0}^{\infty} a_n x^n$ is equal to 1.

27. Prove the following variation on 6.24: Suppose $f: [a, b] \rightarrow R$ is n times differentiable on $[a, b]$ and $f^{(n)}$ is Riemann-integrable on $[a, b]$. Then for all $x, y \in [a, b]$,

$$f(x) = f(y) + \sum_{k=1}^{n} \frac{f^{(k)}(y)}{k!} (x - y)^k + R_n(x)$$

where

$$R_n(x) = \frac{1}{(n-1)!} \int_{y}^{x} f^{(n)}(t)(x - t)^{n-1} \, dt.$$

CHAPTER 7

THE ELEMENTARY
FUNCTIONS

In this concluding chapter, we utilize our previous results to consider some of the so-called elementary functions that the reader has already encountered. Although we have used these functions on previous occasions to illustrate our theorems with examples, none of the theorems so far presented hinges on any unproved facts about these elementary functions.

For each real number $t > 0$, define $L(t) = \int_1^t dx/x$. The reader will recognize this as one way of defining the natural logarithm function. Let us use our knowledge of analysis to investigate the properties of L.

7.1 THEOREM   The function L has the following properties:
(1) L is differentiable at t for all $t > 0$ and $L'(t) = 1/t$.
(2) L is strictly increasing and hence 1–1.
(3) $L(1) = 0$.
(4) $L(xy) = L(x) + L(y)$ for all $x, y > 0$.
(5) $\operatorname{im} L = R$.

Proof: By 5.13, L is differentiable at $t > 0$ and $L'(t) = 1/t$. By 4.9, L is strictly increasing on any closed interval; hence, L is strictly increasing on $\{x : x > 0\}$. Thus, in particular, L is 1–1. Now

$$L(1) = \int_1^1 \frac{dx}{x} = 0.$$

Consider $x, y > 0$. $L(x) = \int_1^x dt/t$ by definition. Define $\phi(t) = yt$. Then by 5.28 (the change of variables theorem),

$$L(x) = \int_1^x \frac{dt}{t} = \int_y^{xy} \frac{d\phi^{-1}}{\phi^{-1}(t)} = \int_y^{xy} \frac{dt}{t}$$

$$= \int_1^{xy} \frac{dt}{t} - \int_1^y \frac{dt}{t} = L(xy) - L(y).$$

Hence,

$$L(xy) = L(x) + L(y).$$

Now for any $x > 0$,

$$0 = L(1) = L\left(x \cdot \frac{1}{x}\right) = L(x) + L\left(\frac{1}{x}\right),$$

hence $L(1/x) = -L(x)$. In order to prove that (5) holds, it will suffice to show that if $t > 0$, then there is $x > 1$ such that $L(x) = t$, since we know $L(1/x) = -L(x)$.

Suppose $t > 0$. Now in Chapter 6, we observed that $\sum_{n=2}^{\infty} 1/n$ is divergent, so there is n_0 such that $\sum_{n=2}^{n_0} 1/n > t$. Now

$$L(n_0) = \int_1^{n_0} \frac{dt}{t} = \int_1^2 \frac{dt}{t} + \int_2^3 \frac{dt}{t}$$

$$+ \cdots + \int_{n_0-1}^{n_0} \frac{dt}{t} \geq \frac{1}{2} + \frac{1}{3} + \cdots + \frac{1}{n_0} > t.$$

Thus, $L(1) = 0 < t < L(n_0)$, and L is continuous; hence, by the intermediate-value theorem, there is $x \in (1, n_0)$ such that $L(x) = t$.

Theorem 7.1 assures us that L is 1–1 and $\operatorname{im} L = R$. Thus, L^{-1} is a 1–1 function from R onto the set of positive real numbers. For obvious reasons, we shall write $E = L^{-1}$. Since L is such a nice function, one would like to conclude that E inherits its nice properties. Unfortunately, the theorems one would like us to use, 3.11 and 4.12, are not applicable, because the domain of L is not a closed interval and is not compact. However, careful consideration of the case we are interested in yields the following lemma, which extends 3.11 and 4.12 and serves our purpose quite nicely.

7.2 LEMMA   Suppose $f: A \to R$ is 1–1 and continuous and that the set A has the property that $a < x < b$ with $a, b \in A$ implies $x \in A$. Then f is monotone, f^{-1} is continuous on $f[A]$, and if f is differentiable on A and $f'(x) \neq 0$ for all $x \in A$, then f^{-1} is differentiable on $f[A]$.

Proof: First of all, let us verify that f must be monotone. If $A = \{x_0\}$, there is nothing to prove. Suppose A has more than one element, and choose $x, y \in A$ with $x < y$. Since f is 1–1, $f(x) \neq f(y)$; let us suppose $f(x) < f(y)$. We shall prove that f is increasing in this case. Choose any $u, v \in A$ with $u < v$. Let $a = \min\{u, v, x, y\}$, and let $b = \max\{u, v, x, y\}$. Define $h: [a, b] \to R$ by $h(x) = f(x)$ for all $x \in [a, b]$. The fact that A has the intermediate-value property implies $[a, b] \subset A = \operatorname{dom} f$. Now h is 1–1 and continuous; hence, by 3.15, h is monotone. We already know that

$$h(x) = f(x) < f(y) = h(y),$$

so

$$f(u) = h(u) < h(v) = f(v).$$

Since u and v are arbitrary, we find that f is increasing. In case $f(x) > f(y)$, the same argument shows that $-f$ is increasing, so f is decreasing.

For the proof of the remainder of the theorem, let us assume f is increasing. The case for f decreasing is quite similar. Let

$$B = \operatorname{im} f = \operatorname{dom} f^{-1}.$$

We shall now show that B also has the intermediate-value property. Suppose $a, b \in B$ and $a < x < b$. Let $\alpha, \beta \in A$ such that $f(\alpha) = a$ and $f(\beta) = b$. Since f is increasing, $\alpha < \beta$. By 3.12, there is $y \in (\alpha, \beta)$ such that $f(y) = x$, hence $x \in B$.

Let us now choose $x \in B$ and prove that f^{-1} is continuous at x. Let $y = f^{-1}(x) \in A$. There are three separate cases to consider: $y = \sup A, y = \inf A$, and $\inf A < y < \sup A$. We shall handle the last two cases and leave the first case to the reader.

Suppose there are $w, z \in A$ such that $w < y < z$. Then

$$f(w) < f(y) = x < f(z).$$

Since both A and B have the intermediate-value property and f is increasing and continuous, $[w, z] \subset A, [f(w), f(z)] \subset B$, and

$$f([w, z]) = [f(w), f(z)].$$

Define $h : [w, z] \to [f(w), f(z)]$ by $h(u) = f(u)$ for all $u \in [w, z]$. The function h is continous and 1–1; hence $h^{-1} : [f(w), f(z)] \to [w, z]$ is continuous. Choose any sequence $\{x_n\}_{n=1}^{\infty}$ in B converging to x. Since $x \in (f(w), f(z))$, there is n_0 such that $n \geq n_0$ implies

$$x_n \in (f(w), f(z)).$$

Now h^{-1} is continuous at x, and for $n \geq n_0, x_n \in \operatorname{dom} h^{-1}$; hence,

$$\{h^{-1}(x_n)\}_{n=1}^{\infty} = \{f^{-1}(x_n)\}_{n=1}^{\infty}$$

converges to $h^{-1}(x) = f^{-1}(x)$. Thus, f^{-1} is continuous at x.

If $y = \inf A$, then $f(y) = x = \inf B$, since f is increasing. Since we have assumed that A has at least two members, there is $z \in A$ such that $y < z$. Thus, as before, $[y, z] \subset A, [f(y), f(z)] \subset B$, and

$$f([y, z]) = [f(y), f(z)].$$

Define $h : [y, z] \to [f(y), f(z)]$ by $h(u) = f(u)$ for all $u \in [y, z]$. The function h is continuous and 1–1; hence, $h^{-1} : [f(y), f(z)] \to [y, z]$ is continuous. Choose any sequence $\{x_n\}_{n=1}^{\infty}$ in B converging to

x. Since $x = \inf B$, $x_n \geq x$ for all n; so there is n_0 such that $n \geq n_0$ implies $x \leq x_n \leq f(z)$. Since h^{-1} is continuous at x and $x_n \in \operatorname{dom} h^{-1}$ for $n \geq n_0$,

$$\{f^{-1}(x_n)\}_{n=1}^{\infty} = \{h^{-1}(x_n)\}_{n=1}^{\infty}$$

converges to $h^{-1}(x) = f^{-1}(x)$. Thus, f is continuous at x.

It should now be obvious how to handle the case $y = \sup A$. Rather than finish the proof, let us analyze the reasoning used so that the reader can supply his own proof for the case in which f is differentiable. In Chapter 3, where 3.11 fails if the domain of f is not compact, we see that the example presented consists of a 1–1 function whose domain does not have the intermediate-value property; hence the function need not be monotone. The facts that f is monotone and A has the intermediate-value property allow one to conclude that f maps open intervals into open intervals and that each $x \in A$ either is an end point of A or belongs to an open interval contained in A.

The property assumed for the set A in this lemma has of course been used before. It is a special case of a more general property used in topology.

DEFINITION A set $A \subset R$ is *connected* iff for all $x, y \in A$, $x < u < y$ implies $u \in A$.

This definition is restricted to sets of real numbers. It would have to be formulated differently if one wanted to generalize. We refer the curious reader to Exercises 8, 9, and 10 for more on connected sets.

Since the domain of L is the set of all positive real numbers, a connected set, the preceding lemma applies and yields part of the following theorem.

7.3 THEOREM The function E has the following properties:
(1) E is differentiable on R, and $E'(x) = E(x)$ for all $x \in R$
(2) E is strictly increasing.
(3) $E(0) = 1$.
(4) $E(x + y) = E(x)E(y)$ for all $x, y \in R$.
(5) $\operatorname{im} E = \{x : x > 0\}$.

Proof: Since $\{x : x > 0\}$ is connected ($x < y < z, x, z > 0$ imply that $y > 0$) and $L'(x) = 1/x \neq 0$ for all $x > 0$, then by the lemma, E is differentiable on its domain R. Now for all $x \in R, L(E(x)) = x$; hence

$$1 = (L \circ E)'(x) = \frac{E'(x)}{E(x)},$$

so $E'(x) = E(x)$. Since $E'(x) = E(x) > 0$ for all x, E is strictly increasing. Now $L(1) = 0$, and so

$$E(0) = E(L(1)) = (E \circ L)(1) = 1.$$

Choose $x, y \in R$. Now

$$L(E(x) \cdot E(y)) = L(E(x)) + L(E(y)) = x + y,$$

so

$$E(x + y) = E(L(E(x) \cdot E(y))) = E(x)E(y).$$

Condition (5) is immediate since

$$\{x : x > 0\} = \operatorname{dom} L = \operatorname{im} L^{-1} = \operatorname{im} E.$$

Let us now indulge in a rather informal discussion of some of these results. First of all, let us define $E(1) = e$. Now $E(0) = 1$, so

$$1 = E(x - x) = E(x)E(-x);$$

hence,

$$E(-x) = \frac{1}{E(x)}.$$

For any integer, this result, coupled with 7.3, condition (4), guarantees that $E(n) = e^n$ where e^n has the usual interpretation for integer n. If m is a positive integer, then by $e^{1/m}$, we mean that positive real number x such that $x^m = e$. If p is rational, $p = n/m, m > 0$, then by e^p we mean $(e^{1/m})^n$. It is easy to see that for all rational $p, E(p) = e^p$. Suppose we define for all real $x, e^x = \sup \{e^p : p$ is rational and $p \leq x\}$. Now E is continuous at x, and E is increasing; hence $E(x) = \sup \{E(p) : p$ is rational and $p \leq x\} = \sup \{e^p : p$

is rational and $p \le x\} = e^x$. This is of course the rationale behind the use of e^x to represent the function E and the use of the name "the exponential function." Note that with this notation,

$$e^{x+y} = E(x+y) = E(x)E(y) = e^x e^y.$$

With this in mind, observe that if $x > 0, L(x) = a$ iff $E(a) = x$; that is, $e^a = x$. Hence, $L(x)$ is referred to as "the natural logarithm of x" or "logarithm to the base e of x." We shall now feel free to write $\log x$ rather than $L(x)$ when we desire and note that

$$\log(xy) = L(xy) = L(x) + L(y) = \log x + \log y.$$

Also,

$$\log e^x = L(E(x)) = x \quad \text{and} \quad e^{\log x} = E(L(x)) = x.$$

Suppose now that $x > 0$ and α is any real number. We seek to define x^α in such a way as to extend the definition for α rational. Now for each rational p, the results of 7.3 guarantee that

$$E(pz) = [E(z)]^p$$

for each $z \in R$. Thus, for rational numbers p,

$$e^{p \log x} = E(pL(x)) = [E(L(x))]^p = x^p.$$

Thus, we shall define $x^\alpha = e^{\alpha \log x}$ for all real α and $x > 0$. Note that the usual rules of exponentiation are preserved in that

$$x^{\alpha + \beta} = e^{(\alpha + \beta) \log x} = e^{\alpha \log x} e^{\beta \log x} = x^\alpha x^\beta$$

and

$$(x^\alpha)^\beta = (e^{\alpha \log x})^\beta = (E(\alpha L(x)))^\beta = E(\beta L(E(\alpha(L(x))))) = E(\beta \alpha(L(x)))$$
$$= e^{\beta \alpha \log x} = x^{\beta \alpha}.$$

Now for fixed α, E is differentiable for all x and αL is differentiable for all $x > 0$, hence the function $f(x) = x^\alpha$ for $x > 0$ is differentiable and

$$f'(x) = (E \circ (\alpha L))'(x) = E'(\alpha L(x))(\alpha L)'(x) = E(\alpha L(x)) \cdot \frac{\alpha}{x} = \frac{\alpha x^\alpha}{x} = \alpha x^{\alpha - 1}.$$

On the other hand, if we fix $x > 0$, then the function

$$h(\alpha) = E(\alpha L(x)) = x^{\alpha}$$

is differentiable for all α and

$$h'(\alpha) = E'(\alpha L(x)) \cdot L(x) = x^{\alpha} \log x.$$

The reader is invited to verify that the function $g(x) = x^x$ for $x > 0$ is differentiable and to compute the derivative.

The properties of these two very important functions are far too numerous to list here. We hope we have aroused the reader's curiosity and supplied him with the necessary foundations to pursue this topic further.

We now attack the trigonometric functions from the same point of view. Define

$$A(x) = \int_0^x \frac{dt}{\sqrt{1 - t^2}}$$

for $-1 < x < 1$. Because $1/\sqrt{1 - t^2}$ is unbounded in any neighborhood of 1 or -1, we are unable to define $A(1)$ and $A(-1)$ in this fashion. However, as the reader may recognize, A is bounded on $(-1, 1)$, so life is not too grim. The usual means of proving this fact is to use some of the properties of the trigonometric functions, but that device is denied us since we are seeking to construct these functions. First of all, note that $A(-x) = -A(x)$ for $x \in (-1, 1)$. Thus, if $A(x)$ is bounded for $0 < x < 1$, then A is bounded on $(-1, 1)$. We shall again appeal to the change of variables theorem to justify the claim that A is bounded. Choose $x \in (0, 1)$. Define $\phi : [0, x] \to R$ by $\phi(t) = 1/(1 - t)$. Then

$$A(x) = \int_0^x \frac{dt}{\sqrt{1 - t^2}} = \int_1^{\frac{1}{1-x}} \frac{dy}{y\sqrt{2y - 1}}.$$

Now $0 < x < 1$, hence $1 < 1/(1 - x)$. Choose a positive integer n_0 such that $1/(1 - x) < n_0$. Thus,

$$A(x) = \int_1^{\frac{1}{1-x}} \frac{dy}{y\sqrt{2y - 1}} \leq \int_1^2 \frac{dy}{y\sqrt{2y - 1}} + \int_2^3 \frac{dy}{y\sqrt{2y - 1}} + \cdots$$

$$+ \int_{n_0 - 1}^{n_0} \frac{dy}{y\sqrt{2y - 1}} \leq 1 + \frac{1}{2\sqrt{2 \cdot 2 - 1}} + \frac{1}{3\sqrt{2 \cdot 3 - 1}} + \cdots$$

$$+ \frac{1}{(n_0 - 1)\sqrt{2(n_0 - 1) - 1}} = \sum_{k=1}^{n_0 - 1} \frac{1}{k\sqrt{2k - 1}}.$$

Now

$$\frac{1}{k\sqrt{2k-1}} \le \frac{1}{k\sqrt{2k-k}} = \frac{1}{k^{3/2}}$$

for $k \ge 1$ and $\sum_{k=1}^{\infty} 1/k^{3/2}$ converges; hence, by the comparison test, $\sum_{k=1}^{\infty} 1/k\sqrt{2k-1}$ converges. Thus, for all $x \in (0, 1)$

$$0 \le A(x) \le \sum_{k=1}^{\infty} \frac{1}{k\sqrt{2k-1}}.$$

Let us now extend the domain of A by defining $A(1) = \sup\{A(x): x \in (-1, 1)\}$ and $A(-1) = \inf\{A(x): x \in (-1, 1)\}$.

We are now ready to list some of the more obvious properties of A.

7.4 THEOREM   The function A defined above has the following properties:

    (1) A is continuous on $[-1, 1]$.

    (2) A is differentiable on $(-1, 1)$, and $A'(x) = 1/\sqrt{1-x^2}$ for all $x \in (-1, 1)$.

    (3) A is 1–1 and increasing on $[-1, 1]$

    (4) $A(-x) = -A(x)$ for all $x \in [-1, 1]$

Proof: By 5.13, A is differentiable on $(-1, 1)$, and for each $x \in (-1, 1)$, $A'(x) = 1/\sqrt{1-x^2}$. Now $A'(x) \ne 0$ for all $x \in (-1, 1)$; hence, A is 1–1 on $(-1, 1)$, so by the lemma, A is monotone on $(-1, 1)$. Now $A(0) = 0$, and if $0 < x < 1$,

$$A(x) = \int_0^x \frac{dt}{\sqrt{1-t^2}} > 0$$

since $1/\sqrt{1-t^2} > 0$ for $-1 < t < 1$. Hence, A is increasing on $(-1, 1)$. The fact that $A(-x) = -A(x)$ for $x \in (-1, 1)$ has already been pointed out.

To finish the proof of 7.4, we must verify that A is continuous at 1 and -1, that $A(-1) = -A(1)$, and that A is 1–1 on $[-1, 1]$. Recall that

$$A(1) = \sup\{A(x): x \in (-1, 1)\}$$

and

$$A(-1) = \inf\{A(x): x \in (-1, 1)\}.$$

Choose $\varepsilon > 0$. There is $x_0 \in (-1, 1)$ such that $A(1) - \varepsilon < A(x_0)$. Thus, if $x_0 < x \leq 1$, then $A(1) - \varepsilon < A(x_0) < A(x) \leq A(1)$; hence, A is continuous at $x = 1$. Suppose $A(1) = A(t)$ for some $t \in [-1, 1]$. Then for $t \leq x \leq 1$, $A(t) \leq A(x) \leq A(1) = A(t)$; hence $A(t) = A(x)$. But A is 1-1 on $(-1, 1)$, so $t = 1$. Now

$$
\begin{aligned}
A(-1) &= \inf\{A(x) : x \in (-1, 1)\} \\
&= \inf\{A(-x) : x \in (-1, 1)\} \\
&= \inf\{-A(x) : x \in (-1, 1)\} \\
&= -\sup\{A(x) : x \in (-1, 1)\} \\
&= -A(1).
\end{aligned}
$$

Thus, (4) holds on $[-1, 1]$. Suppose $\{x_n\}_{n=1}^{\infty}$ is any sequence of points in $[-1, 1]$ converging to -1. Then $\{-x_n\}_{n=1}^{\infty}$ is a sequence of points in $[-1, 1]$ converging to 1, hence $\{A(-x_n)\}_{n=1}^{\infty}$ converges to $A(1)$ by the continuity of A at 1. Therefore,

$$
\{A(x_n)\}_{n=1}^{\infty} = \{-A(-x_n)\}_{n=1}^{\infty}
$$

converges to $-A(1) = A(-1)$. This verifies that A is continuous at -1. Finally, $A(t) = A(-1)$ implies that $A(-t) = A(1)$, hence $-t = 1$, or $t = -1$. Therefore, A is 1-1 on $[-1, 1]$.

Note that we do not assert that A is differentiable at 1 or -1; in fact, we shall see shortly that that is not the case. Define $A(1) = \pi/2$, so $A(-1) = -\pi/2$. (Note that we are defining the number $\pi/2$; $A(1)$ has already been defined.) Now the domain of A is $[-1, 1]$, and by 3.12, the range of A is $[-\pi/2, \pi/2]$. Since A is 1-1 and continuous,

$$
A^{-1} : \left[-\frac{\pi}{2}, \frac{\pi}{2}\right] \to [-1, 1]
$$

is 1-1 and continuous; we shall write $S = A^{-1}$. Let us now consider some of the properties of S.

7.5 THEOREM   The function S has the following properties:

(1) S is 1-1, increasing, and continuous on $[-\pi/2, \pi/2]$, and

$$
S\left(\left[-\frac{\pi}{2}, \frac{\pi}{2}\right]\right) = [-1, 1].
$$

(2) S is differentiable on $[-\pi/2, \pi/2]$ and

$$S'(x) = \sqrt{1 - [S(x)]^2}$$

for all $x \in [-\pi/2, \pi/2]$.

(3) S' is differentiable on $[-\pi/2, \pi/2]$ and

$$S''(x) = -S(x)$$

for all $x \in [-\pi/2, \pi/2]$.

(4)   For all $x \in [-\pi/2, \pi/2]$,

$$S(-x) = -S(x).$$

Proof: Statement 1 follows immediately from our remarks preceding this theorem. By Lemma 7.2, S is differentiable on $(-\pi/2, \pi/2)$ and

$$S'(x) = S'(A(S(x))) = \frac{1}{A'(S(x))} = \sqrt{1 - [S(x)]^2}$$

for $x \in (-\pi/2, \pi/2)$. Since it appears that A is not differentiable at 1 or -1, we suspect that the derivative of S (if it exists at $\pi/2$ and $-\pi/2$) must take the value 0 at $\pi/2$ and $-\pi/2$. Let us prove that S is differentiable at $\pi/2$ and that $S'(\pi/2) = 0$. Choose $\varepsilon > 0$. Define

$$C(x) = \sqrt{1 - [S(x)]^2}$$

for all $x \in [-\pi/2, \pi/2]$. Since C is the composition of continuous functions, C is continuous. In particular,

$$C(\pi/2) = \sqrt{1 - [S(\pi/2)]^2} = 0;$$

hence there is $0 < \delta < \pi/2$ such that $\pi/2 - \delta < x \le \pi/2$ implies that $|C(x)| < \varepsilon$. Now suppose $\pi/2 - \delta < t < \pi/2$. There is $x \in (t, \pi/2)$ such that

$$\frac{S\left(\frac{\pi}{2}\right) - S(t)}{\frac{\pi}{2} - t} = S'(x) = C(x)$$

(since the mean-value theorem applies to S on $[t, \pi/2]$). But then $\pi/2 - \delta < x < \pi/2$, so

$$\left| \frac{S\left(\frac{\pi}{2}\right) - S(t)}{\frac{\pi}{2} - t} \right| = |C(x)| < \varepsilon.$$

Hence, S is differentiable at $\pi/2$, and $S'(\pi/2) = 0$. In particular, the formula

$$S'(x) = \sqrt{1 - [S(x)]^2}$$

also holds for $x = \pi/2$. Statement (4) follows from statement (4) of 7.4, since

$$S(-x) = S(-A(S(x))) = S(A(-S(x))) = -S(x).$$

Using the fact that $S(-x) = -S(x)$, the reader should have no difficulty in proving that S is differentiable at $-\pi/2$ and that $S'(-\pi/2) = 0$.

Let us now consider again the function $C : [-\pi/2, \pi/2] \to R$ defined by

$$C(x) = S'(x) = \sqrt{1 - [S(x)]^2}.$$

Define $g : R \to R$ by $g(x) = 1 - x^2$, and define $h : \{x : x \geq 0\} \to R$ by $h(x) = \sqrt{x}$. Then $C(x) = h(g(S(x)))$ for all $x \in [-\pi/2, \pi/2]$. For each $x \in (-\pi/2, \pi/2)$, S is differentiable at x, g is differentiable at $S(x)$, and h is differentiable at $g(S(x))$, since $g(S(x)) > 0$. Thus, $C = S'$ is differentiable on $(-\pi/2, \pi/2)$ and

$$C'(x) = S''(x) = h'(g(S(x))) \cdot g'(S(x)) \cdot S'(x)$$

$$= \frac{1}{2h(g(S(x)))} \cdot (-2S(x)) \cdot S'(x) = -S(x).$$

It remains to be shown that C is differentiable at $\pi/2$ and at $-\pi/2$ and that

$$C'\left(\frac{\pi}{2}\right) = -S\left(\frac{\pi}{2}\right) \quad \text{and} \quad C'\left(-\frac{\pi}{2}\right) = -S\left(-\frac{\pi}{2}\right).$$

(Note that we cannot appeal to the chain rule at $\pi/2$, since $g(S(\pi/2)) = 0$ and h is not differentiable at 0.) We shall resort to the same device that was used to prove that S was differentiable at $\pi/2$ and $-\pi/2$. Choose $\varepsilon > 0$. By the continuity of $-S$ at $\pi/2$, there is $0 < \delta < \pi/2$ such that $\pi/2 - \delta < x \le \pi/2$ implies $|-S(x) - (-S(\pi/2))| < \varepsilon$. Suppose $\pi/2 - \delta < t < \pi/2$. By the mean-value theorem applied to C, there is $x \in (t, \pi/2)$ such that

$$\frac{C(t) - C\left(\frac{\pi}{2}\right)}{t - \frac{\pi}{2}} = C'(x) = -S(x).$$

But $\pi/2 - \delta < x < \pi/2$, so

$$\left| \frac{S'(t) - S'\left(\frac{\pi}{2}\right)}{t - \frac{\pi}{2}} - (-1) \right| = \left| \frac{C(t) - C\left(\frac{\pi}{2}\right)}{t - \frac{\pi}{2}} - (-1) \right|$$

$$= |-S(x) - (-S(\pi/2))| < \varepsilon.$$

Thus, $S' = C$ is differentiable at $\pi/2$ and

$$C'\left(\frac{\pi}{2}\right) = S''\left(\frac{\pi}{2}\right) = -S\left(\frac{\pi}{2}\right) = -1.$$

Now

$$C(-x) = S'(-x) = \sqrt{1 - [S(-x)]^2} = \sqrt{1 - [S(x)]^2} = C(x).$$

Using this fact, the reader should experience no difficulty in proving that $C = S'$ is differentiable at $-\pi/2$ and

$$C'\left(\frac{-\pi}{2}\right) = S''\left(\frac{-\pi}{2}\right) = -S\left(\frac{-\pi}{2}\right) = 1.$$

The observant reader has of course recognized the functions A, S, and C that we have discussed so far. Let us now define the trigonometric functions sine and cosine and derive a few of the familiar properties.

We wish to define differentiable functions on R which will have period 2π and will agree with S and C on $[-\pi/2, \pi/2]$.

Define S_1 and C_1 on $[-\pi, \pi]$ by

$$S_1(x) = \begin{cases} -S(x+\pi), & x \in \left[-\pi, -\dfrac{\pi}{2}\right) \\[2mm] S(x), & x \in \left[-\dfrac{\pi}{2}, \dfrac{\pi}{2}\right] \\[2mm] -S(x-\pi), & x \in \left(\dfrac{\pi}{2}, \pi\right] \end{cases}$$

and

$$C_1(x) = \begin{cases} -C(x+\pi), & x \in \left[-\pi, -\dfrac{\pi}{2}\right) \\[2mm] C(x), & x \in \left[-\dfrac{\pi}{2}, \dfrac{\pi}{2}\right] \\[2mm] -C(x-\pi), & x \in \left(\dfrac{\pi}{2}, \pi\right]. \end{cases}$$

There is no difficulty in verifying that S_1 and C_1 are differentiable at each point of $[-\pi, \pi]$, except possibly at $-\pi/2$ and $\pi/2$. Let us verify that S_1 is differentiable at $\pi/2$ and leave the remaining cases to the reader. Choose $\varepsilon > 0$. Now

$$S\left(\frac{\pi}{2}\right) = S_1\left(\frac{\pi}{2}\right) = 1 = -S\left(\frac{-\pi}{2}\right) = -S\left(\frac{\pi}{2}-\pi\right).$$

S is differentiable at $\pi/2$ (recall dom $S = [-\pi/2, \pi/2]$); the function $\tilde{S}$ defined by $\tilde{S}(x) = -S(x-\pi)$ is differentiable at $\pi/2$ (dom $\tilde{S} = [\pi/2, \pi]$); and

$$S'\left(\frac{\pi}{2}\right) = 0 = \tilde{S}'\left(\frac{\pi}{2}\right).$$

Thus, there is $0 < \delta < \pi/2$ such that if $\pi/2 - \delta < x < \pi/2$, then

$$\left| \frac{S\left(\dfrac{\pi}{2}\right) - S(x)}{\dfrac{\pi}{2} - x} \right| < \varepsilon,$$

while if $\pi/2 < x < \pi/2 + \delta$, then

$$\left| \frac{\tilde{S}\left(\frac{\pi}{2}\right) - \tilde{S}(x)}{\frac{\pi}{2} - x} \right| < \varepsilon.$$

Since $S_1(x) = \tilde{S}(x)$ for $\pi/2 \le x \le \pi$ and $S_1(x) = S(x)$ for $-\pi/2 \le x \le \pi/2$, this pair of inequalities guarantees that S_1 is differentiable at $\pi/2$ and $S_1'(\pi/2) = 0$.

Let us summarize a few of the more obvious properties of S_1 and C_1.

1. S_1 and C_1 are differentiable on $[-\pi, \pi]$.
2. $S_1' = C_1$ and $C_1' = -S_1$ on $[-\pi, \pi]$.
3. $[S_1(x)]^2 + [C_1(x)]^2 = 1$ for all $x \in [-\pi, \pi]$.
4. $S_1(-x) = -S_1(x)$; $C_1(-x) = C_1(x)$ for all $x \in [-\pi, \pi]$.
5. $S_1(-\pi) = 0 = S_1(\pi)$; $C_1(-\pi) = -1 = C_1(\pi)$.

The reader is invited to verify these facts. Most of them follow immediately from the definitions of S_1 and C_1 and the results proven for S and C.

Let x be any real number. There is a unique integer n such that $-\pi < x + 2n\pi \le \pi$. We define $P(x) = x + 2n\pi$. Thus, for each real x, $-\pi < P(x) \le \pi$. Define $\sin : R \to R$ and $\cos : R \to R$ by

$$\sin x = S_1(P(x)) \quad \text{and} \quad \cos x = C_1(P(x)).$$

Now for $-\pi < x \le \pi, P(x) = x$; hence,

$$\sin x = S_1(x) \quad \text{and} \quad \cos x = C_1(x).$$

$P(-\pi) = \pi$, so

$$\sin(-\pi) = S_1(\pi) = 0 = S_1(-\pi)$$

and

$$\cos(-\pi) = C_1(\pi) = C_1(-\pi).$$

We seek now to show that the functions sin and cos inherit the properties listed above for S_1 and C_1.

7.6 THEOREM   The functions sin and cos have the following properties:

(1)   sin and cos are differentiable on R.

(2)   the derivative of sin is cos, and the derivative of cos is $-\sin$.

(3)   for all $x \in R$, $(\sin x)^2 + (\cos x)^2 = 1$.

(4)   for all real x and all integers n, $\cos(x + 2n\pi) = \cos x$ and $\sin(x + 2n\pi) = \sin x$.

(5)   for all real x, $\cos(-x) = \cos x$ and $\sin(-x) = -\sin x$.

Proof: To show that 1 and 2 are satisfied, we must consider these two cases: when $x = (2n + 1)\pi$ for some integer n and when $x \neq (2n + 1)\pi$ for all integers n.

Suppose $x \neq (2n + 1)\pi$ for all integers n. Thus, there is an integer m such that $-\pi < x + 2m\pi < \pi$, which means that $-\pi < P(x) < \pi$. Now S_1 and C_1 are differentiable at $x + 2m\pi$, and

$$S_1'(x + 2m\pi) = C_1(x + 2m\pi),$$

and

$$C_1'(x + 2m\pi) = -S_1(x + 2m\pi).$$

Since $-\pi < x + 2m\pi < \pi$, there is $\delta > 0$ such that $|x - y| < \delta$ implies that $-\pi < y + 2m\pi < \pi$. Choose $\varepsilon > 0$. There is $\delta' > 0$ such that $\delta' < \delta$ and such that $0 < |x + 2m\pi - z| < \delta'$ implies

$$\left| \frac{C_1(x + 2m\pi) - C_1(z)}{x + 2m\pi - z} - C_1'(x + 2m\pi) \right| < \varepsilon$$

and

$$\left| \frac{S_1(x + 2m\pi) - S_1(z)}{x + 2m\pi - z} - S_1'(x + 2m\pi) \right| < \varepsilon.$$

Now suppose $0 < |x - y| < \delta'$. Then $-\pi < y + 2m\pi < \pi$, and $0 < |(x + 2m\pi) - (y + 2m\pi)| < \delta'$.

Thus

$$
\begin{aligned}
&\left| \frac{\sin x - \sin y}{x - y} - \cos x \right| \\
&= \left| \frac{S_1(x + 2m\pi) - S_1(y + 2m\pi)}{(x + 2m\pi) - (y + 2m\pi)} - C_1(x + 2m\pi) \right| \\
&= \left| \frac{S_1(x + 2m\pi) - S_1(y + 2m\pi)}{(x + 2m\pi) - (y + 2m\pi)} - S_1'(x + 2m\pi) \right| < \varepsilon,
\end{aligned}
$$

and

$$\left| \frac{\cos x - \cos y}{x - y} - (-\sin x) \right|$$

$$= \left| \frac{C_1(x + 2m\pi) - C_1(y + 2m\pi)}{(x + 2m\pi) - (y + 2m\pi)} - (-S_1(x + 2m\pi)) \right|$$

$$= \left| \frac{C_1(x + 2m\pi) - C_1(y + 2m\pi)}{(x + 2m\pi) - (y + 2m\pi)} - C_1'(x + 2m\pi) \right| < \varepsilon.$$

Thus, (1) and (2) hold for any real number x which is not an odd multiple of π.

Suppose now that $x = (2n + 1)\pi$. Then $\cos x = C_1(\pi) = -1$ and $\sin x = S_1(\pi) = 0$. For $(2n - 1)\pi < y < x = (2n + 1)\pi$,

$$\cos y = C_1(y - 2n\pi) \quad \text{and} \quad \sin y = S_1(y - 2n\pi).$$

For $x = (2n + 1)\pi < y < (2n + 3)\pi$,

$$\cos y = C_1(y - 2(n + 1)\pi) \quad \text{and} \quad \sin y = S_1(y - 2(n + 1)\pi).$$

Choose $\varepsilon > 0$. There is $0 < \delta < 2\pi$ such that $\pi - \delta < z < \pi$ implies

$$\left| \frac{S_1(\pi) - S_1(z)}{\pi - z} - S_1'(\pi) \right| < \varepsilon$$

and

$$\left| \frac{C_1(\pi) - C_1(z)}{\pi - z} - C_1'(\pi) \right| < \varepsilon$$

and such that $-\pi < w < -\pi + \delta$ implies

$$\left| \frac{S_1(-\pi) - S_1(w)}{-\pi - w} - S_1'(-\pi) \right| < \varepsilon$$

and

$$\left| \frac{C_1(-\pi) - C_1(w)}{-\pi - w} - C_1'(-\pi) \right| < \varepsilon.$$

Rather than reel off a list of equations as in the last paragraph, let us merely note a few facts to verify that $0 < |x - y| < \delta$ implies

$$\left| \frac{\sin x - \sin y}{x - y} - \cos x \right| < \varepsilon$$

and

$$\left| \frac{\cos x - \cos y}{x - y} - (-\sin x) \right| < \varepsilon.$$

First of all,

$$S_1'(\pi) = C_1(\pi) = -1 = \cos x$$

and

$$S_1'(-\pi) = C_1(-\pi) = -1 = \cos x.$$

Similarly,

$$C_1'(\pi) = -S(\pi) = 0 = \sin x$$

and

$$C_1'(-\pi) = -S(-\pi) = 0 = \sin x.$$

For $(2n - 1)\pi < y < (2n + 1)\pi$,

$$\sin y = S_1(y - 2n\pi), \qquad \cos y = C_1(y - 2n\pi), \qquad y - 2n\pi < \pi,$$

and

$$x - y = (2n + 1)\pi - (2n\pi) - (y - 2n\pi) = \pi - (y - 2n\pi).$$

If $(2n + 1)\pi < y < (2n + 3)\pi$,

$$\sin y = S_1(y - 2(n + 1)\pi), \qquad \cos y = C_1(y - 2(n + 1)\pi),$$

$$-\pi < y - 2(n + 1)\pi,$$

and

$$x - y = ((2n + 1)\pi - 2(n + 1)\pi) - (y - 2(n + 1)\pi)$$
$$= -\pi - (y - (2(n + 1)\pi)).$$

Statement (3) follows immediately from the definition of sin and cos and the similar property for S_1 and C_1.

Suppose x is any real number and n an integer. Then there is an integer m such that $x + 2m\pi \in (-\pi, \pi]$. Then

$$(x + 2n\pi) + 2(m - n)\pi \in (-\pi, \pi].$$

Hence,

$$\sin(x + 2n\pi) = S_1(P(x + 2n\pi)) = S_1(x + 2n\pi + 2(m - n)\pi)$$

$$= S_1(x + 2m\pi) = \sin x,$$

and of course similarly for $\cos x$. Thus (4) holds.

If x is a real number, then there is an integer m such that $-\pi < x + 2m\pi \leq \pi$. Then $-\pi \leq -x - 2m\pi < \pi$. If $-x - 2m\pi = -\pi$, then

$$\cos(-x) = C_1(-x - 2(m - 1)\pi) = C_1(x + 2(m - 1)\pi)$$

$$= C_1(-\pi) = C_1(\pi) = \cos x.$$

If $-x - 2m\pi \in (-\pi, \pi)$, then

$$\cos(-x) = C_1(-x - 2m\pi) = C_1(x + 2m\pi) = \cos x.$$

The details for sin are much the same.

In this chapter, we have left many details to the reader. There are several reasons for these omissions. First of all, many would repeat, with slight variations, arguments already presented. Secondly, we hope by now that the reader has developed sufficient maturity and insight to be able to fill in these details with ease. Perhaps the absence of some detail makes this chapter even more challenging and interesting.

We close the chapter with a few random observations concerning the functions just described and the exercises, which provide interesting problems that invite the reader to apply the facts thus far presented to verify some of the more common properties of these functions which have been omitted.

Consider the sequence $\{(1 + 1/n)^n\}_{n=1}^{\infty}$. In chapter 2, we indicated that this sequence converged to e. We are now in a position to substantiate that fact. Define $x_n = (1 + 1/n)^n$ for all positive integers n. Then

$$L(x_n) = nL\left(1 + \frac{1}{n}\right).$$

The sequence $\{1 + 1/n\}_{n=1}^{\infty}$ converges to 1, so by the differentiability of L at 1,

$$\left\{nL\left(1 + \frac{1}{n}\right)\right\}_{n=1}^{\infty} = \left\{\frac{L\left(1 + \frac{1}{n}\right) - L(1)}{\frac{1}{n}}\right\}_{n=1}^{\infty}$$

converges to $L'(1) = 1$. By the continuity of $E, \{x_n\}_{n=1}^{\infty} = \{E(L(x_n))\}_{n=1}^{\infty}$ converges to $E(1) = e$.

A well-known identity from trigonometry states that

$$\sin(x + y) = (\sin x)(\cos y) + (\sin y)(\cos x)$$

for all $x, y \in R$. Let us prove this fact. Define

$$g(x) = \sin(x + y) - (\sin x)(\cos y) - (\sin y)(\cos x).$$

Then

$$g'(x) = \cos(x + y) - (\cos x)(\cos y) + (\sin y)(\sin x),$$

so for all $x, g''(x) + g(x) = 0$. In particular,

$$0 = 2g'(x)g''(x) + 2g'(x)g(x) = [(g')^2 + (g)^2]'(x).$$

Thus, there is a real number k such that

$$[g'(x)]^2 + [g(x)]^2 = k$$

for all $x \in R$. Now $g(0) = 0$ and $g'(0) = 0$; hence $k = 0$. Therefore,

$$[g'(x)]^2 + [g(x)]^2 = 0$$

for all x, so $g(x) = 0$ for all x. Thus, for all x and y,

$$\sin(x + y) = (\sin x)(\cos y) + (\sin y)(\cos x).$$

It is easy now to observe (by (2) of 7.2) that $\cos(x + y) = (\cos x)(\cos y) - (\sin y)(\sin x)$.

EXERCISES

1. For what values of α does the sequence

$$\left(\frac{\log n}{n^{\alpha}}\right)^{\infty}_{n=1}$$

converge?

2. Let $\phi: R \to R$ be such that $\phi(x + y) = \phi(x)\phi(y)$, ϕ is differentiable at zero, and ϕ is not identically zero. Prove that ϕ is differentiable everywhere and that

$$\phi'(x) = \phi(x)\phi'(0).$$

Prove that $\phi(x) = e^{cx}$ for $c = \phi'(0)$.

3. Prove that if $x > 0$ and α is a real, then $\log x^{\alpha} = \alpha \log x$.

4. For what values of α does the sequence

$$\left(\frac{n^{\alpha}}{e^{n}}\right)^{\infty}_{n=1}$$

converge?

5. Give an honest definition of $\log_{10}$ and state and prove a theorem concerning the differentiability of this function.

6. Prove that the sequence $\{(1 + n)^{1/n}\}_{n=1}^{\infty}$ converges, and compute the limit.

7. Prove that for each real number x, the sequence

$$\left\{\left(1 + \frac{x}{n}\right)^{n}\right\}^{\infty}_{n=1}$$

converges, and determine the limit. (The limit of course should depend on x.)

8. Prove that the only connected sets in R are those of the following types: $\{x : x < a\}, \{x : x \le a\}, \{x : a < x < b\}, \{x : x > a\}, \{x : x \ge a\},$ $\{x : a \le x < b\}, \{x : a < x \le b\}, \{x : a \le x \le b\},$ and R. Is the empty set connected?

9. Prove that a set $A \subset R$ is connected iff there do not exist open sets B and C such that $A \subset B \cup C$, $B \cap C$ is empty and $A \cap B$ and $A \cap C$ are nonempty.

10. Suppose $f: R \to R$ is continuous and $A \subset R$ is connected. Prove that $f[A]$ is connected.

11. For $x > 0$, define $g(x) = x^{x}$. Prove that g is differentiable for all $x > 0$. Does g have a limit at zero?

12. Prove that $3 < \pi < 4$. (Hint: For $0 \le x < 1$,

$$\frac{1}{\sqrt{1 - x^2}} \le \frac{1}{\sqrt{1 - x}}.)$$

13. For $0 < x < \pi/2$, prove that $2/\pi < \sin x/x < 1$.

14. For each positive integer n and x real, prove that $|\sin nx| \leq n|\sin x|$. Show that this may fail for n rational.

15. Prove that for all x, $\sin(\pi/2 - x) = \cos x$ and $\cos(\pi/2 - x) = \sin x$.

16. Prove that

$$\sin \frac{\pi}{4} = \cos \frac{\pi}{4} = \frac{\sqrt{2}}{2},$$

$$\sin \frac{\pi}{6} = \cos \frac{\pi}{3} = \frac{1}{2},$$

and

$$\sin \frac{\pi}{3} = \cos \frac{\pi}{6} = \frac{\sqrt{3}}{2}.$$

17. Define

$$B(x) = \int_0^x \frac{dt}{1+t^2}$$

for all $x \in R$. By methods similar to those used in this chapter, prove that B is differentiable everywhere, $B: R \to (-\pi/2, \pi/2)$, B is 1–1, and

$$B^{-1}(x) = \frac{\sin x}{\cos x}$$

for all $x \in (-\pi/2, \pi/2)$.

18. As in Chapter 2, let $[x]$ denote the greatest integer less than or equal to x for each $x \in R$. What is the graph of the function $f(x) = [\sin n! \ \pi x]^2$? (Hint: Consider first x rational and then x irrational.)

EXTENDED LIMITS

In Chapter 2, we discussed the notion of the limit of a function at an accumulation point of its domain. In particular, we observed that the function $f : (0, 1) \to R$ defined by $f(x) = 1/x$ fails to have a limit at $x = 0$, since it is unbounded in every neighborhood of zero. Consider now the function $g : (0, 1) \to R$ defined by

$$g(x) = \frac{1}{x} \sin \frac{1}{x}.$$

For $x = 1/n\pi$, where n is a positive integer, $g(x) = 0$; and for $x = 2/n\pi$, where n is an odd positive integer, $g(x) = n\pi/2$ or $-n\pi/2$. First of all, g

fails to have a limit at zero since it is unbounded in each neighborhood of zero. However, every neighborhood of zero contains a point x at which $g(x) = 0$; hence, the behavior of g near zero is much different from that of f near zero. In this appendix, we wish to investigate the distinction between functions such as g and f. We wish, of course, to discuss "limits at infinity" and "infinite limits."

As before, R will be the set of all real numbers. We adjoin to the set R two symbols ∞ and $-\infty$ and call the resulting set the set of *extended real numbers*, denoted, in this appendix only, by E. We make a weak stab at extending the order relation and arithmetic operations on R to an order relation and some arithmetic on E as follows:

(i)   for all $x \in R$, $-\infty < x < \infty$;

(ii) $-\infty < \infty$;

(iii)   for all $x \in R$,
$$x + \infty = \infty + x = \infty \quad \text{and}$$
$$x + (-\infty) = (-\infty) + x = -\infty;$$

(iv) $\infty + \infty = \infty$, $(-\infty) + (-\infty) = -\infty$;

(v)   if $x \in R$ and $x > 0$, then
$$x \cdot (\infty) = \infty = (\infty) \cdot x$$
$$\text{and} \quad x \cdot (-\infty) = -\infty = (-\infty) \cdot x;$$

(vi)   if $x \in R$ and $x < 0$, then
$$x(\infty) = -\infty = (\infty) \cdot x \quad \text{and} \quad x \cdot (-\infty) = \infty = (-\infty) \cdot x;$$

(vii) $\infty \cdot \infty = (-\infty)(-\infty) = \infty$ and
$$(-\infty) \cdot \infty = \infty \cdot (-\infty) = -\infty.$$

We have no desire to enter into a discussion of what is the maximal consistent list of properties one may assign to the set of extended real numbers. Rather, we take note of the fact that we do not attempt to assign meaning to $0 \cdot \infty, 0 \cdot (-\infty)$, or $\infty + (-\infty)$. The reasons for this omission shall become apparent later.

Let us now recall a definition from Chapter 2. (We hope that this definition is very familiar to the reader and that he does not need to look back to Chapter 2.) Suppose $f : D \to R$ and x_0 is an accumulation point of D. Then f has a limit L at x_0 if for each $\varepsilon > 0$, there is $\delta > 0$ such that $0 < |x - x_0| < \delta$ and $x \in D$ imply $|f(x) - L| < \varepsilon$. We are interested in generalizing this definition so that either x_0 or L or possibly both may be members of $E \backslash R$—that is, ∞ or $-\infty$. It is clear that the present form of the definition is unacceptable for this purpose, since, if x is real, then

$\infty - x = \infty > \varepsilon$ for all real numbers $\varepsilon > 0$. However, if we rephrase this definition in a slightly different fashion and consider the function f mentioned earlier, perhaps our intuition will lead the way.

First of all, we have seen before (in considering convergence of sequences) that statements involving ε's and δ's may be restated in terms of neighborhoods. Thus $f: D \to R$ has a limit L at x_0 if for each neighborhood Q of L, there is a neighborhood P of x_0 such that $x \in P \cap D$ and $x \neq x_0$ imply $f(x) \in Q$. (The reader should prove that this statement is true.) This is clearly a form for the definition in question that is more suitable for generalization: all one needs to do is decide what to choose for neighborhoods of ∞ and $-\infty$. It seems reasonable to desire that the function f mentioned earlier has ∞ as a "limit" at zero, whereas the function g mentioned earlier does not have a "limit" at zero. Our intuition tells us that $f(x)$ gets larger and larger without bound as x gets close to zero. In fact, if $0 < x < \varepsilon$, then $f(x) > 1/\varepsilon$. For x close to zero, $g(x)$ may be positive, negative, or zero, and it does not have a limit in the usual sense in that it oscillates more and more wildly as x comes close to zero. In light of the preceding, we are led to the following definition of neighborhoods in E.

DEFINITION   Let $x \in E$. If x is a real number, then an *extended-neighborhood* of x is any set $Q \subset E$ which contains an open interval centered at x; in other words, there is $\varepsilon > 0$ such that $(x - \varepsilon, x + \varepsilon) \subset Q$. If $x = \infty$, an *extended-neighborhood* of x is any set Q which contains a set of the form $\{ y \in E : y > M \}$ where $M \in R$. If $x = -\infty$, an *extended-neighborhood* of x is any set Q which contains a set of the form $\{ y \in E : y < M \}$ where $M \in R$.

Since this is an appendix to the text, hence an optional part of the presentation, we feel free to take some leeway with the orderly development of our subject and indulge in a little fun. We now have a set E and, for each $x \in E$, the notion of an extended-neighborhood of x. (We shall hereafter abbreviate extended-neighborhood by *e*-neighborhood.) We have considered a number of topics that can be considered with only the notion of a neighborhood at hand. Let us try to generalize some of those notions for *e*-neighborhoods to see what theorems remain true. This detour is not only for pleasure; but it should deepen the reader's understanding of extended neighborhoods.

Let us make one more convention before proceeding further. If $x \in R$, we shall write x is finite; and if we write x is infinite, we mean x is either ∞ or $-\infty$.

DEFINITION   Let $D \subset E$ and $x \in E$. Then x is an *e-accumulation point* of D if every *e*-neighborhood of x contains infinitely many points of D.

First of all, note that if x is finite, then every neighborhood of x is an *e*-neighborhood of x, and every *e*-neighborhood of x contains a neighborhood of x. In fact, the only distinction between neighborhoods of x and *e*-neighborhoods of x for x finite is the fact that ∞ and $-\infty$ can belong to *e*-neighborhoods. Thus, we suspect that for x finite, x is an *e*-accumulation point of D if x is an accumulation point of D. It is worth considering under what conditions ∞ or $-\infty$ might be accumulation points of D.

I.1 THEOREM   Let $D \subset E$ and $x \in E$. Then
    (a)   if x is finite, then x is an accumulation point of $D \cap R$ iff x is an *e*-accumulation point of D;
    (b) $x = \infty$ is an *e*-accumulation point of D iff $D \cap R$ is not bounded from above;
    (c) $x = -\infty$ is an *e*-accumulation point of D iff $D \cap R$ is not bounded from below.

Proof: (a) Suppose x is finite and x is an accumulation point of $D \cap R$. Then every neighborhood of x contains infinitely many points of $D \cap R$; hence, since each *e*-neighborhod of x contains a neighborhood of x, each *e*-neighborhood of x contains infinitely many points of D, and so x is an *e*-accumulation point of D.

Suppose x is finite and x is an *e*-accumulation point of D. Then each *e*-neighborhood of x contains infinitely many points of D. Since $E \backslash R$ has only two members and each neighborhood of x is an *e*-neighborhood of x, then each neighborhood of x contains infinitely many points of $D \cap R$ so that x is an accumulation point of $D \cap R$.

(b) Suppose ∞ is an e-accumulation point of D. Thus, for each M, there are infinitely many members of D belonging to the set $\{y \in E : y > M\}$, since $\{y \in E : y > M\}$ is an e-neighborhood of ∞. Since $E \backslash R$ has only two members, $\{y \in E : y > M\} \cap D \cap R$ must be infinite; hence, M is not an upper bound for $D \cap R$. Since M was any real number, we conclude that $D \cap R$ is not bounded from above.

Suppose now that $D \cap R$ is not bounded from above. Thus, for each positive integer n, there is $x_n \in D \cap R$ such that $n < x_n$. Let Q be any e-neighborhood of ∞. There is $M \in R$ such that $\{y \in E : y > M\} \subset Q$. Now if n is any positive integer larger than M, $x_n > n > M$; hence, $\{x_n : n > M\} \subset \{y \in E : y > M\} \subset Q$. Finally, the inequality $x_n > n$, which holds for all positive integers n, implies that the set $\{x_n : n > M\}$ is infinite. Hence, ∞ is an e-accumulation point of D.

(c) Exercise 1.

Perhaps now the adventuresome reader might wish to try his own hand at this game. The idea is to generalize notions in Chapters 1 and 2 and try to prove the corresponding theorems. We shall pursue this course and leave some of the intellectual excitement to be discovered in the exercises.

In Chapter 1, we proved that every bounded infinite set of real numbers had at least one accumulation point. Since $-\infty \le x \le \infty$ for all $x \in E$, we see that every subset of E has $-\infty$ as a lower bound and ∞ as an upper bound; hence, every subset of E is bounded in E. Perhaps one might expect that any infinite subset of E has an e-accumulation point. After a little reflection, it becomes clear that this is not such a foolish idea, and in fact, it's very easy to prove.

I.2 THEOREM   Every infinite subset of E has at least one e-accumulation point.

Proof: Suppose that $D \subset E$ is infinite. If $D \cap R$ is bounded as a set of real numbers—that is, if there is $M \in R$ such that $-M \le x \le M$ for all $x \in D \cap R$—then by the Bolzano–Weierstrass theorem, $D \cap R$ has at least one accumulation point. Such an accumulation point must be a real number; hence by I.1, it must be an *e*-accumulation point of *D*. If $D \cap R$ is not bounded, then by I.1, either $-\infty$ or ∞ is an *e*-accumulation point of *D*. So in either case, *D* has an *e*-accumulation point.

Perhaps it is time to consider a few examples. Consider the set *J* of all positive integers and the set *Z* of all integers. The set *J* has precisely one *e*-accumulation point, namely ∞. The set *Z* has two *e*-accumulation points, namely ∞ and $-\infty$. The set of *e*-accumulation points of the set $\{x \in R : x > 0\}$ is the set $\{x \in E : x \geq 0\}$.

Let us skip over sequences for a moment and pass on to the notion of the extended limit of a function. The reason for this omission shall be clear quite soon.

DEFINITION   Suppose $D \subset E$, $f : D \to E$, and x_0 is an *e*-accumulation point of *D*. Then *f* has an *e-limit* *L* at x_0 iff for each *e*-neighborhood *Q* of *L*, there is an *e*-neighborhood *P* of x_0 such that $x \in P \cap D$ and $x \neq x_0$ imply that $f(x) \in Q$.

Let us consider several distinct cases and see how this definition reads in terms of ε's and δ's. Since our main interest will center about functions whose domains are subsets of *R*, we shall restrict our attention to such functions.

Suppose $f : D \to R$ with $D \subset R$ and x_0 an *e*-accumulation point of *D*. We shall consider four cases.

Case 1: $x_0 \in R$, $L \in R$. Then *L* is an *e*-limit of *f* at x_0 iff *L* is a limit of *f* at x_0.

Case 2: $x_0 \in R$, $L = \infty$. Then ∞ is an *e*-limit of *f* at x_0 iff for each $M \in R$, there is $\delta > 0$ such that $0 < |x - x_0| < \delta$ and $x \in D$ imply that $f(x) > M$.

Case 3: $L \in R$, $x_0 = \infty$. Then *L* is an *e*-limit of *f* at x_0 iff for each $\varepsilon > 0$, there is $M \in R$ such that $M < x < \infty$ and $x \in D$ imply that $|f(x) - L| < \varepsilon$.

Case 4: $L = x_0 = \infty$. Then ∞ is an *e*-limit of *f* at ∞ iff for each $M \in R$, there is $N \in R$ such that $N < x < \infty$ and $x \in D$ imply that $f(x) > M$.

We leave other possible cases to the reader; in fact, we shall leave the verification of these statements to the reader.

In our earlier adventures with limits, we proved that if a function has a limit at a point, then it is unique. The proof depended upon the fact that if x and y are distinct real numbers, then there are neighborhoods P and Q of x and y, respectively, such that P and Q are disjoint. A few moments of reflection will yield the same result for E.

I.3 THEOREM   If $x \in E$ and $y \in E$ with $x \neq y$, then there are disjoint e-neighborhoods P and Q of x and y, respectively.

Proof: If x and y are both finite, let $\varepsilon = |x - y|/2$. Then $(x - \varepsilon, x + \varepsilon)$ and $(y - \varepsilon, y + \varepsilon)$ are disjoint e-neighborhoods of x and y, respectively.

If $x = \infty$, then choose a real number w such that $y < w < x$. Then $\{u \in E : u > w\}$ and $\{u \in E : u < w\}$ are disjoint e-neighborhoods of x and y, respectively. The case for $x = -\infty$ is similar.

With this theorem at our disposal, it is quite easy to prove the uniqueness of e-limits.

I.4 THEOREM   If L and L_2 are e-limits of f at x_0, then $L_1 = L_2$. (It is assumed that dom $f \subset E$ and x_0 is an e-accumulation point of dom f.)

Proof: Suppose L_1 is an e-limit of f at x_0 and $L_2 \in E$, with $L_2 \neq L_1$. We shall show that L_2 cannot be an e-limit of f at x_0. By I.3, there are e-neighborhoods P and Q of L_1 and L_2, respectively, such that $P \cap Q$ is empty. There is an e-neighborhood S of x_0 such that if $x \in S \cap \text{dom} f$ and $x \neq x_0$, then $f(x) \in P$. Thus, for all $x \in S \cap \text{dom} f$ with $x \neq x_0, f(x) \notin Q$; hence, L_2 cannot be an e-limit of f at x_0.

Let us return to the functions mentioned earlier and, using a little poetic license, change our examples slightly. Let $D = \{x \in R : x > 0\}$ and define $f : D \to R$ and $g : D \to R$ by

$$f(x) = \frac{1}{x} \quad \text{and} \quad g(x) = \frac{1}{x} \sin \frac{1}{x}$$

for all $x \in D$. By our previous experiences, f and g have finite e-limits at x for all $x \in D$. We shall thus direct our attention to the behavior at 0 and at ∞.

If we have properly conditioned the reader, he should anticipate the result that f has an e-limit at zero and the e-limit is ∞. Let us verify this fact. Let $M \in R$. (We are choosing a neighborhood of ∞, the set $\{x : x > M\}$.) Let $\varepsilon = 1/|M|$. Thus, for $0 < x < \varepsilon$,

$$f(x) = \frac{1}{x} > \frac{1}{\varepsilon} = |M| \geq M;$$

hence $f(x) \in \{w : w > M\}$. Thus, f has an e-limit at zero, which is ∞. Let us now consider the behavior of f at ∞. Intuitively, one suspects that f will have an e-limit at ∞, namely zero. Choose $\varepsilon > 0$, and let $M = 1/\varepsilon$. Then if $M < x < \infty$,

$$0 < f(x) = \frac{1}{x} < \frac{1}{M} = \varepsilon.$$

Hence, f has an e-limit at ∞ and that e-limit is zero.

In light of the last few sentences of the preceding paragraph, it is clear that g also has an e-limit of zero at ∞. The situation near zero is a different story, however. It is clear that neither ∞ nor $-\infty$ can serve as an e-limit of g at zero since every e-neighborhood of zero contains a point x such that $g(x) = 0$. Our previous experience assures us that g cannot have a finite e-limit at zero since g is unbounded on every neighborhood of zero. Hence, g does not have an e-limit at zero.

Early in Chapter 1, a sequence was defined as any function with domain J, the set of positive integers. We have already observed that J has ∞ as its only e-accumulation point. It might be amusing to investigate the behavior of sequences which have e-limits at ∞.

Let $\{a_n\}_{n=1}^{\infty}$ be a sequence of real numbers. Thus, we have a function with domain J such that a_n is the value of the function at n for each $n \in J$. Suppose this function has a finite e-limit A at ∞. Then for each $\varepsilon > 0$, there is N such that $n > N$ implies that $|a_n - A| < \varepsilon$. Surprisingly enough, this is precisely the definition of convergence of a sequence.

With this last result in mind, the reason for the similarity between the results and proofs in Chapters 1 and 2 becomes apparent. The reader might do well to go back and look for these similarities in Chapters 1 and 2.

Our reason for postponing the discussion of convergence of sequences in E is no longer a mystery. A sequence $a = \{a_n\}_{n=1}^{\infty}$ of members

of E *e-converges* iff the function a has an *e*-limit at ∞. Thus, any results for
e-limits of functions yield results for *e*-limits of sequences. To round out
the picture on *e*-convergent sequences, we see that an *e*-convergent sequence
either has a finite limit, in which case it is a convergent sequence, or it has
an infinite limit. If a sequence $\{a_n\}_{n=1}^{\infty}$ *e*-converges to ∞, then for each
$M \in R$ there is $N \in R$ such that $n > N$ implies $a_n > M$. If a sequence
e-converges to $-\infty$, then for each $M \in R$ there is $N \in R$ such that $n > N$
implies $a_n < M$. We see further that I.4 guarantees that an *e*-convergent
sequence has a unique limit. Note that it is not true that *e*-convergent
sequences of real numbers are Cauchy sequences. The sequence $\{n\}_{n=1}^{\infty}$
e-converges to ∞ but is not Cauchy.

   We have just remarked that facts about *e*-convergent sequences
follow from facts about *e*-limits of functions. In Chapter 2, we proved a
theorem relating limits of functions to limits of sequences. Let us seek an
analogue of that theorem. First, we need the following lemma.

   LEMMA   Let $D \subset E$ and $x \in E$. Then x is an *e*-accumulation
point of D iff there is a sequence $\{x_n\}_{n=1}^{\infty}$ of members of $D \backslash \{x\}$
e-converging to x.

Proof: Exercise 6.

I.5 THEOREM   Let $D \subset E$ and let x_0 be an *e*-accumulation
point of D. Then $f : D \to E$ has an *e*-limit at x_0 iff for each
sequence $\{x_n\}_{n=1}^{\infty}$ of members of $D \backslash \{x_0\}$ *e*-converging to x_0, the
sequence $\{f(x_n)\}_{n=1}^{\infty}$ is *e*-convergent.

Proof: Suppose f has an *e*-limit L at x_0. Let $\{x_n\}_{n=1}^{\infty}$ be any
sequence of members of $D \backslash \{x_0\}$ *e*-converging to x_0. Let Q be any
e-neighborhood of L. There is an *e*-neighborhood P of x_0 such that
$x \in P \cap D$ and $x \neq x_0$ imply that $f(x) \in Q$. Since $\{x_n\}_{n=1}^{\infty}$
e-converges to x_0, there is N such that $n > N$ implies that $x_n \in P$.
Thus, for $n > N$, $x_n \in P \cap D$ and $x_n \neq x_0$, hence $f(x_n) \in Q$. Thus,
$\{f(x_n)\}_{n=1}^{\infty}$ *e*-converges to L.

   Suppose now that for each sequence $\{x_n\}_{n=1}^{\infty}$ of members of
$D \backslash \{x_0\}$ which *e*-converges to x_0, it is true that $\{f(x_n)\}_{n=1}^{\infty}$ is

e-convergent. Choose such a sequence $\{x_n\}_{n=1}^{\infty}$, and let L be the e-limit of the sequence $\{f(x_n)\}_{n=1}^{\infty}$. Suppose L is not an e-limit of f at x_0. (We do not assume that f has an e-limit at x_0.) Then there is an e-neighborhood Q of L such that each e-neighborhood of x_0 contains a point $p \neq x_0$ such that $p \in D$ and $f(p) \notin Q$. We shall use this fact to construct a sequence $\{y_n\}_{n=1}^{\infty}$ of members of $D\backslash\{x_0\}$ e-converging to x_0 such that $\{f(y_n)\}_{n=1}^{\infty}$ e-converges to $L_1 \neq L$. We choose y_n according to the following rules:

(1) if x_0 is finite, choose

$$y_n \in \left[\left(x_0 - \frac{1}{n}, x_0 + \frac{1}{n}\right) \cap D\right] \backslash \{x_0\}$$

such that $f(y_n) \notin Q$.

(2) if $x_0 = \infty$, choose

$$y_n \in [\{w \in E : w > n\} \cap D]\backslash\{x_0\}$$

such that $f(y_n) \notin Q$.

(3) if $x_0 = -\infty$, choose

$$y_n \in [\{w \in E : w < -n\} \cap D]\backslash\{x_0\}$$

such that $f(y_n) \notin Q$.

By the choice of the sequence $\{y_n\}_{n=1}^{\infty}$, it is clear that this sequence e-converges to x_0. Hence, $\{f(y_n)\}_{n=1}^{\infty}$ e-converges to L_1, and since $f(y_n) \notin Q$ for each n, $L_1 \neq L$. Define a new sequence $\{z_n\}_{n=1}^{\infty}$ by $z_n = x_n$ if n is even and $z_n = y_n$ if n is odd. Let S be any e-neighborhood of x_0. There are real numbers N_1 and N_2 such that $n \geq N_1$ implies $x_n \in S$ and $n \geq N_2$ implies $y_n \in S$, so for $n \geq \max\{N_1, N_2\}$, $z_n \in S$. Hence, $\{z_n\}_{n=1}^{\infty}$ e-converges to x_0. By our assumption, the sequence $\{f(z_n)\}_{n=1}^{\infty}$ e-converges, call the e-limit L_2. Since $L_1 \neq L$, we must have $L_2 \neq L_1$ or $L_2 \neq L$. Let us suppose the latter. Then there exist (by I.3) disjoint e-neighborhoods P_1 and Q_1 of L_2 and L, respectively. Now there is N such that for $n \geq N, f(x_n) \in Q_1$; hence for all even $n \geq N, f(z_n) \notin P_1$, contrary to $\{f(z_n)\}_{n=1}^{\infty}$ e-converging to L_2. The case for $L_2 \neq L_1$ is similar. Thus, L must be an e-limit of f at x_0.

Note that in the course of the proof, we discover a fact we know to be true for limits of functions, namely that if f has an e-limit at x_0, call it L, then for any sequence $\{x_n\}_{n=1}^{\infty}$ of members of $D\backslash\{x_0\}$ e-converging to x_0, it is true that $\{f(x_n)\}_{n=1}^{\infty}$ e-converges to L.

As a corollary to I.5, we obtain the next theorem. The observant reader will notice that part of its proof is hidden in the last paragraph of the proof for I.5. In Chapter 2, we had an analogue of the following theorem at our disposal, so the analogue of I.5 was a bit simpler to prove.

I.6 THEOREM A sequence $\{a_n\}_{n=1}^{\infty}$ of members of E is e-convergent iff every subsequence of $\{a_n\}_{n=1}^{\infty}$ is e-convergent.

Proof: Consider $a : J \to E$ where $a(n) = a_n$ for each $n \in J$. The sequence $\{a_n\}_{n=1}^{\infty}$ e-converges iff a has an e-limit at ∞. If $\{a_{n_k}\}_{k=1}^{\infty}$ is a subsequence of $\{a_n\}_{n=1}^{\infty}$, then $\{n_k\}_{k=1}^{\infty}$ e-converges to ∞. Thus, if $\{a_n\}_{n=1}^{\infty}$ e-converges to A, then a has A as an e-limit at ∞; hence,

$$\{a_{n_k}\}_{k=1}^{\infty} = \{a(n_k)\}_{k=1}^{\infty}$$

e-converges to A. If every subsequence of $\{a_n\}_{n=1}^{\infty}$ e-converges, then $\{a_n\}_{n=1}^{\infty}$ e-converges since it is one of its subsequences.

Let us pause to point out some of the properties of e-neighborhoods that we have used so far:

(1) if $x \neq y$, then there are disjoint e-neighborhoods P and Q of x and y, respectively. This is necessary for I.4;

(2) for each $x \in E$, there is a sequence $\{Q_n\}_{n=1}^{\infty}$ of e-neighborhoods of x such that for any e-neighborhood P, there is n such that $Q_n \subset P$ and such that

$$\bigcap_{n=1}^{\infty} Q_n = \{x\}.$$

In the case where x is finite, ∞, or $-\infty$, we choose Q_n to be $(x - 1/n, x + 1/n)$, $\{y : y > n\}$, or $\{y : y < -n\}$, respectively. This fact was implicitly used in the proof of I.5 and is necessary for the lemma preceding I.5.

There is one more property we should mention here since it is necessary later:

(3) if P and Q are two e-neighborhoods of x, then $P \cap Q$ is also an e-neighborhood of x.

This is a result we used many times before without specifically mentioning it. For example, if $\{a_n\}_{n=1}^{\infty}$ converges to A and $\{b_n\}_{n=1}^{\infty}$ converges to B, then, given $\varepsilon > 0$, there is N_1 such that $n \geq N_1$ implies $|a_n - A| < \varepsilon$ and N_2 such that $n \geq N_2$ implies $|b_n - B| < \varepsilon$. So if we let $N = \max\{N_1, N_2\}$, then for $n \geq N$ we have

$$|a_n - A| < \varepsilon \quad \text{and} \quad |b_n - B| < \varepsilon.$$

The sets

$$P_1 = \{x \in E : x > N_1\} \quad \text{and} \quad P_2 = \{x \in E : x > N_2\}$$

are e-neighborhoods of ∞ and

$$P = \{x \in E : x > N\}$$

is the intersection of P_1 and P_2 and also an e-neighborhood.

We shall prove (3) in the case where x is finite and leave the rest of the work to the reader. Suppose P and Q are e-neighborhoods of x. Then there are positive real numbers ε_1 and ε_2 such that $(x - \varepsilon_1, x + \varepsilon_1) \subset P$ and $(x - \varepsilon_2, x + \varepsilon_2) \subset Q$. Let

$$\varepsilon = \min\{\varepsilon_1, \varepsilon_2\}.$$

Then $\varepsilon > 0$ and

$$(x - \varepsilon, x + \varepsilon) \subset P \cap Q,$$

so $P \cap Q$ is an e-neighborhood of x. Note that we have also proved that the intersection of two neighborhoods of x is a neighborhood of x.

We are now going to tackle a rather ticklish problem, that of worrying about the arithmetic of e-limits. The reservations about defining addition and multiplication on E were motivated by the desire to have the following theorem.

I.7 THEOREM   Suppose $D \subset E, f : D \to R$ and $g : D \to R$, that x_0 is an e-accumulation point of D, and that f and g each have an e-limit at x_0. Let A be the e-limit of f at x_0, and let B be the e-limit of g at x_0. Then
(1)   if $A + B$ is defined, then $f + g$ has $A + B$ as an e-limit at x_0;
(2)   if $A \cdot B$ is defined, then $f \cdot g$ has $A \cdot B$ as an e-limit at x_0;
(3)   if $f(x) \leq g(x)$ for all $x \in D$, then $A \leq B$.

Proof: To accomplish the proof of this theorem, one is forced to consider a number of cases. We shall present a representative sample of these cases and leave the rest to the reader. If A and B are both finite, then the proofs of Theorems 2.4 and 2.5 may be altered slightly to yield the desired results.

Suppose $A = B = \infty$, and let M be any real number. Then there are e-neighborhoods P_1 and P_2 of x_0 such that $x \in P_1 \cap D$ and $x \neq x_0$, imply that

$$f(x) > |M| + 1;$$

and $x \in P_2 \cap D$ and $x \neq x_0$ imply that

$$g(x) > |M| + 1.$$

$P_1 \cap P_2$ is also an e-neighborhood of x_0, and for $x \in P_1 \cap P_2 \cap D$ and $x \neq x_0$, we have

$$f(x) + g(x) > 2|M| + 2 > M \quad \text{and} \quad f(x)g(x) > (|M| + 1)^2 > M.$$

Hence, $f + g$ and fg both have

$$A + B = \infty + \infty = \infty = \infty \cdot \infty = A \cdot B$$

as an e-limit at x_0. The case where $A = B = -\infty$ is left to the reader.

Suppose $A = \infty$ and $B \in R$, and let M be any real number. There are e-neighborhoods P_1 and P_2 of x_0 such that $x \in P_1 \cap D$ and $x \neq x_0$ imply that

$$f(x) > |M| - B + 1;$$

and $x \in P_2 \cap D$ and $x \neq x_0$ imply that

$$B - 1 < g(x) < B + 1.$$

Thus, $P = P_1 \cap P_2$ is an e-neighborhood of x_0 such that $x \in P \cap D$ and $x \neq x_0$ imply that

$$f(x) + g(x) > |M| - B + 1 + B - 1 = |M| \geq M.$$

Thus, $f + g$ has $\infty = A + B$ as an e-limit at x_0. We leave the case $A = -\infty, B \in R$ for the reader.

Suppose now that $A = \infty$, $B \in E$, and $B < 0$ (this includes the case $B = -\infty$). Since $B < 0$, there is a real number r such that $B < r < 0$. Choose any real number M (that is, an e-neighborhood of $-\infty$). There are e-neighborhoods P_1 and P_2 of x_0 such that $x \in P_1 \cap D$ and $x \neq x_0$ imply that

$$f(x) > \left| \frac{M}{r} \right|$$

and such that $x \in P_2 \cap D$ and $x \neq x_0$ imply that

$$g(x) < r.$$

Thus, $P_1 \cap P_2$ is an e-neighborhood of x_0 such that

$$x \in P_1 \cap P_2 \cap D$$

and $x \neq x_0$ imply that

$$f(x)g(x) < \left| \frac{M}{r} \right| \cdot r = -|M| \leq M.$$

Thus, fg has $-\infty = A \cdot B$ as an e-limit at x_0.

We leave the remaining cases and the proof of part (3) to the reader.

Note that the proof given breaks down when the sum or product of A and B fails to be defined. Let us consider several examples to illustrate the reason for this failure.

First of all, $A + B$ fails to be defined if $A = \infty$ and $B = -\infty$. One might be tempted to define $\infty + (-\infty)$ to be zero, but the folly of this will be quickly revealed. Define $f: R \rightarrow R$ by $f(x) = x$, $g: R \rightarrow R$ by $g(x) = 1 - x$, and $h: R \rightarrow R$ by $h(x) = x^2$. Now f, g, and h have e-limits at ∞, and those e-limits are ∞, $-\infty$, and ∞, respectively. Also, $f - f, f + g$, and $f - h$ have e-limits at ∞ and those e-limits are $0, 1$, and $-\infty$, respectively. Thus, regardless of how one decides to define $\infty + (-\infty)$, part 1 of I.7 will be false.

The reader now suspects that the problem with $0 \cdot \infty$ will be much the same. Again, a few simple examples serve to justify this suspicion. Define $f: R \rightarrow R$ by

$$f(x) = x;$$

$g : R \to R$ by

$$g(x) = \frac{1}{x}$$

for $x \neq 0$, $g(0) = 9$; $h : R \to R$ by

$$h(x) = \sqrt{|x|} \, ;$$

and $k : R \to R$ by

$$k(x) = x^2.$$

Now g has zero as an e-limit at ∞ while f, h, and k have ∞ as an e-limit at ∞. However, fg, hg, and kg have $1, 0$, and ∞ as e-limits at ∞. Thus, again, we may not extend part 2 of I.7 by merely defining $0 \cdot \infty$.

We have purposely omitted reference to quotients in I.7, because we wish to consider them separately. Perhaps we should mention that the assumption in I.7 that the images of f and g are subsets of R was made so that $f + g$ and fg were defined on D.

I.8 THEOREM   Suppose $D \subset E, f : D \to R$ and $g : D \to R, x_0$ is an e-accumulation point of D, and $g(x) \neq 0$ for all $x \in D$. Let us suppose further that A is the e-limit of f at x_0 and B is the e-limit of g at x_0. Then
   (1)   if A is finite and $B \neq 0$, then f/g has an e-limit at x_0 and that e-limit is zero if B is infinite or A/B in case B is finite;
   (2)   if A is infinite and B is finite and not zero, then f/g has ∞ as an e-limit if $A = \infty$ and $B > 0$ or $A = -\infty$ and $B < 0$; if $A = -\infty$ and $B > 0$ or if $A = \infty$ and $B < 0$, then f/g has $-\infty$ as an e-limit.

Proof: If A and B are both finite and $B \neq 0$, the proof is like that of Theorem 2.4. Let us suppose now that A is finite and B is infinite. We wish to show that zero is an e-limit of f/g. Choose a real number $\varepsilon > 0$. There is an e-neighborhood P_1 of x_0 such that $x \in P_1 \cap D$ and $x \neq x_0$ imply that

$$A - 1 < f(x) < A + 1.$$

Let $M = \max\{|A - 1|, |A + 1|\}$. There is an e-neighborhood P_2 of x_0 such that $x \in P_2 \cap D$ and $x \neq x_0$ imply that

$$g(x) > \frac{M}{\varepsilon}$$

if $B = \infty$ or

$$g(x) < -\frac{M}{\varepsilon}$$

if $B = -\infty$. Thus, $P_1 \cap P_2$ is an e-neighborhood of x_0 such that $x \in P_1 \cap P_2 \cap D$ and $x \neq x_0$ imply that

$$-\varepsilon < \frac{f(x)}{g(x)} < \varepsilon.$$

Hence, zero is an e-limit of f/g at x_0.

Suppose now that $A = \infty$ and B is finite with $B > 0$. We shall show that f/g has ∞ as an e-limit and leave the remaining cases to the reader. Choose any real number M. Since $B > 0$, there is a real number r such that $0 < r < B$. There are e-neighborhoods P_1 and P_2 of x_0 such that if $x \in P_1 \cap D$ and $x \neq x_0$, then

$$f(x) > \frac{|M|}{r}$$

and such that if $x \in P_2 \cap D$ and $x \neq x_0$, then

$$g(x) > r.$$

Thus, $P_1 \cap P_2$ is an e-neighborhood of x_0 such that

$$x \in P_1 \cap P_2 \cap D$$

and $x \neq x_0$ imply that

$$\frac{f(x)}{g(x)} > \left(\frac{|M|}{r}\right) \cdot r = |M| \geq M.$$

Hence, ∞ is an e-limit of f/g at x_0.

The cases where A and B are both infinite or where $B = 0$ yield problems similar to those discussed following I.8. The reader is invited to construct a few examples to see this.

It goes without saying that I.7 and I.8 yield results for *e*-convergent sequences.

To illustrate the results presented so far let us consider what are referred to as "improper integrals."

DEFINITION   Suppose $a \in R$ and $f : \{x : x > a\} \to R$ is Riemann-integrable on $[a, b]$ for each $b \geq a$. Define

$$F(x) = \int_a^x f(t)\, dt$$

for each real number $x \geq a$. The function F is referred to as an *improper integral of the first kind* and is denoted by

$$\int_a^\infty f(t)\, dt.$$

The improper integral is said to *converge* if F has a finite *e*-limit at ∞. If F has a finite *e*-limit at ∞, we shall also denote it by

$$\int_a^\infty f(t)\, dt.$$

This peculiar usage is not new since we used the notation

$$\sum_{n=1}^\infty a_n$$

for both the infinite series and its sum if it converged. Improper integrals of the form

$$\int_{-\infty}^b f(t)\, dt$$

may also be defined in an obvious way. If $f : R \to R$ is such that f is Riemann-integrable on each interval and if there is $a \in R$ such that

$$\int_a^\infty f(t)\, dt \quad \text{and} \quad \int_{-\infty}^a f(t)\, dt$$

are both convergent, we say that the integral

$$\int_{-\infty}^\infty f(t)\, dt$$

is convergent and we define its value to be

$$\int_a^\infty f(t)\, dt + \int_{-\infty}^a f(t)\, dt.$$

Suppose $g(x) = 1/x$ for $x \geq 1$ and $f(x) = 1/x^2$ for $x \geq 1$. For each $x \geq 1$,

$$G(x) = \int_1^x g(t)\, dt = \log x \quad \text{and} \quad F(x) = \int_1^x f(t)\, dt = 1 - \frac{1}{x}.$$

Now G and F both have e-limits at ∞, but the e-limit of G at ∞ is ∞ whereas the e-limit of F at ∞ is 1. Thus, the improper integral

$$\int_1^\infty \frac{dt}{t}$$

is not convergent, whereas the improper integral

$$\int_1^\infty \frac{dt}{t^2}$$

is convergent and

$$\int_1^\infty \frac{dt}{t^2} = 1.$$

In some respects, the theory of improper integrals of the first kind is similar to the theory of infinite series. One may draw a parallel between the partial sums

$$\sum_{n=0}^k a_n$$

and the "partial" integrals

$$\int_a^b f(t)\, dt$$

and between the infinite sum

$$\sum_{n=0}^\infty a_n$$

and the infinite integral

$$\int_a^\infty f(t)\, dt.$$

Perhaps the reader recalls the "integral test" for convergence of infinite series, which we present next.

I.9 THEOREM   Suppose $f: \{x \in R : x \geq 1\} \to R$ is decreasing and $f(x) \geq 0$ for all $x \geq 1$. Further, assume that f is Riemann-integrable on $[1, x]$ for each $x \geq 1$. Then

$$\sum_{n=1}^{\infty} f(n)$$

converges iff

$$\int_1^{\infty} f(t)\, dt$$

converges.

Proof: Since f is decreasing and non-negative, for each integer $n \geq 1$,

$$f(n + 1) \leq \int_n^{n+1} f(t)\, dt \leq f(n);$$

hence, for each integer $n \geq 1$,

$$\sum_{k=1}^{n} f(k) \leq f(1) + \int_1^n f(t)\, dt$$

and

$$\int_1^n f(t)\, dt \leq \sum_{k=1}^{n-1} f(k).$$

Since $f(k) \geq 0$ for all integers k, the series

$$\sum_{k=1}^{\infty} f(k)$$

converges iff the sequence of partial sums is bounded. If we can prove that

$$\int_1^{\infty} f(t)\, dt$$

converges iff the set

$$\left\{ \int_1^x f(t)\, dt : x \geq 1 \right\}$$

is bounded, we'll be in business. In general, this is not true, but in the case of $f(t) \geq 0$ for all $t \geq 1$, it indeed is true. We shall thus digress for the moment to prove two theorems which satisfy our desires.

I.10 THEOREM   Suppose $f : \{x : x \geq a\} \to R$ is monotone. Then f has a finite e-limit at ∞ iff f is bounded on some e-neighborhood of ∞.

Proof: We shall handle the case where f is increasing; the case for f decreasing will be left to the reader.

If f is increasing and not bounded on any e-neighborhood of ∞, then f must not be bounded from above. Choose $M \in R$. Since f is not bounded from above, then there is $x \in \{x : x \geq a\}$ such that $f(x) > M$. Thus, for $y > x$,

$$f(y) \geq f(x) > M.$$

Hence, ∞ is the e-limit of f at ∞.

Suppose f is increasing and bounded on $\{x : x > M\}$. Thus, the set $\{f(x) : x > M\}$ is a set bounded from above; let

$$s = \sup \{f(x) : x > M\}.$$

We shall show that s is the e-limit of f at ∞. Choose $\varepsilon > 0$. Then $s - \varepsilon$ is not the supremum of $\{f(x) : x > M\}$, so there is y such that $s - \varepsilon < f(y)$. Thus, for $x > y$,

$$s - \varepsilon < f(y) \leq f(x) \leq s.$$

Hence, s is the e-limit of f at ∞.

I.11 THEOREM   Suppose $f : \{x : x \geq a\} \to R$ is non-negative and Riemann-integrable on $[a, b]$ for each $b \geq a$. Then

$$\int_a^\infty f(t)\,dt$$

converges if the set

$$\left\{ \int_a^b f(t)\,dt : b \geq a \right\}$$

is bounded.

Proof: Define

$$F(b) = \int_a^b f(t)\,dt$$

for all $b \geq a$. Since f is non-negative, F is increasing and non-negative and hence has a finite e-limit at ∞ iff F is bounded. This, however, is equivalent to the boundedness of the set

$$\left\{ \int_a^b f(t)\,dt : b \geq a \right\}.$$

The integral test now allows us to use results from the theory of infinite series to study improper integrals and vice versa. Let us consider some of the topics in Chapter 6 and see what the corresponding results are for improper integrals. Roughly speaking, one would suspect that

$$\int_a^\infty f(t)\,dt$$

will converge only if $f(t)$ tends to zero "fast enough" as t gets large.

I.12 THEOREM   Suppose $f : \{x \in R : x \geq a\} \to R$ is Riemann-integrable on $[a, b]$ for all $a \leq b$. Then the improper integral

$$\int_a^\infty f(t)\,dt$$

converges iff for each $\varepsilon > 0$, there is $M \in R$ such that $M \leq c \leq d$ implies that

$$\left| \int_c^d f(t)\,dt \right| < \varepsilon.$$

Proof: Define

$$F(b) = \int_a^b f(t)\,dt$$

for all $a \leq b$. Then

$$|F(d) - F(c)| = \left| \int_c^d f(t)\,dt \right|$$

for all $a \leq c \leq d$. Suppose F has a finite e-limit L at ∞, and choose $e > 0$. Then $M \in R$ such that $M < x$ implies that $|F(x) - L| < \varepsilon/2$. Hence, for $M + 1 \leq c \leq d$,

$$|F(d) - F(c)| \leq |F(d) - L| + |F(c) - L| < \frac{\varepsilon}{2} + \frac{\varepsilon}{2} = \varepsilon.$$

Suppose now that the condition is satisfied in that for each $\varepsilon > 0$, there is $M \in R$ such that $M \leq c \leq d$ implies that

$$\left| \int_c^d f(t)\, dt \right| < \varepsilon.$$

Choose any sequence $\{x_n\}_{n=1}^{\infty}$ of members of $\{x : x \geq a\}$ which e-converges to ∞. Choose $\varepsilon > 0$. There is $M \in R$ such that $M \leq c \leq d$ implies that

$$\left| \int_c^d f(t)\, dt \right| < \varepsilon.$$

There is $N \in R$ such that $n \geq N$ implies that $M < x_n$. Thus, for $m \geq N$ and $n \geq N$,

$$|F(x_n) - F(x_m)| = \left| \int_{x_m}^{x_n} f(t)\, dt \right| < \varepsilon;$$

hence, the sequence $\{F(x_n)\}_{n=1}^{\infty}$ is Cauchy, and hence convergent. Thus, by I.5, F has an e-limit at ∞, and since Cauchy sequences have finite e-limits,

$$\int_a^{\infty} f(t)\, dt$$

is convergent.

It is not true that the convergence of

$$\int_a^{\infty} f(t)\, dt$$

implies that f has an e-limit of zero at ∞ even when f is continuous. To see this, define $f(x) = \sin x^2$ for all real x. Every e-neighborhood of ∞ contains points x and y such that $f(x) = 0$ and $f(y) = 1$; hence, f does not have an e-limit at ∞. We shall see shortly that

$$\int_1^{\infty} \sin x^2 \, dx$$

is convergent.

Just as in studying infinite series, one may consider absolute and conditional convergence of improper integrals. The example mentioned above,

$$\int_1^{\infty} \sin x^2 \, dx,$$

fails to converge absolutely.

DEFINITION   An improper integral

$$\int_a^\infty f(t)\,dt$$

converges *absolutely* if the improper integral

$$\int_a^\infty |f(t)|\,dt$$

is convergent. If an improper integral converges but fails to converge absolutely, it is said to converge *conditionally*.

We have introduced a convention in this definition designed to make matters a bit simpler. When we speak of an improper integral

$$\int_a^\infty f(t)\,dt,$$

we shall automatically imply that $f: \{x \in R : x \geq a\} \to R$ and that f is Riemann-integrable on $[a, b]$ for all $a \leq b$.
Since

$$\left| \int_c^d f(t)\,dt \right| \leq \int_c^d |f(t)|\,dt$$

for all $a \leq c \leq d$, it is clear that absolute convergence implies convergence, by I.12. (Note that the integrability of f implies the integrability of $|f|$.) Of course, there are cases where $|f|$ is integrable on $[a, b]$ but f is not. Our unwritten hypotheses, of course, rule out such examples here.

I.13 THEOREM   The improper integral

$$\int_1^\infty x^{-p} \sin x\,dx$$

converges absolutely for $p > 1$ and converges conditionally for $0 < p \leq 1$.

Proof: Suppose $p > 1$. Then for all $b \geq 1$,

$$0 \leq \int_1^b |x^{-p} \sin x|\,dx \leq \int_1^b x^{-p}\,dx = \frac{-1}{p-1}\left[\frac{1}{b^{p-1}} - 1\right] = F(b).$$

Since $p - 1 > 0$, then by I.7 and I.8, F has an e-limit at ∞ and that e-limit is finite. F is monotone, and hence bounded, since it has a finite e-limit at ∞; hence by I.11,

$$\int_1^\infty |x^{-p} \sin x| \, dx$$

is convergent, which means

$$\int_1^\infty x^{-p} \sin x \, dx$$

is absolutely convergent.

Suppose now that $0 < p \leq 1$. Then, invoking integration by parts (x^{-p} and $\cos x$ are both functions of bounded variation), we have for all $b \geq 1$,

$$\int_1^b x^{-p} \sin x \, dx = b^{-p}(-\cos b) - (-\cos 1)$$
$$- \int_1^b (-\cos x)(-px^{-p-1}) \, dx.$$

Define

$$G_1(x) = x^{-p}(-\cos x) + \cos 1$$

and

$$G_2(x) = \int_1^x t^{-p-1} \cos t \, dt.$$

Since $|\cos x| \leq 1$ for all x and $p > 0$, G_1 has a finite e-limit at ∞. For all $x \geq 1$,

$$\int_1^x |\cos t| \, t^{-p-1} \, dt \leq \int_1^x t^{-p-1} \, dt = \frac{-1}{p}\left[\frac{1}{x^p} - 1\right];$$

hence the improper integral $\int_1^\infty (\cos t) t^{-p-1} \, dt$ converges absolutely. Hence, G_2 has a finite e-limit at ∞. Thus, by I.7,

$$\int_1^\infty x^{-p} \sin x \, dx$$

converges for $0 < p \leq 1$.

It now remains to show that

$$\int_1^\infty |x^{-p} \sin x| \, dx$$

does not converge for $0 < p \leq 1$. This will be accomplished if we can prove that the set

$$\left\{ \int_1^b |x^{-p} \sin x| \, dx : b \geq 1 \right\}$$

is unbounded. For each positive integer n,

$$\int_1^{n\pi} x^{-p} |\sin x| \, dx \geq \int_\pi^{n\pi} x^{-p} |\sin x| \, dx$$

$$= \sum_{k=1}^{n-1} \int_{k\pi}^{(k+1)\pi} x^{-p} |\sin x| \, dx \geq \sum_{k=1}^{n-1} \frac{1}{[(k+1)\pi]^p} \int_{k\pi}^{(k+1)\pi} |\sin x| \, dx$$

$$= 2 \sum_{k=1}^{n-1} \frac{1}{\pi^p} \frac{1}{(k+1)^p}.$$

Since $p < 1$, the series

$$\sum_{k=1}^\infty \frac{1}{(k+1)^p}$$

diverges, hence the partial sums are unbounded. Thus, the set

$$\left\{ \int_1^b x^{-p} |\sin x| \, dx : b \geq 1 \right\}$$

is unbounded.

Consider now $\int_1^\infty \sin x^2 \, dx$. By the change of variable theorem,

$$\int_1^b \sin x^2 \, dx = \frac{1}{2} \int_1^{b^2} \frac{\sin t}{\sqrt{t}} \, dt.$$

Hence, by I.13, $\int_1^\infty \sin x^2 \, dx$ converges conditionally.

Theorem I.13 is obviously open to generalization. We invite the reader to go over the proof carefully to find suitable generalizations. Also, note that we essentially used a type of comparison test in this proof. The reader is invited to state and prove a comparison test for improper integrals.

We close this appendix with the fond hopes that we have inspired the reader to study further the topics introduced herein and have equipped him adequately for such study.

EXERCISES

1. Prove part c of I.1
2. Define $f : \{x : x \neq 0\} \to R$ by $f(x) = \sin 1/x$. Does f have an e-limit at zero, at ∞, or at $-\infty$?
3. Define a set $A \subset E$ to be e-open if for each $a \in A$ there is an e-neighborhood Q of a such that $Q \subset A$. Define a set $B \subset E$ to be e-closed if $E \backslash B$ is e-open. Prove that B is e-closed iff each e-accumulation point of B belongs to B.
4. Using the definitions of Exercise 3, define a set $A \subset E$ to be e-compact if each e-open cover of A has a finite subcover so that, for each collection $\{A_\lambda\}_{\lambda \in \Lambda}$ of e-open sets such that $A \subset \bigcup_{\lambda \in \Lambda} A_\lambda$, there are $\lambda_1, \ldots, \lambda_n \in \Lambda$ such that $A \subset \bigcup_{i=1}^{n} A_{\lambda_i}$. Prove that a set $A \subset E$ is e-compact iff A is e-closed. In particular, E is e-compact.
5. Let $D \subset E$ and $f : D \to E$. Define f to be e-continuous at $x_0 \in D$ if for each e-neighborhood Q of $f(x_0)$, $f^{-1}(Q)$ is an e-neighborhood of x_0. Define $f : E \to [-1, 1]$ by

$$f(x) = \frac{x}{|x| + 1}$$

   for $x \in R$, $f(\infty) = 1$, and $f(-\infty) = -1$. Prove that f is e-continuous, f is 1–1, $f(E) = [-1, 1]$, and $f^{-1} : [-1, 1] \to E$ is e-continuous.
6. Prove the lemma preceding I.5.
7. Prove that the sequence $\{y_n\}_{n=1}^{\infty}$ in the proof of I.5 e-converges to x_0.
8. Prove part 3 of I.7.
9. Show by examples that it is foolish to try to define $-\infty/0$, $\infty/0$, ∞/∞, $\infty/-\infty$, $-\infty/-\infty$, or $-\infty/\infty$ in such a way as to extend the results of I.8.
10. Generalize I.13 by translating 6.14 for infinite series to a result for improper integrals.
11. Convert the limit comparison test for infinite series (cf. Exercise 6, Chapter 6) to an analogous result for improper integrals.
12. Prove that every monotone sequence of real numbers is e-convergent.
13. Prove that every sequence of real numbers has an e-convergent subsequence.

SEQUENCES AND SERIES
OF FUNCTIONS

In Chapter 6, we devoted some time to the consideration of power series, and we left many rather obvious questions unasked and unanswered. In this appendix, we shall seek out these questions and try to answer some of them.

Suppose $\sum_{n=0}^{\infty} a_n x^n$ is a power series which converges for $-r < x < r$ where $r > 0$. For each integer $n \geq 0$, define $S_n : (-r, r) \to R$ by

$$S_n(x) = \sum_{k=0}^{n} a_k x^k$$

for all $x \in (-r, r)$. Therefore, for each $x \in (-r, r)$ and each integer $n \geq 0, S_n(x)$ is the nth partial sum of the convergent series $\sum_{n=0}^{\infty} a_n x^n$, so the sequence $\{S_n(x)\}_{n=0}^{\infty}$ converges to $\sum_{n=0}^{\infty} a_n x^n$. It is natural to define a function $S : (-r, r) \to R$ by defining $S(x)$ to be the limit of the convergent sequence $\{S_n(x)\}_{n=0}^{\infty}$ or, equivalently,

$$S(x) = \sum_{n=0}^{\infty} a_n x^n,$$

for all $x \in (-r, r)$. It is customary to denote the limit of a convergent sequence $\{a_n\}_{n=1}^{\infty}$ by $\lim_{n \to \infty} a_n$. We have avoided this usage because of possible conflict with the notation in Chapter 2. However, especially if he has read Appendix I, the reader should not be disturbed by this notation. Thus, we would write

$$S(x) = \lim_{n \to \infty} S_n(x)$$

for each $x \in (-r, r)$. Each S_n is a polynomial, and hence is continuous everywhere, differentiable everywhere, and Riemann-integrable on every interval of finite length. Does S inherit any of these nice properties? If S is differentiable at $x \in (-r, r)$, is it true that

$$S'(x) = \lim_{n \to \infty} S_n'(x) = \sum_{n=0}^{\infty} n a_n x^{n-1} \, ?$$

If S is Riemann-integrable on $[a, b] \subset (-r, r)$, is it true that

$$\int_a^b S(t)\, dt = \lim_{n \to \infty} \int_a^b S_n(t)\, dt = \sum_{n=0}^{\infty} a_n \left[\frac{b^{n+1} - a^{n+1}}{n+1} \right] ?$$

Perhaps there lurks in the reader's past some experience with Fourier series—that is, series of the type

$$\sum_{n=0}^{\infty} (a_n \cos nx + b_n \sin nx).$$

Here again, define $T_n : R \to R$ by

$$T_n(x) = \sum_{k=0}^{n} (a_k \cos kx + b_k \sin kx)$$

for each integer $n \geq 0$. If this series converges for all $x \in E$, one may define a function $T : E \to R$ by

$$T(x) = \lim_{n \to \infty} T_n(x) = \sum_{n=0}^{\infty} (a_n \cos nx + b_n \sin nx)$$

for all $x \in E$. Again, the same questions may be asked concerning the nature of T. These last remarks lead us to suspect that it may be more profitable to consider the situation in general rather than concentrate our attention on power series alone.

DEFINITION Suppose $\{f_n\}_{n=0}^{\infty}$ is a sequence of functions and that E is a subset of R such that $E \subset \operatorname{dom} f_n$ for each integer $n \geq 0$. Then $\{f_n\}_{n=0}^{\infty}$ *converges pointwise* on E if for each $x \in E$, the sequence

$$\{f_n(x)\}_{n=0}^{\infty}$$

converges. If $\{f_n\}_{n=0}^{\infty}$ converges pointwise on E, define $f : E \to R$ by

$$f(x) = \lim_{n \to \infty} f_n(x)$$

for each $x \in E$.

We say that $\{f_n\}_{n=0}^{\infty}$ converges pointwise to f on E. It is common practice to call f the *limit function* of the sequence $\{f_n\}_{n=0}^{\infty}$ and write $f = \lim_{n \to \infty} f_n$.

As a simple and familiar example, for each integer $n \geq 0$, define $f_n : (-1, 1) \to R$ by

$$f_n(x) = \sum_{k=0}^{n} x^k$$

for each $x \in (-1, 1)$. Then $\{f_n\}_{n=1}^{\infty}$ converges pointwise on $(-1, 1)$ to the function $g(x) = 1/(1 - x)$.

We depart from the realm of power series to seek other examples. Define for each integer $n > 0, f_n : [0, 1] \to R$ by

$$f_n(x) = x^n$$

for each $x \in [0, 1]$. For $x \in [0, 1)$,

$$\{f_n(x)\}_{n=1}^{\infty}$$

converges to zero and for $x = 1$,

$$\{f_n(x)\}_{n=1}^{\infty}$$

converges to 1. Thus, the limit function is not continuous although each f_n is continuous.

For each positive integer n, define $g_n : [0, 1] \to R$ by

$$g_n(x) = n$$

for $0 < x \leq 1/n$,

$$g_n(0) = 0 \quad \text{and} \quad g_n(x) = 0$$

for $1/n < x \le 1$. Then $\{g_n\}_{n=1}^{\infty}$ converges pointwise on $[0, 1]$ to the function g, which is zero for all $x \in [0, 1]$. Each g_n is Riemann-integrable on $[0, 1]$, as is g, but

$$\left\{ \int_0^1 g_n(t)\, dt \right\}_{n=1}^{\infty}$$

converges to 1, whereas $\int_0^1 g(t)\, dt = 0$.

Consider the sequence $\{h_n\}_{n=1}^{\infty}$ defined by

$$h_n(x) = \frac{1}{x}$$

for $1/n \le x < 1$ and

$$h_n(x) = n^2 x$$

for $0 \le x < 1/n$. The sequence $\{h_n(x)\}_{n=1}^{\infty}$ converges to $1/x$ for $0 < x < 1$ and converges to zero at $x = 0$. Here each h_n is continuous, but the limit function is unbounded, and hence not Riemann-integrable. Note further that the sequence

$$\left\{ \int_0^1 h_n(t)\, dt \right\}_{n=1}^{\infty}$$

is unbounded.

The sequence $\{f_n\}_{n=1}^{\infty}$ given above yields an example of a sequence of differentiable functions which converges to a function that fails to be differentiable. We now present a sequence of differentiable functions $\{k_n\}_{n=1}^{\infty}$ such that the limit function k is differentiable, but for some x,

$$k'(x) \ne \lim_{n \to \infty} k_n'(x).$$

To this end, define for each positive integer n, $k_n : [-1, 1] \to R$ by

$$k_n(x) = \frac{x}{1 + nx^2}$$

for all $x \in [-1, 1]$. For each positive integer n, k_n is differentiable on $[-1, 1]$ and

$$k_n'(x) = \frac{1 - nx^2}{(1 + nx^2)^2}.$$

From this, it is easy to see that the minimum and maximum values of k_n occur at $-1/\sqrt{n}$ and $1/\sqrt{n}$, respectively. Hence,

$$|k_n(x)| \le \frac{1}{2\sqrt{n}}$$

for all $x \in [-1, 1]$ and all positive integers n. It follows quite easily that $\{k_n(x)\}_{n=1}^{\infty}$ converges to zero for all $x \in [-1, 1]$. The limit function is thus constant on $[-1, 1]$, hence differentiable with the derivative equal to zero everywhere on $[-1, 1]$. However, $k_n'(0) = 1$ for all n.

Rather than be discouraged by this list of examples, we shall examine these examples more carefully with the hope of finding a substitute for pointwise convergence that yields affirmative answers to some of the questions posed earlier.

Suppose $\{f_n\}_{n=1}^{\infty}$ converges pointwise to a function f on a set E. This means that for each $\varepsilon > 0$ and each $x \in E$, there is N (probably depending on both x and ε), such that for each positive integer n, $n \ge N$ implies

$$|f_n(x) - f(x)| < \varepsilon.$$

Again, for each positive integer n, define $f_n(x) = x^n$ for each $x \in [0, 1]$. Given $0 < x < 1$ and $\varepsilon > 0$, there is a lower bound for the possible values of N; in fact, N must be larger than $|\log \varepsilon / \log x|$. For x close to 1 but different from 1, N must be quite large, for, given any $0 < \varepsilon < 1$ and any positive integer m, there is $0 < x < 1$ such that $x^m > \varepsilon$. These last remarks are especially meaningful in light of the fact that the discontinuity of the limit function occurred at 1. We are led to suspect that a notion of "uniform" convergence, so-named because of the similar distinction between continuity and uniform continuity, might be in order.

DEFINITION   A sequence $\{f_n\}_{n=1}^{\infty}$ of functions is said to *converge uniformly* on E if there is a function $f: E \to R$ such that for each $\varepsilon > 0$, there is N such that for each positive integer n, $n \ge N$ implies that

$$|f_n(x) - f(x)| < \varepsilon$$

for all $x \in E$. We may also express this by writing "the sequence $\{f_n\}_{n=1}^{\infty}$ converges uniformly to f on E".

Naturally, a series $\sum_{n=0}^{\infty} f_n$ of functions will converge pointwise or converge uniformly on E as the sequence $\{S_n\}_{n=0}^{\infty}$ of partial sums, defined by

$$S_n(x) = \sum_{k=0}^{n} f_k(x),$$

converges pointwise or uniformly on E.

The following theorem arises quite naturally after our previous experience with sequences. The proof will be left to the reader.

II.1 THEOREM   A sequence of functions $\{f_n\}_{n=1}^{\infty}$ converges uniformly on E iff for each $\varepsilon > 0$ there is a real number N such that for all positive integers m and n, $m \geq N$ and $n \geq N$ imply that

$$|f_n(x) - f_m(x)| < \varepsilon$$

for all $x \in E$.

For infinite series of functions, there is a very convenient test for uniform convergence, called the Weierstrass M-test.

II.2 THEOREM   (Weierstrass M-test) Suppose $\{f_n\}_{n=1}^{\infty}$ is a sequence of functions defined on E and $\{M_n\}_{n=1}^{\infty}$ is a sequence of non-negative real numbers such that

$$|f_n(x)| \leq M_n$$

for all $x \in E$ and all positive integers n. If $\sum_{n=1}^{\infty} M_n$ converges, then $\sum_{n=1}^{\infty} f_n$ converges uniformly on E.

Proof: Choose $\varepsilon > 0$. Since $\sum_{n=1}^{\infty} M_n$ converges, there is a real number N such that for all positive integers m and n, $N \leq n \leq m$ implies that

$$\sum_{k=n}^{m} M_k < \varepsilon.$$

(Recall that $M_n \geq 0$ for all positive integers n.) Thus, for all positive integers m and n, $N \leq n \leq m$ implies that

$$|S_m(x) - S_n(x)| = \left| \sum_{k=n+1}^{m} f_k(x) \right| \leq \sum_{k=n+1}^{m} M_k < \varepsilon$$

for all $x \in E$. By II.1, $\sum_{k=1}^{\infty} f_k$ converges uniformly on E.

We have exhibited remarkable confidence in the definition of uniform convergence by proving the last two theorems before having any concrete evidence that this new concept is really useful. The next few theorems serve to show that this confidence is not unfounded.

Suppose $\{f_n\}_{n=1}^{\infty}$ is a sequence of functions converging uniformly to f on E such that for each positive integer n, f_n is continuous at $x_0 \in E$. Choose $\varepsilon > 0$. There is N such that for each positive integer n, $n \geq N$ implies that

$$|f_n(x) - f(x)| < \varepsilon$$

for all $x \in E$. Since f_N is continuous at x_0, there is $\delta > 0$ such that $|x - x_0| < \delta$ and $x \in E$ imply that

$$|f_N(x) - f_N(x_0)| < \varepsilon.$$

Hence, for $|x - x_0| < \delta$ and $x \in E$, we have

$$|f(x) - f(x_0)| \leq |f(x) - f_N(x)| + |f_N(x) - f_N(x_0)|$$
$$+ |f_N(x_0) - f(x_0)| < \varepsilon + \varepsilon + \varepsilon = 3\varepsilon.$$

It seems we have just proved a theorem. What is really necessary for this proof to yield the desired conclusion—that f is continuous at x_0?

First of all, it is sufficient that infinitely many members of the sequence $\{f_n\}_{n=1}^{\infty}$ be continuous at x_0. Second, uniform convergence on all of E is unnecessary. We now present a slight modification of our original definition of uniform convergence which will suffice for this proof.

DEFINITION   Suppose $\{f_n\}_{n=1}^{\infty}$ is a sequence of functions converging pointwise to a function f on a set E. Then $\{f_n\}_{n=1}^{\infty}$ *converges uniformly at* $x_0 \in E$ if for each $\varepsilon > 0$, there are positive real numbers N and δ such that for each positive integer n, $n \geq N$, $|x - x_0| < \delta$ and $x \in E$ imply that

$$|f_n(x) - f(x)| < \varepsilon.$$

It is immediate that if $\{f_n\}_{n=1}^{\infty}$ converges uniformly to f on E, then $\{f\}_{n=1}^{\infty}$ converges uniformly at x for each $x \in E$. Conversely, if E is compact and $\{f_n\}_{n=1}^{\infty}$ converges uniformly at x for each $x \in E$, then $\{f_n\}_{n=1}^{\infty}$ converges uniformly on E. Can you prove this?

II.3 THEOREM   Suppose $\{f_n\}_{n=1}^{\infty}$ converges pointwise to f on E, $x_0 \in E$, and infinitely many members of the sequence are continuous at x_0. If $\{f_n\}_{n=1}^{\infty}$ converges uniformly at x_0, then f is continuous at x_0.

Proof: Choose $\varepsilon > 0$. There are positive real numbers N and δ such that for each positive integer $n \geq N$,

$$|f_n(x) - f(x)| < \frac{\varepsilon}{3}$$

for all $x \in E$ such that $|x - x_0| < \delta$. There is a positive integer $n_0 \geq N$ such that f_{n_0} is continuous at x_0; hence there is $\delta_1 > 0$ such that $|x - x_0| < \delta_1$ and $x \in E$ imply that

$$|f_{n_0}(x) - f_{n_0}(x_0)| < \frac{\varepsilon}{3}.$$

Let $\delta_2 = \min \{\delta, \delta_1\}$. Then for $|x - x_0| < \delta_2$ and $x \varepsilon E$, we have

$$|f(x) - f(x_0)| \leq |f(x) - f_{n_0}(x)| + |f_{n_0}(x) - f_{n_0}(x_0)|$$

$$+ |f_{n_0}(x_0) - f(x_0)| < \frac{\varepsilon}{3} + \frac{\varepsilon}{3} + \frac{\varepsilon}{3} = \varepsilon.$$

Consequently, f is continuous at x_0.

In particular, it follows from II.3 that if $\{f_n\}_{n=1}^{\infty}$ is a sequence of functions continuous on E and converging uniformly to f on E, then f is continuous. (Of course, it is implicit that $E = \text{dom } f$.)

The example presented earlier to convince the reader that the limit of a sequence of continuous functions need not be Riemann-integrable yielded a limit function that was unbounded. The added hypothesis of uniform convergence will serve to eliminate such occurrences.

II.4 THEOREM   If $\{f_n\}_{n=1}^{\infty}$ is a sequence of functions converging uniformly to f on E and for each positive integer n, f_n is bounded on E, then f is bounded on E.

Proof: Let $\varepsilon = 1$. There is a real number N such that for each positive integer $n, n \geq N$ implies that

$$|f_n(x) - f(x)| < 1$$

for all $x \in E$. There is M such that $|f_N(x)| \leq M$ for all $x \in E$. Hence, for all $x \in E$,

$$|f(x)| \leq |f(x) - f_N(x)| + |f_N(x)| \leq 1 + M.$$

One should now hope that if $\{f_n\}_{n=1}^{\infty}$ converges uniformly to f on $[a, b]$ and for each positive integer n, f_n is Riemann-integrable on $[a, b]$, then f is Riemann-integrable on $[a, b]$. This and more is the content of the next theorem.

II.5 THEOREM   Let $\{f_n\}_{n=1}^{\infty}$ be a sequence of functions, each Riemann-integrable on $[a, b]$, converging uniformly to f on $[a, b]$. Define

$$F_n(t) = \int_a^t f_n(x)\, dx$$

for each $t \in [a, b]$ and each positive integer n. Then f is Riemann-integrable on $[a, b]$, and $\{F_n\}_{n=1}^{\infty}$ converges uniformly on $[a, b]$ to the function F defined by

$$F(t) = \int_a^t f(x)\, dx$$

for each $t \in [a, b]$.

Proof: Each f_n is bounded on $[a, b]$, so by II.4, f is also bounded. We may suppose $a < b$. Choose $\varepsilon > 0$. There is a real number N such that for each positive integer $n, n \geq N$ implies that

$$|f_n(x) - f(x)| < \frac{\varepsilon}{3(b - a)}$$

for all $x \in [a, b]$. There is a partition P of $[a, b]$ such that

$$U(P, f_N) - L(P, f_N) < \frac{\varepsilon}{3}.$$

For each $x \in [a, b]$,

$$f_N(x) - \frac{\varepsilon}{3(b-a)} < f(x) < f_N(x) + \frac{\varepsilon}{3(b-a)}.$$

Thus,

$$L(P, f_N) - \frac{\varepsilon}{3} < L(P, f) \le U(P, f) < U(P, f_N) + \frac{\varepsilon}{3}.$$

Consequently,

$$U(P, f) - L(P, f) < U(P, f_N) - L(P, f_N) + \frac{2\varepsilon}{3}.$$

Hence, f is Riemann-integrable on $[a, b]$.

Again, choose $\varepsilon > 0$ and N such that for each positive integer n, $n \ge N$ implies that

$$|f_n(x) - f(x)| < \frac{\varepsilon}{3(b-a)}$$

for all $x \in [a, b]$. Then for each positive integer $n, n \ge N$ implies that

$$|F_n(t) - F(t)| = \left| \int_a^t f_n(x)\, dx - \int_a^t f(x)\, dx \right| \le \int_a^t |f_n(x) - f(x)|\, dx$$

$$\le (t - a)\frac{\varepsilon}{3(b-a)} \le \frac{\varepsilon}{3} < \varepsilon$$

for all $t \in [a, b]$. Therefore, $\{F_n\}_{n=1}^{\infty}$ converges uniformly to F on $[a, b]$.

Very soon, we shall prove that the power series $\sum_{n=0}^{\infty} x^n$ converges uniformly on any closed interval $[a, b] \subset (-1, 1)$. (Do you want to try the proof now? Why not?) Assuming this fact, let us see what results we can obtain with the aid of II.5. Choose any closed interval $[a, b] \subset (-1, 1)$. It is no surprise that

$$\sum_{n=0}^{\infty} x^n = \frac{1}{1 - x}$$

is Riemann-integrable on $[a, b]$. But II.5 implies even more; it implies also that

$$\sum_{n=0}^{\infty} \int_0^x t^n \, dt = \sum_{n=0}^{\infty} \frac{x^{n+1}}{n+1}$$

converges uniformly to $\int_0^x dt/(1-t)$ on $[a, b]$. From Chapter 7, recall that

$$\int_0^x \frac{dt}{1-t} = -\log(1-x),$$

so we have a power series $\sum_{n=0}^{\infty} x^{n+1}/(n+1)$ which converges to $-\log(1-x)$ on $(-1, 1)$ and converges uniformly on any closed subinterval of $(-1, 1)$.

The concept of uniform convergence does not allow affirmative answers to all the questions posed at the beginning of this appendix. The sequence $\{k_n\}_{n=1}^{\infty}$, defined on $[-1, 1]$ by

$$k_n(x) = \frac{x}{1 + nx^2}$$

for each positive integer n and each $x \in [-1, 1]$, converges uniformly to the function which is zero everywhere on $[-1, 1]$. However, $\{k_n'(0)\}_{n=1}^{\infty}$ converges to 1. Consequently, one must have some additional hypothesis to gain the type of result we have in mind.

II.6 THEOREM   Suppose $\{f_n\}_{n=1}^{\infty}$ is a sequence of functions, each of which is differentiable on $[a, b]$. Suppose further that for some $x_0 \in [a, b]$,

$$\{f_n(x_0)\}_{n=1}^{\infty}$$

converges and that $\{f_n'\}_{n=1}^{\infty}$ converges uniformly to g on $[a, b]$. Then
  (1) $\{f_n\}_{n=1}^{\infty}$ converges uniformly on $[a, b]$ to a function f;
  (2) f is differentiable on $[a, b]$ and $f'(x) = g(x)$ for all $x \in [a, b]$.

Proof: Assume $b > a$ and choose $\varepsilon > 0$. There is a real number N such that for all positive integers m and $n, m \geq N$ and $n \geq N$ imply that

$$|f_n(x_0) - f_m(x_0)| < \frac{\varepsilon}{2}$$

and for all $t \in [a, b]$,

$$|f'_n(t) - f'_m(t)| < \frac{\varepsilon}{2(b-a)}.$$

For each pair of positive integers m and $n, f_n - f_m$ is differentiable on $[a, b]$; hence, for each $u \in [a, b]$ and $v \in [a, b]$, there is $w \in [a, b]$ such that

$$[f_n(u) - f_m(u)] - [f_n(v) - f_m(v)] = [f'_n(w) - f'_m(w)](u - v).$$

Therefore, for all positive integers m and $n, m \geq N$ and $n \geq N$ imply

$$|f_n(x) - f_m(x)| \leq |f_n(x) - f_m(x) - f_n(x_0) + f_m(x_0)|$$
$$+ |f_n(x_0) - f_m(x_0)|$$
$$< \frac{\varepsilon|x - x_0|}{2(b-a)} + \frac{\varepsilon}{2} \leq \frac{\varepsilon}{2} + \frac{\varepsilon}{2} = \varepsilon.$$

for all $x \in [a, b]$. Consequently $\{f_n\}_{n=1}^{\infty}$ converges uniformly on $[a, b]$; define

$$f(x) = \lim_{n \to \infty} f_n(x)$$

for each $x \in [a, b]$.

Choose $x \in [a, b]$ and for each positive integer n, define $F_n : [a, b] \to R$ by

$$F_n(y) = \frac{f_n(x) - f_n(y)}{x - y}$$

for all $y \in [a, b] \setminus \{x\}$ and $F_n(x) = f'_n(x)$. Define $F : [a, b] \to R$ by

$$F(y) = \frac{f(x) - f(y)}{x - y}$$

for all $y \in [a, b] \setminus \{x\}$ and $F(x) = g(x)$. The function f will be differentiable at x with $f'(x) = g(x)$ if F is continuous at x. For each positive integer n, F_n is continuous at x by the differentiability of f_n at x. If we can show that $\{F_n\}_{n=1}^{\infty}$ converges uniformly to F on $[a, b]$, then F will be continuous at x, and hence f will be differentiable at x with $f'(x) = g(x)$. Choose $\varepsilon > 0$. As before, there is a real number N such that for all positive integers m and $n, m \geq N$ and $n \geq N$ imply that for all $t \in [a, b]$,

$$|f_n'(t) - f_m'(t)| < \frac{\varepsilon}{2}.$$

Then for all positive integers m and $n, m \geq N$ and $n \geq N$ imply

$$|F_n(y) - F_m(y)| = \left| \frac{f_n(x) - f_n(y)}{x - y} - \frac{f_m(x) - f_m(y)}{x - y} \right|$$

$$= \left| \frac{1}{x - y} \right| \cdot |f_n(x) - f_n(y) - f_m(x) + f_m(y)|$$

$$\leq \frac{1}{|x - y|} \cdot \frac{\varepsilon}{2} \cdot |x - y| < \varepsilon$$

for all $y \in [a, b] \backslash \{x\}$ and

$$|F_n(x) - F_m(x)| = |f_n'(x) - f_m'(x)| < \frac{\varepsilon}{2} < \varepsilon.$$

Thus, by II.1, $\{F_n\}_{n=1}^{\infty}$ converges uniformly on $[a, b]$, and it is clear that $\{F_n\}_{n=1}^{\infty}$ converges to F. This concludes the proof.

Before examining in more detail the results of II.3, II.5, and II.6, we return to consider the convergence of power series. The Weierstrass M-test suggests the following theorem.

II.7 THEOREM   Let $\sum_{n=0}^{\infty} a_n x^n$ be a power series that converges for $-r < x < r, r > 0$. Then $\sum_{n=0}^{\infty} a_n x^n$ converges uniformly on $-t \leq x \leq t$ for each $0 < t < r$.

Proof: If $0 < t < r$, then $\sum_{n=0}^{\infty} a_n t^n$ converges absolutely. For $-t \leq x \leq t$,

$$|a_n x^n| \leq |a_n| t^n.$$

Thus, by the Weierstrass M-test, $\sum_{n=0}^{\infty} a_n x^n$ converges uniformly on $[-t, t]$.

Consider a power series $\sum_{n=0}^{\infty} a_n x^n$. To apply the results of II.6, one must consider the question of convergence of the series

$$\sum_{n=0}^{\infty} na_n x^{n-1}.$$

It is not at all clear from casual observation that this series should converge for any $x \neq 0$. Even though $\sum_{n=0}^{\infty} a_n x^n$ converges, it seems reasonable that $\{na_n x^{n-1}\}_{n=0}^{\infty}$ might not even converge to zero. Indeed, if $a_n = 1/n$ and $x = -1$, this is the case. We have, from Chapter 6, a result which allows the direct determination of the interval of convergence of $\sum_{n=0}^{\infty} na_n x^{n-1}$. Perhaps considerations of this type will give us the proper perspective.

II.8 LEMMA If $\{b_n\}_{n=1}^{\infty}$ is a bounded sequence of real numbers, then $\{\sqrt[n]{n}\, b_n\}_{n=1}^{\infty}$ is a bounded sequence of real numbers and
$$\limsup_{n \to \infty} b_n = \limsup_{n \to \infty} \sqrt[n]{n}\, b_n.$$

Proof: Let
$$b = \limsup_{n \to \infty} b_n.$$

In Chapter 1, we proved that $\{\sqrt[n]{n}\}_{n=1}^{\infty}$ converges to 1. Thus, $\{\sqrt[n]{n}\, b_n\}_{n=1}^{\infty}$ must be bounded. Let
$$c = \limsup_{n \to \infty} \sqrt[n]{n}\, b_n.$$

Let $\{b_{n_k}\}_{k=1}^{\infty}$ be a subsequence of $\{b_n\}_{n=1}^{\infty}$ converging to b. Then
$$\{\sqrt[n_k]{n_k}\, b_{n_k}\}_{k=1}^{\infty}$$

also converges to b and $b \leq c$. Suppose
$$\{\sqrt[m_j]{m_j}\, b_{m_j}\}_{j=1}^{\infty}$$

converges to c. Since $\{\sqrt[m_j]{m_j}\}_{j=1}^{\infty}$ converges to $1 \neq 0$, we conclude that
$$\{b_{m_j}\}_{j=1}^{\infty} = \left\{\sqrt[m_j]{m_j}\, b_{m_j} \cdot \frac{1}{\sqrt[m_j]{m_j}}\right\}_{j=1}^{\infty}$$

converges to c. Consequently, $c \leq b$. We have shown $b \leq c$ and $c \leq b$, so $c = b$.

Lemma II.8 and Theorem 6.18 yield the fact that

$$\sum_{n=0}^{\infty} a_n x^n \quad \text{and} \quad \sum_{n=0}^{\infty} n a_n x^n$$

have the same radius of convergence. It is easy to see that this implies that

$$\sum_{n=0}^{\infty} a_n x^n \quad \text{and} \quad \sum_{n=0}^{\infty} n a_n x^{n-1}$$

also have the same radius of convergence.

II.9 THEOREM   Suppose $\sum_{n=0}^{\infty} a_n x^n$ converges to f on $(-r, r)$ with $r > 0$. Then

(1)   for each $0 < t < r$, $\sum_{n=0}^{\infty} a_n x^n$ converges uniformly on $[-t, t]$;
(2) f is n-times differentiable on $(-r, r)$ for each positive integer n;
(3)   for each $0 < t < r$ and each positive integer m,

$$\sum_{n=0}^{\infty} n(n-1)\cdots(n-m+1)a_n x^{n-m}$$

converges uniformly to $f^{(m)}(x)$ on $[-t, t]$;
(4) $f^{(n)}(0) = n! \, a_n$. (We make the convention that $f^{(0)}(x) = f(x)$ for all $x \in (-r, r)$.)

Proof: Part 1 of this theorem, a repetition of II.7, is included only for the sake of completeness.

The proof of parts 2, 3, and 4 shall be by induction. Choose any $x_0 \in (-r, r)$. There is $0 < t < r$ such that $|x_0| < t$. Since $\sum_{n=0}^{\infty} a_n x^n$ converges on $(-r, r)$, Lemma II.8 shows that

$$\sum_{n=0}^{\infty} n a_n x^{n-1}$$

converges on $(-r, r)$. By II.7,

$$\sum_{n=0}^{\infty} n a_n x^{n-1}$$

converges uniformly on $[-t, t]$. Define $g : [-t, t] \to R$ by $g(x) = f(x)$ for all $x \in [-t, t]$. Theorem II.6 guarantees that g is differentiable on $[-t, t]$ and

$$g'(x) = \sum_{n=0}^{\infty} n a_n x^{n-1}$$

for all $x \in [-t, t]$. Thus since $x_0 \in (-t, t)$, f is differentiable at x_0 and

$$f'(x_0) = g'(x_0) = \sum_{n=0}^{\infty} n a_n x^{n-1}.$$

Since x_0 was any point in $(-r, r)$, we have f differentiable on $(-r, r)$,

$$f'(x) = \sum_{n=0}^{\infty} n a_n x^{n-1}$$

for all $x \in (-r, r)$, and $\sum_{n=0}^{\infty} n a_n x^{n-1}$ converges uniformly to $f'(x)$ on any closed subinterval of $(-r, r)$. In particular, $f'(0) = a_1$.

Assume the theorem holds for $n = k$. Thus, f is k-times differentiable on $(-r, r)$; for each $0 < t < r$,

$$\sum_{n=0}^{\infty} n(n-1)\cdots(n-k+1) a_n x^{n-k}$$

converges uniformly to $f^{(k)}(x)$ on $[-t, t]$; and

$$f^{(k)}(0) = k! \, a_k.$$

Define $h : (-r, r) \to R$ by

$$h(x) = f^{(k)}(x)$$

for each $x \in (-r, r)$ and define

$$b_n = (n+k)(n+k-1)\cdots(n+1) a_{n+k}$$

for each non-negative integer n. Then

$$h(x) = \sum_{n=0}^{\infty} b_n x^n$$

for all $x \in (-r, r)$. By the results in the preceding paragraph, h is differentiable on $(-r, r)$; for each $0 < t < r$,

$$\sum_{n=0}^{\infty} n b_n x^{n-1}$$

converges uniformly to $h'(x)$ on $[-t, t]$; and $h'(0) = b_1$. Thus, $f^{(k)}$ is differentiable on $(-r, r)$; for each $0 < t < r$,

$$\sum_{n=0}^{\infty} n b_n x^{n-1} = \sum_{n=0}^{\infty} n(n-1)\cdots(n-k) a_n x^{n-k-1}$$

converges uniformly to $f^{(k+1)}(x)$ on $[-t, t]$; and

$$f^{(k+1)}(0) = b_1 = (k+1)! \, a_{k+1}.$$

This completes the induction.

Theorem II.9 tells us that inside the interval of convergence (not necessarily at the end points), a power series may be differentiated term by term, and the resulting power series will converge to the derivative of the limit function of the original series. Theorem II.5, coupled with II.7, justifies the formula

$$\int_a^b \sum_{n=0}^{\infty} a_n x^n dx = \sum_{n=0}^{\infty} a_n \int_a^b x^n dx$$

for $-r < a \le b < r$ if $\sum_{n=0}^{\infty} a_n x^n$ converges for $-r < x < r$.

Recall that $\sum_{n=0}^{\infty} x_n$ converges to $1/(1-x)$ for $-1 < x < 1$. Hence, by II.9,

$$\sum_{n=0}^{\infty} n x^{n-1}$$

converges to $1/(1-x)^2$ and

$$\sum_{n=0}^{\infty} n(n-1) x^{n-2}$$

converges to $2/(1-x)^3$ for $-1 < x < 1$.

If $f: E \to R$ with E a neighborhood of 0, and if f has derivatives of all orders at zero, one can always consider the power series

$$\sum_{n=0}^{\infty} \frac{f^{(n)}(0)}{n!} x^n .$$

This series converges to $f(0)$ at zero, but it is not necessarily true that there is $r > 0$ such that

$$f(x) = \sum_{n=0}^{\infty} \frac{f^{(n)}(0)}{n!} x^n$$

for $-r < x < r$. The classic example is the function $f: R \to R$ defined by

$$f(x) = e^{-1/x^2}$$

for $x \ne 0$ and $f(0) = 0$. In this case, $f^{(n)}(0)$ exists and equals 0 for each positive integer n, but then

$$\sum_{n=0}^{\infty} \frac{f^n(0)}{n!} x^n = 0$$

for all x, and $f(x) = 0$ only for $x = 0$.

We close this appendix with two examples, each of which may strike a familiar note. Consider the differential equation

$$x^2 f''(x) + x(1 - 2x) f'(x) + (x^2 - x) f(x) = 0.$$

In Chapter 1, we proved that $\{\sqrt[n]{n}\}_{n=1}^{\infty}$ converges to 1 by assuming convergence and showing that then the limit must be 1; and then we proved that the sequence converged to 1. A similar device will be used here. Suppose there is a function f satisfying this differential equation, and suppose that

$$f(x) = \sum_{n=0}^{\infty} a_n x^n$$

for $-r < x < r$ with $r > 0$. Then for $-r < x < r$,

$$f'(x) = \sum_{n=0}^{\infty} n a_n x^{n-1}$$

and

$$f''(x) = \sum_{n=0}^{\infty} n(n-1) a_n x^{n-2}.$$

Consequently, for $-r < x < r$,

$$
\begin{aligned}
0 &= x^2 f''(x) + x(1 - 2x) f'(x) + (x^2 - x) f(x) \\
&= x^2 \sum_{n=0}^{\infty} n(n-1) a_n x^{n-2} + x(1 - 2x) \sum_{n=0}^{\infty} n a_n x^{n-1} \\
&\quad + (x^2 - x) \sum_{n=0}^{\infty} a_n x^n \\
&= \sum_{n=0}^{\infty} n(n-1) a_n x^n + \sum_{n=0}^{\infty} n a_n x^n - 2 \sum_{n=0}^{\infty} n a_n x^{n+1} + \sum_{n=0}^{\infty} a_n x^{n+2} \\
&\quad - \sum_{n=0}^{\infty} a_n x^{n+1} = (a_1 - a_0)x + \sum_{n=2}^{\infty} [n^2 a_n - (2n-1)a_{n-1} + a_{n-2}]x^n.
\end{aligned}
$$

This equation will be satisfied if $\{a_n\}_{n=0}^{\infty}$ is chosen so that $a_1 = a_0$ and for each integer $n \geq 2$,

$$n^2 a_n - (2n-1)a_{n-1} + a_{n-2} = 0.$$

Thus, we may choose $a_0 = a_1$ and

$$a_n = \frac{(2n-1)a_{n-1} - a_{n-2}}{n^2}$$

for each integer $n \geq 2$.

Several questions must be considered at this time. First of all, if a sequence $\{a_n\}_{n=0}^{\infty}$ is chosen so that

$$a_0 = a_1 \quad \text{and} \quad a_n = \frac{(2n-1)a_{n-1} - a_{n-2}}{n^2}$$

for each integer $n \geq 2$, is it true that $\sum_{n=0}^{\infty} a_n x^n$ will converge for some $x \neq 0$? Secondly, there may be other methods of choosing the sequence

$\{a_n\}_{n=0}^{\infty}$ to satisfy the equation above. More to the second point, does there exist a sequence $\{b_n\}_{n=0}^{\infty}$ such that $\sum_{n=0}^{\infty} b_n x^n$ converges to zero on an interval of positive length with $b_n \neq 0$ for some integers n? We answer the second question first.

II.10 THEOREM   Suppose $\{a_n\}_{n=0}^{\infty}$ and $\{b_n\}_{n=0}^{\infty}$ are two sequences of real numbers, $r > 0$, and for all $x \in (-r, r)$,

$$\sum_{n=0}^{\infty} a_n x^n = \sum_{n=0}^{\infty} b_n x^n.$$

Then for each integer $n \geq 0$, $a_n = b_n$.

Proof: Define $f : (-r, r) \to R$ by

$$f(x) = \sum_{n=0}^{\infty} a_n x^n = \sum_{n=0}^{\infty} b_n x^n$$

for each $x \in (-r, r)$. Then, by II.9, f has derivatives of all orders on $(-r, r)$, and for each integer $n \geq 0$,

$$f^{(n)}(0) = n! \, a_n = n! \, b_n.$$

Thus, for each integer $n \geq 0$, $a_n = b_n$.

In particular, II.10 allows one to conclude that if $\sum_{n=0}^{\infty} a_n x^n$ converges to zero for all $x \in (-r, r)$ with $r > 0$, then $a_n = 0$ for each integer $n \geq 0$. Therefore, any solution to the differential equation

$$x^2 f''(x) + x(1 - 2x)f'(x) + (x^2 - x)f(x) = 0$$

which is expressible as a power series $\sum_{n=0}^{\infty} a_n x^n$, convergent on an interval of positive radius, must satisfy

$$a_1 = a_0 \quad \text{and} \quad a_n = \frac{(2n - 1)a_{n-1} - a_{n-2}}{n^2}.$$

The question concerning the convergence of such a power series is still unanswered. To simplify matters, choose $a_0 = a_1 = 1$. Then $a_2 = \frac{1}{2}, a_3 = \frac{1}{6}, \ldots, a_n = 1/n!, \ldots$. The solution then is

$$f(x) = \sum_{n=0}^{\infty} \frac{x^n}{n!} = e^x,$$

and this solution is valid for all x since $\sum_{n=0}^{\infty} x^n/n!$ converges for all x. In this case, it is trivial to check that this is a solution, since the function $f(x) = e^x$ is well known to us.

Consider the differential equation $f'(x) - xf(x) = 0$ with the condition $f(0) = 1$. We will attempt to solve this equation by the method of successive approximations. If f is a function which satisfies this equation for all $x \in (-r, r)$, and if f' is Riemann-integrable on any closed interval $[a, b] \subset (-r, r)$, then for all $x \in (-r, r)$,

$$f(x) = 1 + \int_0^x t f(t)\, dt.$$

If one can construct a sequence $\{f_n\}_{n=1}^{\infty}$ of continuous functions that will converge uniformly on any closed interval $[a, b] \subset (-r, r)$ which satisfies

$$f_n(x) = 1 + \int_0^x t f_{n-1}(t)\, dt$$

for all $x \in (-r, r)$, then the limit function should be the desired solution. As an initial guess, set $f_1(x) = 1$ for all $x \in R$. Define

$$f_2(x) = 1 + \int_0^x t f_1(t)\, dt = 1 + \frac{x^2}{2}$$

for all $x \in R$. Continuing in this fashion, we define

$$f_n(x) = 1 + \int_0^x t f_{n-1}(t)\, dt$$

for each $x \in R$ and obtain a sequence of functions $\{f_n\}_{n=1}^{\infty}$. It is not too hard to see that for each $x \in R$ and each positive integer n,

$$f_n(x) = \sum_{k=0}^{n} \frac{x^{2k}}{2^k k!},$$

which is the nth partial sum of the power series

$$\sum_{n=0}^{\infty} \frac{x^{2n}}{2^n n!}.$$

By our previous results on power series (the ratio test works quite well here), the series converges for all $x \in R$, and hence converges uniformly on any closed interval. Define $f : R \to R$ by

$$f(x) = \sum_{n=0}^{\infty} \frac{x^{2n}}{2^n n!}$$

for each $x \in R$. Choose any $x \in R$ with $x \neq 0$, and choose $\varepsilon > 0$. There is a real number N such that for each positive integer $n \geq N$, we have

$$|f_n(t) - f(t)| < \frac{\varepsilon}{|x|}$$

for all t satisfying $|t| \leq |x|$. Thus, for each positive integer $n \geq N$.

$$|t f_n(t) - t f(t)| \leq |x| \cdot \frac{\varepsilon}{|x|} = \varepsilon;$$

hence, the sequence $\{t f_n(t)\}_{n=1}^{\infty}$ converges uniformly to $t f(t)$ for all t such that $|t| \leq |x|$. By II.5,

$$\left\{ \int_0^x t f_{n-1}(t) \, dt \right\}_{n=0}^{\infty}$$

then converges to $\int_0^x t f(t) \, dt$. Since

$$f_n(x) = 1 + \int_0^x t f_{n-1}(t) \, dt$$

for each integer $n \geq 2$, we may conclude that

$$f(x) = 1 + \int_0^x t f(t) \, dt$$

for each $x \in R$. The fact that $\{f_n\}_{n=1}^{\infty}$ converges uniformly on any closed interval shows that f is continuous on R. Therefore, f is differentiable on R (since

$$f(x) = 1 + \int_0^x t f(t) \, dt$$

with $t f(t)$ continuous on R), and

$$f'(x) = x f(x) \quad \text{or} \quad f'(x) - x f(x) = 0$$

for all $x \in R$. If we consider the power series

$$\sum_{n=0}^{\infty} \frac{x^{2n}}{2^n n!}$$

and recall earlier examples of convergent power series, it becomes clear that $f(x) = e^{x^2/2}$. Here again, it is easy to verify that this is indeed a solution to the differential equation

$$f'(x) - x f(x) = 0.$$

EXERCISES

1. Let $\{r_n\}_{n=1}^{\infty}$ be a sequence containing each rational number in $[0, 1]$ exactly once. Define for each positive integer n,

    $$f_n(x) = 0$$

    if x is irrational,

    $$f_n(r_i) = 0$$

    if $i > n$, and

    $$f_n(r_i) = 1$$

    if $i \leq n$. Show that $\{f_n\}_{n=1}^{\infty}$ converges pointwise on $[0, 1]$ to a function f which is not Riemann-integrable.

2. For each positive integer n, define $h_n : [0, 1] \to R$ by

    $$h_n(x) = \frac{1}{x}$$

    for $1/n \leq x \leq 1$ and

    $$h_n(x) = n^2 x$$

    for $0 \leq x < 1/n$. Show that $\{h_n\}_{n=1}^{\infty}$ does not converge uniformly on $[0, 1]$ but does converge uniformly on $[a, 1]$ for each $0 < a < 1$.

3. Prove that the sequence $\{k_n\}_{n=1}^{\infty}$, defined by

    $$k_n(x) = \frac{x}{1 + nx^2}$$

    for all $x \in R$ and each positive integer n, converges uniformly on R.

4. Let $f : (a, b) \to R$ be differentiable. Construct a sequence of continuous functions which converges pointwise to f' on (a, b).

5. Assume E is compact and $\{f_n\}_{n=1}^{\infty}$ is a sequence of functions which converges uniformly on each point of E. Prove that $\{f_n\}_{n=1}^{\infty}$ converges uniformly on E.

6. Suppose that both $\{f_n\}_{n=1}^{\infty}$ and $\{g_n\}_{n=1}^{\infty}$ converge uniformly on E. Prove that $\{f_n + g_n\}_{n=1}^{\infty}$ converges uniformly on E. What can one prove about the uniform convergence of $\{f_n g_n\}_{n=1}^{\infty}$?

7. Let $f : R \to R$ be uniformly continuous, and for each positive integer n and each $x \in R$, define

    $$f_n(x) = f\left(x + \frac{1}{n}\right).$$

    Prove that $\{f_n\}_{n=1}^{\infty}$ converges uniformly to f on R.

8. If $A \subset E \subset R$, A is *dense* in E if $E = \bar{A} \cap E$. Assume $\{f_n\}_{n=1}^{\infty}$ is a sequence of functions continuous on E and converging uniformly on a set A dense in E. Prove that $\{f_n\}_{n=1}^{\infty}$ converges uniformly on E.

9. Suppose E is compact and $\{f_n\}_{n=1}^{\infty}$ a sequence of continuous functions defined on E which converges pointwise to a function f, also continuous on E. If, for each positive integer n,

$$f_n(x) \leq f_{n+1}(x)$$

for all $x \in E$, prove that $\{f_n\}_{n=1}^{\infty}$ converges uniformly to f.

10. (Cf. Exercise 3, Chapter 4.) Search the literature for an example of a continuous, nowhere-differentiable function. Such an example will probably be more meaningful in light of the contents of this appendix.

11. If $\{f_n\}_{n=1}^{\infty}$ is a sequence of continuous functions which converges pointwise to f on $[a, b]$, then there is at least one point $x_0 \in (a, b)$ such that $\{f_n\}_{n=1}^{\infty}$ converges uniformly at x_0. Search the literature for a proof of this theorem.

INDEX